1955

(ORIG. 1934) (1941, 1942)

4th ED. © 1955
(ORIG. 1934)

SHOP THEORY

4th ED. © 1955
(1934, 1941, 1942)

SHOP THEORY

The Shop Theory Department of the

HENRY FORD TRADE SCHOOL

Dearborn, Michigan. Revised by

FRED NICHOLSON *Formerly Academic*

Supervisor, Henry Ford Trade School

Fourth Edition

McGraw-Hill Book Company, Inc.

New York

Toronto

London

SHOP THEORY

Preface

The subject of shop theory has become of increasing importance to men engaged in producing the tools and machines of industry. It is recognized that the ability to work skillfully with the hands can be developed more readily and accurately when the work to be performed in the shop is understood in both its practical and its theoretical aspects. Because of the attention now given to the theory of shop work, the young men of today who enter the toolmaking or one of the related skilled trades have a much better opportunity to succeed in their chosen field than did those of previous generations.

Vocational education has made rapid strides in the past few decades and now takes an equal place with other educational groups. One of the reasons for its growth and prestige has been the dedicated zeal of teachers of vocational subjects in acquiring adequate teaching material for their students. This zeal expressed itself among the classroom teachers of the Henry Ford Trade School, who were journeymen mechanics as well as educators. These men were not satisfied with the teaching material available to them, and so they developed, over the years, their own instruction sheets, which they used in their classrooms and shared with their fellow teachers. Constant revision of these instructional units was made and eventually the instructors collaborated in combining their efforts into one volume and producing it in the school's printing shop. It met their own needs satisfactorily and later, because of the interest of other schools and individuals, the book was placed on the market. There it was received with enthusiasm and has served the needs of many high schools, colleges, vocational schools, technical institutes, apprentice schools within industry, and United States Army and Navy schools, as well as the needs of many individuals in the United States and foreign countries.

The improvements that are constantly being made in the tools and machines of the toolroom, and the continuing development of new techniques and materials, have indicated the need for a revision of many sections of this book. It was considered expedient, as a preliminary step in the project of bringing the work up to date, to make a survey of those who were using the book, in order to discover what improvements and changes they desired, and also to obtain their suggestions about the organization and style of the book. After the survey had been made and the results tabulated, each chapter of the book was examined carefully. The content, organization, and relevance of the units of instruction to present-day practice were all carefully considered, and, as a result, a great many changes, deletions, and additions were made. In many chapters, new tools and machines were introduced, together with adequate instructional units, which, in keeping with past policy, included supplementary illustrations. All out-of-date illustrations of tools and machines were replaced with new ones representing the latest designs. Finally, an appendix and an index were added.

It is hoped that this revision of *Shop Theory* will make the book more valuable to those who have used it in the past and that it will more adequately serve the needs of an ever-increasing number of students who seek a useful and rewarding career in industry.

Fred Nicholson

Contents

Chapter 1 SMALL TOOLS

Tools are one of man's greatest assets. The proper use of them makes hard jobs easy, difficult ones simple. Of all tools, the most valuable and versatile is man's own hand. But the skill of the hand can be increased and its power multiplied by the use of an endless variety of other tools that man has been designing and improving since the beginning of time. Modern man is heir to all the ingenuity of his ancestors. Those of us who will use tools all through life should acquire a great deal of pride in the ability to use them well. The ownership of good tools should be a never-ending source of satisfaction and pleasure. With this in mind, we should be eager to get acquainted with them.

Most of the tools introduced in this chapter are the ones used by machinists and toolmakers.

Fig. 1–1. Ball-peen hammer. (Stanley Tools)

Hammers are one of man's earliest tools. They have been improved since the day when the Stone Age man fashioned one by tying a stone to a branch torn from a tree, but they still consist of two principal parts: head and handle. Several varieties of hammers are used today.

1. Describe the most common hammers used by machinists, and tell the purpose for which each one is used.

Ans. The hammers commonly used by machinists are the ball-peen (Fig. 1–1), the flat face of which is used for general work and the rounded end particularly for riveting, the straight-peen

(Fig. 1–2), and the cross-peen (Fig. 1–3). Both the latter are used for general work and their peens, for peening or hand swaging. The steel heads of this group vary in size from 6 oz to 2 1/2 lb.

2. What is meant by peening or swaging?

Ans. Peening or swaging is the stretching or spreading of metal by hammering it, such as flattening the end of a rivet; spreading babbitt to fit tightly in a bearing; and straightening bars by stretching the short side. There are many other metal-stretching operations.

3. Name the principal parts of a hammer head.

Ans. The parts of the head of a hammer are the

Fig. 1–2. Straight-peen hammer. (Stanley Tools)

face, peen, eye, and post. The face is the lower or flat part of the head; the peen is the opposite end. The eye is the name for the hole that receives the handle. The post is the portion between the face and the eye.

The claw hammer (Fig. 1–4) is used by carpenters for driving or pulling nails. Wooden handles are used on most hammers.

4. What are soft hammers, and for what special purposes are they used?

Ans. Hammers with heads made of solid lead, copper, or babbitt (Fig. 1–5) are known as *soft hammers.* They are used to seat work in a machine vise, to drive a mandrel, or to perform any similar

Fig. 1–3. Cross-peen hammer. (Stanley Tools)

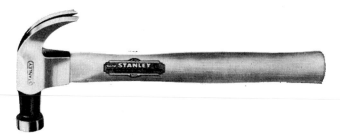

Fig. 1–4. Claw hammer. (Stanley Tools)

operation where the hard surface of a steel hammer might injure the edge or surface of a machined piece of work.

Fig. 1–5. Soft hammer. (Goodell-Pratt Co.)

5. What are soft-faced hammers or mallets, and why are they used?

Ans. Hammers with metal heads in the ends of which are inserted cylinders of plastic or rawhide (Fig. 1–6) are known as *soft-faced hammers* or *mallets.* They are used for the same purposes as soft hammers, but especially for hammering a finished surface or some relatively soft material.

Fig. 1–6. Soft-faced hammer or mallet. (Stanley Tools)

6. Why should a hammer handle be gripped near the end?

Ans. A hammer handle should be gripped near

the end so that full leverage may be obtained when swinging the hammer. A solid blow is difficult to deliver when the handle is held too close to the head of the hammer.

7. Why does the eye in a hammer head taper from each end toward the middle?

Ans. This taper makes for a very secure fit. The hammer handle is formed to fit one end of the tapered eye. The narrowing down of the eye prevents the head from slipping up the handle. After the handle has been fitted into the hammer head, wedges are driven into the end of the handle to expand it. The outward pressure of the wedges, combined with the inward pressure of the other end of the tapered eye, hold the head securely on the handle (see Fig. 1–7).

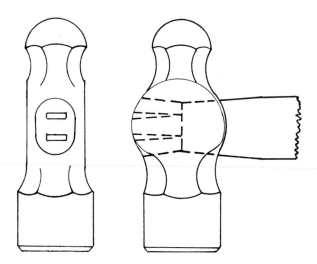

Fig. 1–7. Hammer handle is wedged into tapered eye of hammer head.

8. Why must a hammer handle be set square with the head?

Ans. The hammer handle must be set square with the head to ensure a proper balance of the two parts. When the parts are out of balance, it is more difficult to strike accurately the place aimed for.

9. What is a hand punch?

Ans. A hand punch is a tool that is held in the hand and struck on one end with a hammer. There are many kinds of punches, designed to do a variety of jobs. Most punches are made of tool steel. The part held in the hand is usually octagon-shaped, or it may be knurled. This is to prevent the tool from slipping around in the hand. The other end is shaped to do a particular operation.

10. What is a drift punch and for what purpose is it used?

Ans. A drift punch (Fig. 1–8) is a long, tapered steel tool used to align holes in two or more pieces of material that are to be joined together, so that bolts or rivets may be more easily placed in the holes.

Fig. 1–8. Drift punch. (Stanley Tools)

11. What is a pin punch and how is it used?

Ans. A pin punch (Fig. 1–9) is a tool with a long, straight nose that is used to drive, or remove, straight pins, tapered pins, cotter pins, and keys. This style of punch is made in several sizes, from 1/16 to 3/8 in. in diameter.

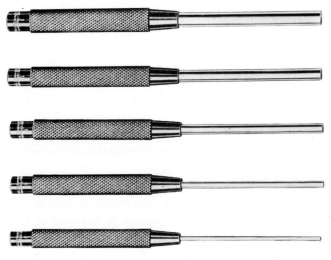

Fig. 1–9. Pin punches. (L. S. Starrett Co.)

12. What is a prick punch?

Ans. A prick punch (Fig. 1–10) is made of hardened tool steel, ground to a slender point. It is used to mark or identify scribed or layout lines on a piece of work. These marks are made at short intervals so that the lines will be easily located.

Fig. 1–10. Prick punch. (Stanley Tools)

13. What is a center punch?

Ans. A center punch (Fig. 1–11) is similar to a prick punch except that the point is ground to a conical shape, the angle of which is usually 90 deg. It is used to mark the location of holes to be drilled and also to help to start the drill in the correct spot.

Fig. 1–11. Center punch. (Stanley Tools)

The automatic center punch (Fig. 1–12) makes punch marks of a uniform size without the use of a hammer. The knurled cap may be turned to control the depth of the punch mark.

Fig. 1–12. Automatic center punch. (Lufkin Rule Co.)

14. What is a scriber?

Ans. A scriber (Fig. 1–13) is a slender steel tool used by toolmakers to scribe (scratch) or mark

Fig. 1–13. Scribers. (Lufkin Rule Co.)

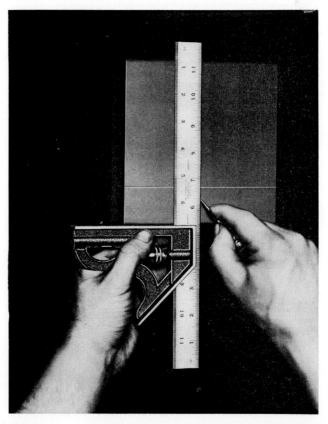

Fig. 1–14. Marking lines with a scriber. (L. S. Starrett Co.)

lines on metal when making measurements, as in Fig. 1–14.

The points of prick punches, center punches, and scribers must be kept sharp to ensure accurate marking of measurements.

The heads of punches become sharp and ragged after much hammering. Such sharp edges should be ground off to prevent injury to the hands.

15. What is a screw driver?

Ans. A screw driver (Fig. 1–15) is a hand tool that is designed to turn screws. The blade is made of steel, attached to one end of which is a wooden or plastic handle. The other end is flattened to fit slots in the heads of screws or bolts. Screw drivers are made in many sizes.

Fig. 1–15. Screw driver. (Stanley Tools)

16. What is a heavy-duty screw driver?

Ans. A heavy-duty screw driver (Fig. 1–16) is of average length but is made with a heavy blade, the shank of which is square. The shape of the shank permits the use of a wrench to assist in tightening a screw. Heavy (thick) material is used for the blade so that it will resist being twisted when a wrench is used.

Fig. 1–16. Heavy-duty screw driver. (Stanley Tools)

17. What is a Phillips screw driver?

Ans. A Phillips screw driver (Fig. 1–17) is specially designed to fit the heads of Phillips screws. It differs from other screw drivers in that the end of the blade is fluted instead of flattened. It is made in several sizes.

Fig. 1–17. Phillips-type screw driver. (Stanley Tools)

18. What is a helical-ratchet screw driver?

Ans. A helical-ratchet screw driver (Fig. 1–18) drives or draws screws by pushing on the handle. It can be locked rigid and used as an ordinary screw driver. It also has a ratchet movement. It may be changed from right-handed to left-handed or locked rigid by moving a small button called a *shifter.*

Fig. 1–18. Helical-ratchet screw driver with automatic, quick return. (Millers Falls Co.)

19. What is the purpose of a double-ended off-set screw driver?

Ans. A double-ended offset screw driver (Fig. 1–19) is used for turning screws in awkward places where there is not enough room to use a regular screw driver.

Fig. 1–19. Double-ended offset screw driver. (Stanley Tools)

20. How should the blade of a worn screw driver be ground?

Ans. A screw-driver blade should be ground so that the faces will be almost parallel with the sides of the screw slot as in Fig. 1–20. The end of the blade should be made as thick as the slot in the screw will permit. A blade ground to a chisel point, as in Fig. 1–21, has a tendency to slip out of the screw slot and, also, to leave a ragged edge on the slot.

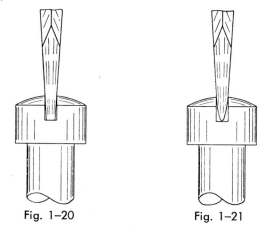

Fig. 1–20   Fig. 1–21

Fig. 1–20. Blade of screw driver correctly ground.
Fig. 1–21. Blade of screw driver incorrectly ground.

Excessive heat at the time of grinding, indicated by a blue color appearing on the blade, will draw the temper of the steel and cause the blade to become soft. This will result in the end of the blade being bent out of shape when a heavy pressure is applied to tighten a screw.

21. What are pliers?

Ans. The word *pliers* is a plural name for a single tool. Pliers are made in many styles and are used to perform as many different operations. Figure 1–22 shows the common slip-joint pliers. They are used for holding and gripping small articles in situations where it may be inconvenient or unsafe to use hands. It is not a good practice to use pliers in place of a wrench.

Fig. 1–22. Slip-joint pliers. (J. H. Williams & Co.)

22. What are needle-nose pliers?

Ans. Needle-nose pliers (Fig. 1–23) are made, as the name implies, with a thin nose or jaws. This tool can be used for placing and removing small items in narrow spaces. It is also preferred for electrical and radio repair work.

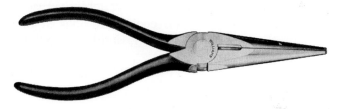

Fig. 1–23. Needle-nose pliers. (J. H. Williams & Co.)

23. What are linemen's side-cutting pliers?

Ans. Linemen's side-cutting pliers (Fig. 1–24) are made with cutting blades on one side of the jaws. They are used mostly for gripping and cutting wire.

Fig. 1–24. Linemen's side-cutting pliers. (J. H. Williams &Co.)

24. What are diagonals?

Ans. Diagonals (Fig. 1–25) are a special type of pliers used exclusively for cutting and stripping electrical wire.

Fig. 1–25. Diagonals (J. H. Williams & Co.)

25. What is a wrench?

Ans. A wrench is a tool for turning or twisting nuts or bolts. It is usually made of steel. There are many kinds of wrenches. They may consist of a slot, socket, pins, or movable jaws for grasping the nut, fastened to a handle for holding the tool.

26. What is a single-ended wrench?

Ans. A single-ended wrench (Fig. 1–26) is one that is made to fit one size of nut or bolt. This is the most inexpensive type of wrench and is quite efficient in ordinary situations.

Fig. 1–26. Single-ended wrench. (J. H. Williams & Co.)

27. What is a double-ended wrench?

Ans. A double-ended wrench (Fig. 1–27) has two openings, one at each end of the handle, to fit two different sizes of nuts or bolt heads.

Fig. 1–27. Double-ended wrench. (J. H. Williams & Co.)

28. What is a closed-end wrench?

Ans. A closed-end wrench (Fig. 1–28) is similar to a single-ended wrench, but, as it entirely encloses a nut, there is little danger of the wrench slipping off the nut or of the jaws spreading apart.

For these reasons, it is preferred for some jobs. It is also known as a *box wrench.*

Fig. 1–28. Closed-end wrench. (Billings & Spencer Co.)

29. What is a twelve-point box wrench?

Ans. A twelve-point box wrench (Fig. 1–29) is one that is designed with twelve notches or points inside a closed end. The points of a nut may be gripped by any one of the twelve notches of the wrench, which permits the turning of a nut where only a short pull of the wrench is possible.

Fig. 1–29. Twelve-point box wrench. (J. H. Williams & Co.)

30. What is an adjustable open-end wrench?

Ans. An adjustable open-end wrench (Fig. 1–30) has a movable jaw which makes it adjustable to various sizes of nuts. A heavy type of adjustable wrench is the monkey wrench shown in Fig. 1–31. When using this type of tool, point the jaws in the direction of the force applied. This will prevent the jaws from springing apart, and the wrench will be less likely to slip off a nut. The movable jaw should be adjusted so that it is tight against the part to be turned. It is not good practice to use a wrench as a hammer.

Fig. 1–30. Adjustable open-end wrench. (Billings & Spencer Co.)

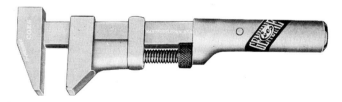

Fig. 1–31. Monkey wrench. (Billings & Spencer Co.)

31. What is a lever-jaw wrench?

Ans. A lever-jaw wrench (Fig. 1–32) is a combination gripping tool with adjustable jaws that may be locked in place. It may be used as a wrench, clamp, pliers, or vise.

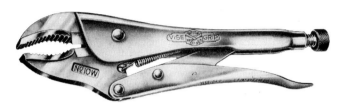

Fig. 1–32. Lever-jaw wrench. (Petersen Mfg. Co.)

32. What is a pinhook spanner wrench?

Ans. A pinhook spanner wrench is designed, as shown in Fig. 1–33, to fit around the edge of large round nuts which have holes in them to fit the pins of the wrench.

Fig. 1–33. Pinhook spanner wrench. (J. H. Williams & Co.)

33. What is an adjustable-hook spanner wrench used for?

Ans. An adjustable-hook spanner wrench (Fig. 1–34) is used on round nuts having notches or slots cut on their periphery to receive the hook at the end of the wrench. Being adjustable, it will fit many sizes of nuts.

Fig. 1–34. Adjustable-hook spanner wrench. (J. H. Williams & Co.)

34. What is an adjustable pin-face wrench?

Ans. An adjustable pin-face wrench is designed, as in Fig. 1–35, with two arms, each having a pin in one end. This tool is used to adjust nuts that are enclosed so that an ordinary wrench cannot be placed around them. A nut in this situation is made with holes around the face to accommodate the pins in the ends of the adjustable legs of the wrench.

Fig. 1–35. Adjustable pin-face wrench. (J. H. Williams & Co.)

35. What is a T-socket wrench?

Ans. A T-socket wrench is made in the form of a T, as shown in Fig. 1–36. The hole in the end or socket is made in a variety of shapes, such as square, hexagon, or octagon. It is generally used on jobs where there is insufficient space to permit the use of an ordinary wrench. The handle may be removed from the head of the wrench, which is hexagon-shaped, to permit the use of another wrench to turn it when more pressure is required than can be applied with the handle.

Fig. 1–36. T-socket wrench. (J. H. Williams & Co.)

36. What is an offset socket wrench?

Ans. An offset socket wrench (Fig. 1–37) is made with the same variety of sockets as a T-socket wrench. It is designed to be used on nuts requiring

great leverage or in places where a T-socket wrench cannot be used.

Fig. 1–37. Offset socket wrench. (Billings & Spencer Co.)

37. What is a ratchet wrench?

Ans. A ratchet wrench may be either of the socket type, as in Fig. 1–38, or the open-end type. The ratchet device in the handle permits a nut to be turned in spaces where only a short swing of the handle is possible. Another advantage of this type of wrench is that it is not necessary to remove it from the nut or bolt until it is tight.

Fig. 1–38. Ratchet wrench. (Billings & Spencer Co.)

38. What is a hollow-setscrew wrench?

Ans. A hollow-setscrew wrench, sometimes called an *Allen* wrench (Fig. 1–39), is made of hexagon-shaped stock to fit the holes in the head of safety setscrews or socket-head screws. They are available in many sizes.

Fig. 1–39. Hollow-setscrew or Allen wrench.

39. What is a strap wrench?

Ans. A strap wrench (Fig. 1–40) is used for turning cylindrical parts or pipes, removing bezels, or for holding or revolving any job on which the surface finish must be preserved.

Fig. 1–40. Strap wrench. (Lowell Wrench Co.)

40. What is a pipe wrench?

Ans. A stillson-type pipe wrench (Fig. 1–41) is designed with adjustable jaws that are serrated, making it possible to grip round pipe and other cylindrical parts. The serrated edges tend to cut into the metal being gripped, so care should be used to protect plated or finished surfaces.

Fig. 1–41. Stillson pipe wrench.

41. What are chain pipe tongs?

Ans. Chain pipe tongs (Fig. 1–42) are designed to hold pipe between a serrated head and an adjustable length of chain. They are especially useful for holding pipe while cutting or threading it, and for turning extra-large sizes of pipe.

Fig. 1–42. Chain pipe tongs. (J. H. Williams & Co.)

42. What is a pipe cutter?

Ans. A pipe cutter (Fig. 1–43) is a tool especially designed to cut pipe. The cutting blade is a hardened-steel wheel. The cutter is adjustable for cutting various sizes of pipe. The two rollers force the pipe against the cutting wheel. The pressure is constantly increased by the operator while he revolves the pipe cutter around the pipe.

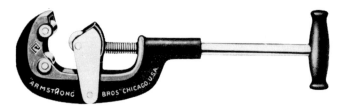

Fig. 1–43. Pipe cutter. (Armstrong Bros. Tool Co.)

Many devices have been designed to hold work securely while it is being measured or machined. Some of them are for one specific piece of work; others are of a more general nature. These include many types of clamps and vises.

43. What is a toolmaker's clamp?

Ans. A toolmaker's clamp (Fig. 1–44) consists of two flat steel jaws that may be adjusted to fit a piece of work by means of a screw passing through the center of each jaw. Another screw in the end of one jaw is used to exert pressure on the other jaw. This pressure tightens the opposite ends of the jaws. It is used by toolmakers for holding small parts both at the bench and at machines. This tool is also known as a *parallel clamp*.

Fig. 1–44. Toolmaker's clamp. (Lufkin Rule Co.)

44. What is a C clamp?

Ans. A C clamp (Fig. 1–45) is an all-purpose clamp that is in general use for all kinds of work. It is made in many sizes.

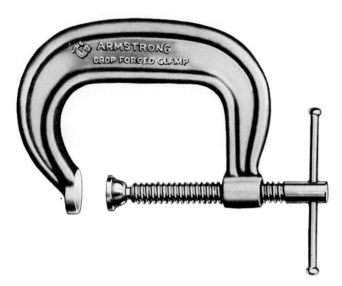

Fig. 1–45. C clamp. (Armstrong Bros. Tool Co.)

45. *What are V blocks with clamps used for?*

Ans. V blocks with clamps, either singly or in pairs, as in Fig. 1–46, are used to hold cylindrical work securely during the laying out of measurements or for machining operations.

Fig. 1–46. V blocks with clamp. (Brown & Sharpe Mfg. Co.)

46. *What is a toolmaker's hand vise?*

Ans. A toolmaker's hand vise (Fig. 1–47) is a small steel vise with two interchangeable blocks. The choice of block to be used depends on the size of the article to be held by the vise. It is used by toolmakers at the bench for small machining oper-

ations such as drilling or tapping. Another type of hand vise is shown in Fig. 1–48.

Fig. 1–47. Toolmaker's hand vise. (Brown & Sharpe Mfg. Co.)

Fig. 1–48. Combination hand vise. (L. S. Starrett Co.)

47. *What is a drill vise?*

Ans. A drill vise (Fig. 1–49) is a sturdy steel vise with a movable jaw that is easily moved back or forth by raising the handle. Turning the same handle tightens the work between the jaws. This vise is not usually fastened to the drilling machine but is held in position by holding the handle with one hand while operating the drill with the other hand.

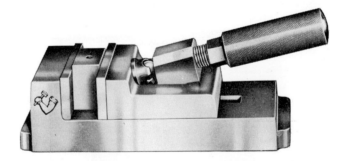

Fig. 1–49. Drill vise. (Armstrong Bros. Tool Co.)

48. *What is a bench vise?*

Ans. A bench vise, usually swivel-based as in Fig. 1–50, is the kind most favored for general shop work. It is securely fastened to the bench with bolts. The faces of the jaws are usually lightly serrated and hardened to ensure a firm grip on the work. Finished surfaces should be protected when placed in the vise, by using brass or copper jaw caps, as in Fig. 1–51. Tightening the vise by hammering on the handle is a poor method and marks one as an inferior workman.

When it is necessary to hammer a piece of work that is held in a vise, it is best to support the work by placing a block of wood or metal under it to prevent the work from being driven down through the jaws of the vise.

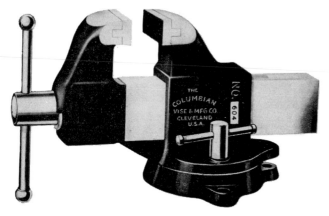

Fig. 1–50. Bench vise. (Columbian Vise & Mfg. Co.)

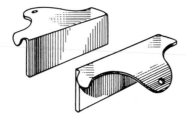

Fig. 1–51. Protective jaw caps for vise. (Columbian Vise & Mfg. Co.)

Fig. 1–52. Pipe vise. (Armstrong Bros. Tool Co.)

49. What is a pipe vise?

Ans. A pipe vise (Fig. 1–52) is a vise with serrated jaws that are V-shaped to grip pipe and cylindrical bars firmly. It is usually bolted securely to the end of a bench. The swinging clamp on one side of the vise holds the two jaws in place, and, when it is lifted, the two jaws are easily separated. Another type of pipe vise is shown in Fig. 1–53.

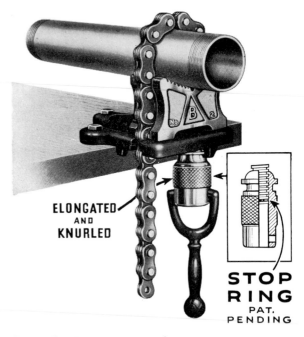

ELONGATED AND KNURLED

STOP RING PAT. PENDING

Fig. 1–53. Chain pipe vise. (Billings & Spencer Co.)

50. What are tinner's snips?

Ans. Tinner's snips (Fig. 1–54), also called *tin snips*, are a common cutting tool used for cutting thin sheets of metal, plastic, fiber, and so forth. They are not only used by tinsmiths, but as a utility tool by all bench workers. They are made in many sizes.

Fig. 1–54. Tinner's snips. (Bartlett Mfg. Co.)

Precision machines do an excellent job in producing surfaces that are accurate in measurement and smooth in finish. However, there are some operations, such as the fitting of bearing surfaces, that are better done by skillful handwork. Scrapers are used for this work.

51. *What is a bearing scraper?*

Ans. A bearing scraper (Fig. 1–55) is a slender tool made of hardened steel especially shaped and curved. It is used for scraping the surface of cylindrical bearings when fitting shafts into them.

Fig. 1–55. Bearing scraper. (Goodell-Pratt Co.)

52. *What is a flat scraper used for?*

Ans. A flat scraper (Fig. 1–56) is used to scrape the high spots off a flat bearing surface that must be perfectly matched to another flat surface. This is a hand operation requiring much skill.

Fig. 1–56. Flat scraper. (Nicholson File Co.)

53. *What is a three-cornered scraper?*

Ans. A three-cornered scraper (Fig. 1–57) is a hardened-steel tool that is used to remove burrs or sharp internal edges from soft bushings and similar parts.

Fig. 1–57. Three-cornered scraper.

Every mechanic should have a toolbox of his own where he may keep his tools when he is not using them. There should be a place for every tool, and each tool should be kept in its place. A popular style of toolbox is shown in Fig. 1–58.

The condition in which a mechanic keeps the various tools he uses can affect his efficiency as well as the judgment that others pass upon him in the performance of his daily work. A workman is frequently judged by the way in which he handles his tools.

All tools should be wiped clean before they are placed in the toolbox, and, if they are not to be used again for some time, they should be oiled to prevent rusting.

Fig. 1–58. Machinist's toolbox. (Kennedy Mfg. Co.)

Tools that are being used while working on a machine or at a bench should be kept within easy reach of the operator and placed so that they will not fall on the floor. Tools ought not to be placed on the finished parts of a machine.

Chapter 2 CHISELS AND CHIPPING

One of the earliest methods of shaping a piece of wood, stone, or metal was to chip away the unwanted material with a hammer and chisel. This practice is still common today for jobs that are done at the workbench and in instances where it is not practical to do the work on a machine. In this chapter, we shall be concerned with the chipping of metal.

On any work of this nature, there is always the danger that flying particles of metal may injure the eyes of the workman who is doing the chipping and of other persons who may be near by.

To do a job safely is the most important rule in any shop. For this reason, goggles should be worn by the person who is chipping, and a guard placed

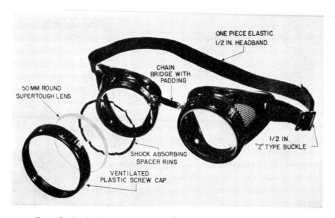

Fig. 2–1. Safety goggles. (Willson Products, Inc.)

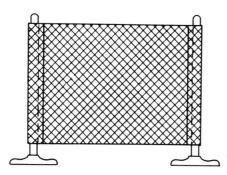

Fig. 2–2. Chipping guard.

to protect those who are near or passing by (see Figs. 2–1 and 2–2).

1. What is a chisel?

Ans. A chisel is a tool made from hexagon- or octagon-shaped tool steel, commonly called *chisel steel,* of a convenient size for handling. One end is shaped for the cutting operation. The other end is left blunt to receive the blows from a hammer. Chisels are usually forged to the required shape, then annealed, hardened, and tempered. Finally, a cutting edge is ground.

2. For what purpose are chisels annealed, hardened, and tempered?

Ans. Annealing relieves the internal strains of the metal which develop during the forging operation, and thus makes a chisel tough and strong. The hardening of the metal makes it possible for a chisel to maintain a sharp cutting edge. Tempering reduces the brittleness of the metal so that the cutting edge of the chisel is less liable to be fractured. All these processes, annealing, hardening, and tempering, are known as *heat-treatments.*

3. Is a chisel hardened all over?

Ans. No. Only the cutting end, and usually for a distance of 1 in. from the end. It is better for the opposite end to remain relatively soft, to avoid its being chipped by the blows of the hammer.

4. What is a flat cold chisel?

Ans. A flat cold chisel (Fig. 2–3) is the most common type of chisel. It is used for chipping flat surfaces and for the cutting of thin sheet metal. It

Fig. 2–3. Flat cold chisel. (Stanley Tools)

is called a *cold chisel* because it is used to cut metals that have not been heated in a furnace.

5. *What is a cape chisel?*

Ans. A cape chisel is a narrow chisel shaped as in Fig. 2–4. It is used mostly for the chipping of grooves and keyways.

Fig. 2–4. Cape chisel. (Stanley Tools)

6. *What is a roundnose chisel used for?*

Ans. A roundnose chisel (Fig. 2–5) is used for roughing out small concave surfaces such as a filleted corner. It is also used on drill-press work, to cut a small groove in the sloping edge of a hole that is off center, for the purpose of drawing the drill back to place, concentric with the layout.

Fig. 2–5. Roundnose chisel. (Stanley Tools)

7. *What is a diamond-point chisel used for?*

Ans. A diamond-point chisel (Fig. 2–6) is used for cutting V-shaped grooves or for chipping in sharp corners.

Fig. 2–6. Diamond-point chisel. (Stanley Tools)

All the chisels mentioned above are designed for hand use. Chisels with cutting edges similar to these, but with a different striking end, as in Fig. 2–7, are designed to be used with an electric hammer (Fig. 2–8).

8. *What is a hot chisel?*

Ans. A hot chisel is one that is designed to cut or chip metal while it is red hot. The cutting edge of the chisel is long and slender, as shown in Fig. 2–9. This type of chisel is mounted on a wooden handle in the same manner as a hammer.

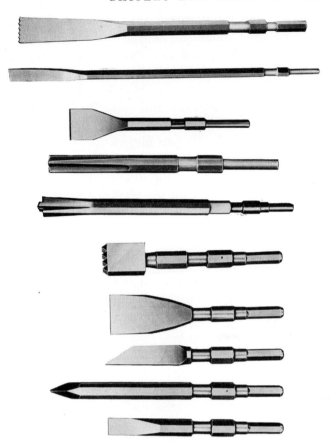

Fig. 2–7. Chisels and cutting tools for use in an electric hammer. (Black & Decker Mfg. Co.)

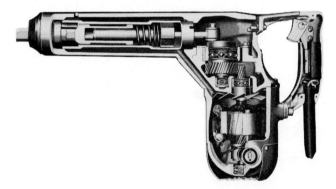

Fig. 2–8. Electric hammer, cut-away view. (Black & Decker Mfg. Co.)

Fig. 2–9. Hot chisel. (Stanley Tools)

9. *Describe the method of chipping by hand.*

Ans. A hammer, weighing from 1 to 1 3/4 lb, a chisel selected for the particular job to be done, goggles, and safety guard are the essential tools. The hammer should be held at the extreme end, grasped by the thumb, second and third fingers, with the first and fourth fingers closed loosely around the handle. The hammer handle may thus be swung more steadily and more freely without tiring the hand as much as if the handle were grasped rigidly by all four fingers.

The chisel should be held with the head of the chisel about 1 in. above the thumb and first finger, and gripped firmly with the second and third fingers. The first finger and thumb should be slack, as the muscles are then relaxed, and the fingers and hand are less likely to be injured if struck with the hammer. The edge of the chisel should be held on the point where the cut is desired, at an angle that will cause the cutting edge to follow the desired finished surface (see Fig. 2–10). After each blow of the hammer, the chisel must be re-set to the proper position for the next cut.

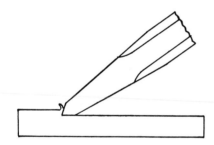

Fig. 2–10. Chisel held at correct angle.

10. To what size angle should the cutting edge of a flat cold chisel be ground?

Ans. The correct cutting angle depends upon the hardness of the material to be cut. An angle of 70 deg is suitable for iron and steel. For soft metals, the angle should be less. The use of a chisel with a cutting angle of 90 deg or larger will tend to remove stock by pushing it off instead of cutting it off (see Figs. 2–11 and 2–12).

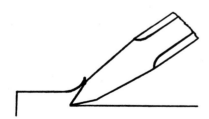

Fig. 2–11. Angle at cutting edge of chisel is ground small for soft metals.

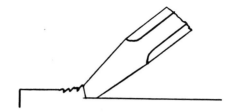

Fig. 2–12. Cutting edge of chisel is dull and cutting angle is too large.

11. What is the correct procedure in sharpening a cold chisel?

Ans. A cold chisel should be held at the required angle and moved back and forth across the face of the grinding wheel to insure an even surface. The pressure of the chisel against the wheel must be enough to prevent chattering, that is, vibrating or bouncing of the chisel against the wheel. It is also necessary to avoid pressing so hard that the edge of the chisel becomes overheated, as this will draw the temper of the steel and make the cutting edge soft. Curving the cutting edge of the chisel as shown in Fig. 2–13 results in a better cutting action.

Fig. 2–13. Cutting edge slightly rounded to give better cutting action.

12. When chipping, should the cutting edge or the head of a chisel be watched?

Ans. For accurate cutting of the material, watch the cutting edge of the chisel. The ability to hit the head of the chisel without watching it is soon acquired.

13. What is meant by a "mushroom head" on a chisel?

Ans. A mushroom head on a chisel is a head that has been hammered until the end spreads out to resemble a mushroom.

14. Why are mushroom-head chisels dangerous?

Ans. The mushroomed part of the head of the chisel may break off when struck by a hammer, and the flying particles of steel injure someone. The ragged edge may also injure the hand of the person holding the chisel.

15. Draw a sketch showing the shape of the cutting edge and facet of each of the following: a flat chisel, a cape chisel, a roundnose chisel, and a diamond-point chisel. These are correctly shown in Fig. 2–14.

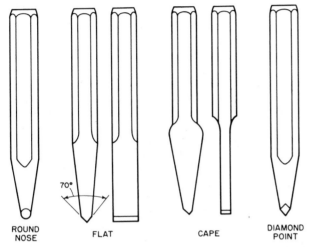

Fig. 2–14. Roundnose, flat, cape, and diamond-point chisels.

Figure 2–15 shows a student in the act of chipping a piece of work that is held in a vise at the workbench. Several items of safety and good shop practice are indicated by numbers. Can you identify them?

Fig. 2–15. Chipping at the bench.

Chapter 3 HACK SAWS AND SAWING

A tool that receives a lot of use by the machinist working at a bench, as well as by workers in general, is the hack saw. This is a handsaw especially designed for cutting metal. It consists of a metal frame (Fig. 3–1), in the ends of which are metal clips to hold the cutting blade. One clip is threaded on one end for a wing nut which is used for tightening the blade in the frame. There are many other styles of hack saws. The frame is adjustable to suit various lengths of blades.

Fig. 3–1. Hack saw. (L. S. Starrett Co.)

1. What is a hack-saw blade?
Ans. A hack-saw blade (Fig. 3–2) is a piece of thin steel about 0.027 in. thick, 1/2 in. wide, and varying in length from 6 to 12 in. On one edge of the blade are serrations known as *teeth.*

Fig. 3–2. Hack-saw blade. (L. S. Starrett Co.)

2. How are hack-saw blades held in the frame?
Ans. Hack-saw blades are made with a hole in each end to fit over pins in the clips at each end of the hack-saw frame.

3. How is the length of a hack-saw blade determined?
Ans. The length of a blade is the distance from the center of the hole in one end of the blade to the center of the hole in the opposite end.

4. Do all hack-saw blades have teeth of the same size?
Ans. No. Blades for handsaws are manufactured with teeth of different sizes ranging from 14 to 32 teeth per inch.

5. What is meant by the set of a saw?
Ans. The set of a saw means the bending to one side or the other of the teeth of a saw. The standard practice is to bend the teeth alternately; that is, one tooth is turned to the right side, the next one to the left side, and so on, as in Fig. 3–3. The teeth are actually turned very little. Sometimes, in the case of fine-toothed saw blades, the teeth are set alternately in pairs. This is known as *double-alternate* setting.

Fig. 3–3. Alternate setting of teeth.

6. For what purposes are the teeth of a hack-saw blade set?
Ans. The teeth are set so that the slot which is made by the saw will be slightly wider than the thickness of the blade. This prevents the blade from binding in the slot, which makes the cutting operation easier for the workman, and, because the friction between blade and work is reduced, the effective life of the blade is increased. The set of the teeth also permits the blade to be guided from left to right when sawing to simplify following a layout line.

7. Of what kinds of steel are hack-saw blades made?
Ans. Hack-saw blades are made of high grades of steel such as tool steel, high-speed steel, or tungsten-alloy steel.

8. *What is meant by an all-hard blade?*

Ans. An all-hard blade is one that has been hardened all over.

9. *For what kinds of material is it desirable to use all-hard blades?*

Ans. All-hard blades are used for cutting hard materials such as steel, cast iron, and brass and particularly when cutting solid stock where a straight, even cut is desired.

10. *What is meant by a flexible-back blade?*

Ans. A flexible-back blade is one in which only the part where the teeth are cut is hardened, the rest of the blade remaining relatively soft.

11. *For what kinds of material are flexible-back blades preferred?*

Ans. Flexible-back blades are preferred for cutting the softer metals, such as tin, copper, aluminum, and babbitt, and, in particular, for the cutting of tubing, and various structural shapes with thin cross sections. In the process of cutting such materials, there is a tendency for the blade to be twisted or pulled out of line. The flexible blade will yield under these conditions, whereas an all-hard blade will break.

12. *Is there a particular way of placing a hacksaw blade in a frame?*

Ans. Yes. Best results are obtained when the cutting is done on the forward, or pushing, stroke. For this reason, the blade should be placed in the frame so that the teeth point forward.

13. *Can the blade be adjusted in the frame to suit special conditions?*

Ans. Yes. The blade may be set in four different positions, so that the teeth may face down, up, left, or right. The clips in the ends of the frame may be turned to four different positions for this purpose. Figure 3–4 shows a blade turned to the right so that a long strip may be conveniently cut from a metal sheet. In all cases, the blade should be drawn tight enough so that it will not bend. A flexible-back blade has a tendency to stretch because of the heat produced by friction. For this reason, it is necessary to increase the tension after the cutting has been started.

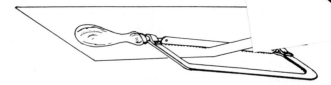

Fig. 3–4. Hack saw with blade turned at right angles to the frame.

14. *It is important that a piece of material to be cut be placed in a vise correctly, if the greatest efficiency is to be obtained from the saw blade. Explain how various materials should be held.*

Ans. Depending upon the shape of the material, it is placed in a vise so that as much as possible of the surface may be presented to the edge of the blade. Avoid starting to saw on a corner. Corners have a tendency to strip teeth from the blade. The work should be held securely and adjusted so that the cutting will take place close to the end of the vise jaw. This will prevent chattering or vibrating of the work, which is hard on the nerves of the

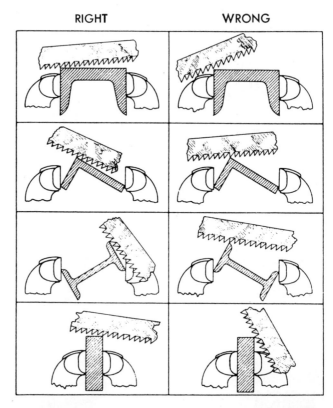

Fig. 3–5. Methods of holding work in a vise for sawing.

workman and on the teeth of the saw blade. Figure 3–5 shows the correct and incorrect ways of placing material in a vise.

15. How should thin steel stock be supported while being cut with a hack saw?

Ans. Clamp thin stock between two pieces of wood or soft steel, and then saw through all three together. Thin stock that is not supported in this manner will bend under the pressure of the saw.

16. Why are hack-saw blades made with teeth of different sizes?

Ans. It has been found by experience that all materials do not cut equally well with the same size of saw teeth. The greatest efficiency is obtained by using a blade with teeth of the proper size for a given operation. The size of the teeth on a saw blade is referred to as the *pitch*.

17. On what kind of jobs should a hack-saw blade with 14 teeth per inch be used?

Ans. Use a blade with 14 teeth per inch for sawing machine steel, cold-rolled steel, and structural-steel units having thick sections. The main advantage of the coarse pitch is that it makes the saw free- and fast-cutting, and for that reason is preferred where a smooth cut is not important.

18. When should a blade with 18 teeth per inch be used?

Ans. Use an 18-pitch blade for sawing any solid stock, including such materials as aluminum, babbitt, cast iron, high-speed steel, tool steel, and so forth. This pitch of blade is recommended for general use where a smooth cut surface is required.

19. On what kind of jobs should a blade with 24 teeth per inch be used?

Ans. Use a 24-pitch blade for cutting pipe, tin, brass, copper, small structural-steel units, and sheet metal over 18 gage. Although a fine-pitch blade cuts slowly, if a coarser blade is used for such items, the comparatively thin stock will tend to strip the teeth from the saw blade. There is less danger of stripping the teeth when two or more teeth are in contact with the work at all times.

20. When should a blade with 32 teeth per inch be used?

Ans. Use a 32-pitch blade for cutting small tubing, conduit, and sheet metal less than 18-gage thickness. These very thin materials require a very fine pitch in the saw blade, to prevent the stripping of the teeth.

21. Does a saw blade cut on the return stroke of the saw?

Ans. No. The teeth are designed to cut in one direction only. For this reason, the pressure on the saw should be released during the return stroke, to avoid damage to the teeth.

22. At what speed should a hand hack saw be used?

Ans. Under ordinary conditions, 35 to 40 strokes per minute is satisfactory. About 50 strokes per minute should be the maximum. Hard materials should not be sawed so fast as this, for it will un-

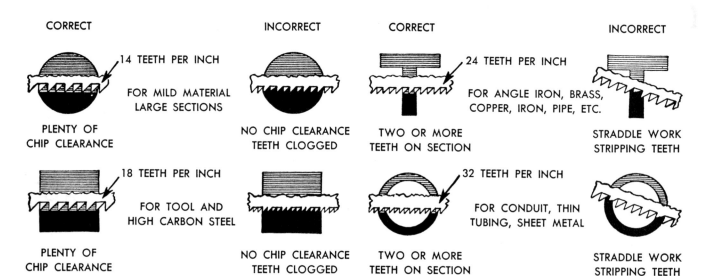

Fig. 3–6. Chart for selecting hack-saw blades of the correct pitch for the job. (L. S. Starrett Co.)

necessarily dull the blade. In cutting hard material, such as drill rod, for example, it is very effective to saw slowly and to use greater pressure than one would use for ordinary materials.

23. *Describe slotting hack-saw blades.*

Ans. Slotting hack-saw blades are similar to other hack-saw blades. They are usually 8 in. long by 1/2 in. wide, and of four different thicknesses, approximately 0.049, 0.065, 0.083, and 0.109 in. They are very handy when slotting a few screws for a special job which is needed at once. When slotting saw blades are not available, two or more ordinary saw blades may be placed in the frame side by side and used as a substitute.

24. *Why should a new cut be started after replacing a worn blade with a new one?*

Ans. The set of the teeth of the old blade will be worn slightly, and so the cut made by it will be narrower than the new blade. The new blade will break if it is forced into the old cut.

25. *Name three common causes for the breaking of hack-saw blades.*

Ans. (1) Using a coarse blade on thin material. (2) Drawing the blade too tightly in the frame and then canting (tilting) it over while in the act of sawing. (3) Using too much pressure on the blade.

26. *Give some of the rules to be followed in using a hand hack saw.*

Ans. (1) Use a blade with teeth of the correct pitch for the job to be done. (2) Saw as close as possible to the point where the work is clamped, to prevent chattering. (3) Do not cut too fast. (4) Relieve the pressure on the saw on the return stroke. (5) Do not press too hard on the work. (6) Saw carefully when the blade is almost through the cut.

Chapter 4 FILES AND FILING

Filing is a method of removing small amounts of material from the surface of a piece of metal or other hard substance. In some respects, this operation compares to smoothing a piece of wood with a chisel or plane. Just as there are many types of chisels and planes to suit many different operations with wood, so there are many types of files designed for specific types of work and for various kinds of metal.

1. What is a file?

Ans. A file is a hardened-steel instrument having parallel rows of cutting edges or teeth on its surfaces. On the two wide surfaces, the rows are usually diagonal to the edge. One end of the file is shaped so that it may be inserted into a wooden handle.

2. What are the names of the various parts of a file?

Ans. The parts of a file are named as shown in Fig. 4–1: tang, heel, face, edge, and tip.

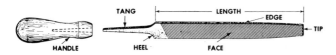

Fig. 4–1. Nomenclature of a file.

3. How is the length of a file measured?

Ans. The length of a file is the distance from the heel to the tip (see Fig. 4–1).

4. What is meant by the safe edge of a file?

Ans. The safe edge of a file is the one on which no teeth have been cut. This edge keeps one side of a piece of work safe while filing an adjacent surface.

5. Are files the same width from tip to heel?

Ans. With one exception, no. Files normally ta-

per in width from the heel to the tip. The exception is known as a blunt file.

6. What are some of the different shapes of files?

Ans. Cross sections of some of the most commonly used files, and their names, are shown in Fig. 4–2.

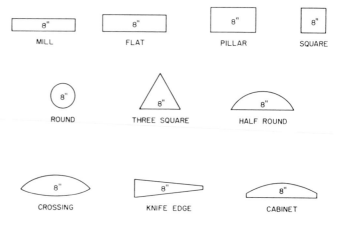

Fig. 4–2. Cross sections of files. (Nicholson File Co.)

7. How are files classified?

Ans. They are divided into two classes: single-cut and double-cut.

8. What are some of the characteristics of the two classes of files?

Ans. Single-cut files have rows of teeth running in one direction across their wide surfaces, as in Fig. 4–3. Double-cut files have rows of teeth the same as single-cut files and, in addition, have a second row of teeth cut diagonally to the first row, as in Fig. 4–4. Single-cut files do not remove stock as fast as double-cut files, but the surface finish produced by the use of single-cut files is smoother.

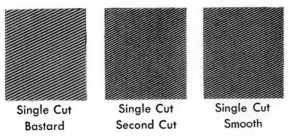

Single Cut Bastard   Single Cut Second Cut   Single Cut Smooth

Fig. 4–3. Types of single-cut files. (Nicholson File Co.)

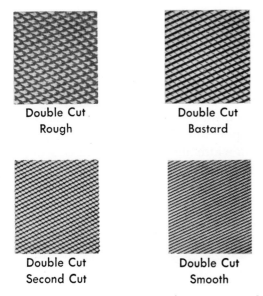

Double Cut Rough   Double Cut Bastard

Double Cut Second Cut   Double Cut Smooth

Fig. 4–4. Types of double-cut files. (Nicholson File Co.)

9. *Do all single-cut files have fine teeth and all double-cut files, coarse teeth?*

Ans. No. Both classes of files are made in similar grades or pitch such as dead-smooth, smooth, second-cut, bastard, coarse, rough. The degree of roughness on small files is indicated by numbers from 00 to 6, with 00 being the roughest.

10. *Is the pitch of file teeth the same for all sizes of files?*

Ans. No. The smaller the file, the finer the pitch. Figure 4–5 illustrates the difference in pitch of a 6-in. second-cut file and a 16-in. second-cut file.

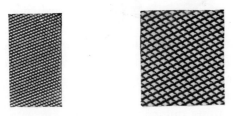

Fig. 4–5. The pitch of a 6-in. and a 16-in. second-cut file. (Nicholson File Co.)

11. *Describe the use of a mill file.*

Ans. The mill file (Fig. 4–6), which is single-cut, is used mostly in smooth and second-cut grades. It derives its name from the fact that it was first used for filing mill saws. It is also used for work on a lathe, draw filing, and for finishing various compositions of brass and bronze. This type of file produces a fine finish. It is available in lengths of from 6 to 16 in.

Fig. 4–6. Mill file. (Nicholson File Co.)

12. *Describe the use of a flat file.*

Ans. Most flat files (Fig. 4–7) are double-cut and are preferred in bastard or second-cut grades. They are used by machinists, machinery builders, ship and engine builders, repair men, and toolmakers, when a fast-cutting file is needed. This type of file produces a comparatively rough finish. It is usually available in lengths of from 6 to 18 in.

Fig. 4–7. Flat file. (Nicholson File Co.)

13. *Describe the pillar file.*

Ans. The pillar file (Fig. 4–8) is similar to the flat file, except that it is narrower and one or both edges are safe edges. The pillar file is used for filing slots and keyways and for filing against shoulders. It is available in lengths of from 6 to 16 in.

Fig. 4–8. Pillar file. (Nicholson File Co.)

14. *Describe the square file.*

Ans. The square file has a cross section that is square and has double-cut teeth on all four sides (see Fig. 4–9). It is used for filing small square or rectangular holes, for finishing the bottoms of narrow slots, and so forth. The grade commonly used is bastard, 4 to 16 in. in length.

Fig. 4–9. Square file. (Nicholson File Co.)

15. Describe the round file.

Ans. The round file (Fig. 4–10) has a circular cross section. It is generally tapered. The small sizes are often called *rattail* files. It is used for enlarging round holes, for rounding irregular holes, and for finishing fillets. The grade commonly used is bastard, 4 to 16 in. in length.

Fig. 4–10. Round file. (Nicholson File Co.)

16. Describe the three-square file.

Ans. The three-square file shown in Fig. 4–11—commonly called the *three-cornered file*—is triangular in section, with angles of 60 deg. It tapers to the point, the corners are left sharp. It is double-cut on all three sides and single-cut on the edges. It is generally used for filing internal angles that are less than 90 deg, for clearing out square corners, and for filing taps, cutters, and so forth. The bastard and second-cut grades are preferred. It is available in 4 to 16 in. lengths. Three-cornered files

Fig. 4–11. Three-square file. (Nicholson File Co.)

Fig. 4–12. Three-square file used in saw-sharpening machine. (Henry Disston & Sons, Inc.)

are also used for sharpening saws, either by hand, or held in a machine, as in Fig. 4–12.

17. Describe a half-round file.

Ans. The half-round file (Fig. 4–13), so named because one half is flat, the other half rounded, is a double-cut file that is used when filing concave surfaces. The bastard grade is used mostly, in lengths of from 6 to 16 in.

Fig. 4–13. Half-round file. (Nicholson File Co.)

18. Describe a knife file.

Ans. The knife file shown in Fig. 4–14 is made knife-shaped, the included angle of the sharp edge being approximately 10 deg. This file tapers to the point in width and thickness, and is double-cut on both flat sides, and single-cut on both edges. It is used for finishing the sharp corners of many kinds of slots and grooves. The grade preferred is bastard, in lengths of from 6 to 12 in.

Fig. 4–14. Knife file. (Nicholson File Co.)

19. Describe a warding file.

Ans. A warding file (Fig. 4–15) is rectangular in section, but tapers to a narrow point in the width. It is used mostly by locksmiths for filing notches in keys and locks. It is made double-cut and is available in sizes of from 4 to 12 in. in length. The four-inch file is only 3/64 in. in thickness.

Fig. 4–15. Warding file. (Nicholson File Co.)

20. What are Swiss pattern files?

Ans. Swiss pattern files are similar to ordinary files but are made to more exacting measurements. The points of Swiss pattern files are smaller, and the tapered files have longer tapers. They are also made in much finer cuts. They are primarily finishing tools, used for removing burrs left over from previous finishing operations; truing up narrow grooves, notches, and keyways; rounding out slots, and cleaning out corners; smoothing small parts; doing the final finishing on all sorts of delicate and intricate pieces. The grades vary from No. 00, the coarsest, to No. 6, the finest.

21. *Describe a Swiss pattern crossing file.*

Ans. The Swiss pattern crossing file shown in Fig. 4–16 has a double circular section, one side having the same radius as the half-round file and the other side having a flatter curve, or larger radius. It tapers to the point in both width and thickness and is double-cut on both sides. They are available in all grades from 00 to 6, in lengths of from 3 to 10 in.

Fig. 4–16. Swiss pattern crossing file. (Nicholson File Co.)

22. *What are needle files?*

Ans. Needle files are members of the Swiss pattern family. They usually come in sets of assorted shapes, as in Fig. 4–17. This type of file is used by tool and die makers, and also by watch- and clockmakers. One end of the file is corrugated so that it may be held in the hand. They are available in grade Nos. 0, 2, 4, and 6, and in lengths of 4, 5 1/2, and 6 1/4 in.

Fig. 4–17. Swiss pattern needle files. (Nicholson File Co.)

23. *Describe a cabinet file.*

Ans. The cabinet file (Fig. 4–18) is similar to a half-round file but is wider and thinner. It is dou-ble-cut, usually coarse or bastard in grade. The length is from 6 to 16 in. It is used for smoothing wood.

Fig. 4–18. Cabinet file. (Henry Disston & Sons, Inc.)

24. *What is a rasp?*

Ans. The flat rasp shown in Fig. 4–19 is similar to a file but has coarse teeth raised by a pointed triangular punch. It is also made in half-round and other shapes, 6 to 16 in. in length. It is used for shaping and finishing articles made of wood. The comparative coarseness of rasps is shown in Fig. 4–20.

Fig. 4–19. Flat rasp. (Nicholson File Co.)

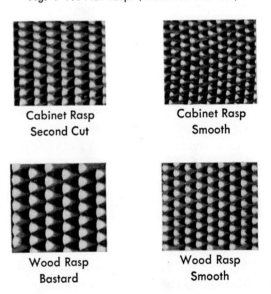

Fig. 4–20. Comparative coarseness of rasps. (Nicholson File Co.)

25. *What is a vixen file?*

Ans. A vixen file, also called a rigid flat file, (Fig. 4–21) has large cutting edges as shown in Fig. 4–22. It is used for filing lead, babbitt, and similar soft materials. The cutting edge is curved. A simi-

Fig. 4–21. Vixen or rigid flat file. (Nicholson File Co.)

lar tool with straight cutting edges is called a *lead float* (see Fig. 4–23).

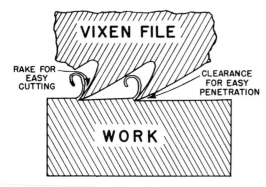

Fig. 4–22. Cutting edges of a vixen file.

Fig. 4–23. Flat lead-float file. (Nicholson File Co.)

26. *Why are files made with convex surfaces?*

Ans. Files are generally made with convex surfaces, that is, they are thicker in the middle than at the ends (see Fig. 4–24). This is done to prevent all the teeth from cutting at the same time, as that would require too much pressure on a file and make it hard to control. A flat surface could not be obtained if the face of the file were straight, as there is a tendency to rock the file. The convex surface helps to overcome the results of rocking.

The convexity of files also serves another purpose. The pressure applied to a file to make it bite into the work also bends the file a little, and, if the file in its natural state was perfectly flat, it would be concave during the cutting operation. This would prevent the production of a flat surface, because the file would cut away more at the edges of the work than in the center and thus leave a convex surface.

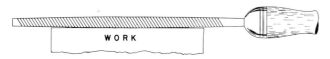

Fig. 4–24. The edge of a file is slightly convex.

27. *What are increment-cut files?*

Ans. Files were originally made by hand, and the teeth were more or less irregular, according to the skill of the mechanic who cut them. Some of the teeth were higher than others, giving fewer contact points. This proved desirable as it in-

creased the cutting life of the file, but the cost of the handmade files was necessarily great. Machines are now used to increase or decrease the cuts of the teeth, resulting in the same type of file as the earlier hand-cut ones.

28. *What is the proper way to hold a file?*

Ans. Grasp the handle in the right hand so that it rests against the palm of the hand, with the thumb placed on top. Place the left hand at the end of the file and let the fingers curl under it.

29. *What should be the position of the body when filing?*

Ans. It is important to have the body in the correct position, as the muscles must move freely. The left foot should point forward and the right foot be brought up close enough to the left to give the necessary balance. When filing, the body should lean forward on the beginning of the forward stroke and then return to the original position at the finish of the stroke. The file must be held straight, or the surface will not be flat. The strokes should not be too fast as this will ruin the file and the work. Enough pressure should be applied to make the file cut evenly.

30. *Should the file be lifted from the work on the return stroke? Explain.*

Ans. No, but the downward pressure should be released during the return stroke in order to avoid dulling the file by wearing away the back of the teeth. This would destroy the cutting edges. This procedure does not hold true in the filing of soft metals, such as lead or aluminum. The file should be drawn back along those metals on the return stroke, as an aid in cleaning the teeth.

31. *When does a file cut best?*

Ans. A file cuts best after it has cut about 2,500 strokes, or after it has removed about 1 cu in. of material because, at that time, most of the cutting edges will be in contact with the work. It must be remembered, however, that after continued use, the worn-down edges will continue to cut less and less until the life of the file is gone.

32. *What is meant by draw filing?*

Ans. Draw filing is the operation of pushing and pulling a file sidewise across the work. For this purpose, the file should be held firmly in both hands so that only a few inches of the file in the center are actually used. Files are normally made to cut on a longitudinal forward stroke, so a file with a short-angle cut ought not to be used for draw filing because of the possibility of scratching or scoring the work, instead of shaving or shearing off the metal smoothly. When it is properly done, draw filing produces a surface with a finer finish than is usually obtained with straight filing. However, the main objective in draw filing is to obtain a perfectly smooth, level surface. A single-cut mill file is preferred for the finishing operation.

33. What is meant by crossing the stroke?

Ans. Crossing the stroke means changing the angle at which one is holding a file by about 45 deg. This will show the high spots and also tend to keep the work flat.

34. What grade of file should be used to remove stock rapidly?

Ans. A large double-cut bastard, or double-cut coarse-tooth, file should be used to remove stock rapidly.

35. What grade of file should be used for finishing work?

Ans. For ordinary finishing work, a 12-in. single-cut smooth file is preferred.

36. What precaution should be taken before filing cast iron?

Ans. Before attempting to file cast iron, you must remove the scale from the surface of the casting. This can be done by chipping, scraping with the edge of a file, tumbling, sand-blasting, or pickling. A good pickling solution is 4 to 10 parts of water to 1 part of sulfuric acid.

37. What two files are generally used in filing on the lathe?

Ans. For filing work that is being machined on a lathe, a double-cut flat file is used for rough filing and a single-cut file for finish filing.

38. What is considered a good technique for filing lathe work?

Ans. Use long, slow strokes. Bear down hard enough on the file to make it cut, but not so hard that the cutting edges will become clogged.

39. What is the result when short, quick strokes are taken to remove a small amount of material from a job by filing it on the lathe?

Ans. Either a series of small flats will be found on the periphery or the work will become out-of-round.

40. How much material should be left for finishing with a file on lathe work?

Ans. Only a small amount of material should be removed by filing. The average amount is 0.003 in. for a finishing operation.

41. What is the effect when a lot of material is removed by filing lathe work?

Ans. The work will have a tendency to be out-of-round, if a lot of material is removed by filing.

42. What three factors affect the cutting efficiency of a file?

Ans. The three important factors are the shape, the sharpness, and the hardness of the teeth.

43. What is meant by pinning of a file?

Ans. When filing soft metals, narrow surfaces, or corners, small particles of the material being filed tend to become clogged in the gullets between the teeth of the file. This is called *pinning* a file. Pinning reduces the efficiency of the file and causes scratches on the surface of the work.

44. What is the cause of pinning?

Ans. The main cause of pinning is the application of too much pressure on the file, especially when using smooth files. It is helpful when using a new file to allow the rough edges and burrs to become worn slightly before taking heavy cuts. Rubbing chalk on a file will also help to prevent pinning.

45. How may a file that is pinned be cleaned?

Ans. A file may be cleaned with a file brush (Fig. 4–25). One side of the brush has fine wires which are used to loosen the embedded material. The other side has bristles which are used to finish the job. In the handle of the file brush is a piece of metal, called a *scorer*, which is used to remove burrs that cannot be loosened by the wires.

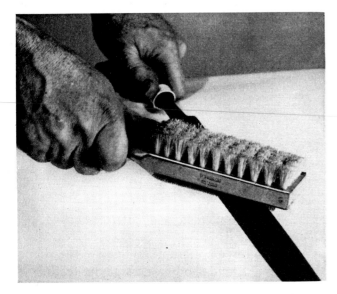

Fig. 4–25. File-cleaning brush and manner of using it. (Henry Disston & Sons, Inc.)

46. Is it permissible to use a file without a handle?

Ans. No. Never use a file without a handle. This is a safety rule. Make sure that the handle is firmly attached to the file. A good type of file handle is the Lutz design shown in Fig. 4–26.

Fig. 4–26. Lutz file handle. (Lutz File & Tool Co.)

47. Mention two precautions that should not be overlooked when filing.

Ans. (1) Do not rub the hand over the work that is being filed. The grease and perspiration of the hand produce a glazed surface, and the sharp edge of the work may cut the hand. (2) Always make sure that finished surfaces are protected by placing some soft material between the work and the hardened jaws of the vise.

48. In placing an order for files, how should a required file be designated?

Ans. A file should be designated by its length, shape, and grade. When ordering files, the quantity desired should be specified first as:

12—6-in. half-round, second-cut files
6—12-in. flat, bastard files

49. What is a filing machine?

Ans. A filing machine is a device for holding a file and moving it with a vertical reciprocating action. The work is placed on the table and pressed

Fig. 4–27. Filing machine. (Oliver Instrument Co.)

Fig. 4–28. Files for use in a filing machine. (Nicholson File Co.)

against the moving file (see Fig. 4–27). The table may be adjusted to a required angle. When adjusting the table, use the same amount of force in setting the protractor against the file to obtain the proper angle as will be used when forcing the work against the file.

50. Are special files used with a filing machine?
Ans. Yes. Files with straight shanks, as in Fig. 4–28, are used in a filing machine. In placing a file in the machine, the roller guide must be adjusted to give the proper amount of friction against the file.

Chapter 5 SOLDERING

Soldering is an ancient art that has not changed very much during the period when great technological improvements were taking place in most industrial areas. It was at one time the special activity of itinerant menders of pots and pans who were called *tinkers*.

1. What is soldering?
Ans. Soldering is the process of joining two metals together by a third soft metal, called *solder*, which is applied in the molten state.

2. What is solder?
Ans. Solder is an alloy of metals that melt at low temperatures.

3. What kinds of solder are commonly used?
Ans. Two kinds are commonly used. One is a soft solder, an alloy of tin and lead. A common proportion is three parts of tin and two parts of lead. Small amounts of bismuth and cadmium are frequently added to lower the melting point of the solder.

Another kind is hard solder, sometimes called *spelter*, an alloy of copper and zinc. A common proportion is four parts of copper and one part of zinc.

4. What is the effect of mixing zinc with solder?
Ans. The addition of zinc causes solder to flow sluggishly. The addition of aluminum has the same effect.

5. Why does solder contain lead?
Ans. Lead is used because it has a low melting point, 620.6°F, and because it is inexpensive.

6. What is the effect of phosphorus on a mixture of solder?
Ans. The addition of a small percentage of phosphorus causes solder to flow more freely. It should be added in the form of phosphor-tin.

7. What peculiar property does bismuth have?
Ans. Bismuth expands when it cools. Most metals shrink when cooling. The presence of bismuth in a solder helps to prevent it from shrinking.

8. What is one of the most important operations in soldering?
Ans. One of the most important operations, and one that is often overlooked, is that of cleaning the surface to be soldered.

9. What is a flux and why is it used?
Ans. Flux is a cleanser and is used to remove and prevent the oxidation of the metals, allowing the solder to flow freely and to unite more firmly with the surfaces to be joined.

10. Why cannot two pieces of metal be soldered together successfully without the aid of a flux after their surfaces have been cleaned?
Ans. A cleaned metal surface tarnishes immediately upon exposure to the air. A thin coating of oxide is formed when the oxygen in the air combines with the metal. Solder will not unite with a metal that has a coating of oxide. A flux is used to remove the oxide the instant the solder comes in contact with the metal.

11. What is the most commonly used flux in the machine shop?
Ans. Prepared soldering paste is the most commonly used flux in the machine shop, but tinsmiths favor "killed" muriatic acid (zinc chloride).

12. What is "killed" muriatic acid?

Ans. Muriatic (hydrochloric) acid is killed by adding small scraps of zinc, a few at a time, until the acid fails to eat the zinc. It is then called a *saturated solution.* The killed, or cut, acid is known as chloride of zinc.

CAUTION: Do not kill the acid near any machines or tools, as the escaping fumes may cause the machines or tools to rust.

13. On what kind of metals is chloride of zinc used as a flux?

Ans. Chloride of zinc is used as a flux on steel, cast iron, brass, zinc, nickel, monel metal, stainless steel, lead, and galvanized iron.

14. For what metal is chloride of zinc flux diluted?

Ans. When chloride of zinc is used as a flux for soldering tin, it is diluted with about 50 percent alcohol.

15. Is muriatic acid ever used in the raw state as a flux?

Ans. Muriatic acid is frequently used in the raw state as a flux for soldering galvanized iron. It is also used as a cleaner for cast iron, galvanized iron, and sheet steel.

CAUTION: Where muriatic acid or zinc chloride is used as a flux, the parts should be cleaned after soldering to prevent the acid from eating the metal.

16. What kind of flux is used for soldering copper and brass?

Ans. Zinc chloride or a commercially prepared soldering flux.

17. What kind of flux is used for soldering lead?

Ans. Rosin, tallow, or zinc chloride may be used as a flux for soldering lead.

18. What kind of flux is used for soldering sheet tin?

Ans. Beeswax, rosin, or any of the commercially prepared fats, pastes, or liquid fluxes are considered good. Zinc chloride may be used by diluting it with 50 percent alcohol.

19. What kind of flux should be used for soldering wrought iron or steel?

Ans. Zinc chloride is the best flux to use for soldering wrought iron or steel.

20. What kind of flux is used by canneries and packing houses when sealing cans?

Ans. Rosin is generally used as a flux in the sealing of cans for food because it is nonpoisonous. Palm oil or cocoa oil is also used.

21. What kind of flux is best to use for soldering commutator wires and electrical connections?

Ans. An alcoholic solution of rosin is considered best for the soldering of commutator wires and electrical connections. Do not use an acid flux, as this will cause a corrosive action.

22. What is a soldering iron?

Ans. A soldering iron, sometimes called a *copper,* is a steel rod with a piece of copper attached to one end and a wooden handle on the other end (Fig. 5–1). They are made in several sizes and styles. Two of the styles are shown in Fig. 5–2 and Fig. 5–3.

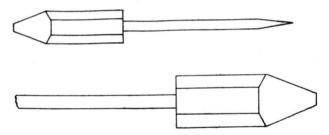

Fig. 5–1. Square-point copper. (Electric Materials Co.)

Fig. 5–2. Bottoming copper. (Electric Materials Co.)

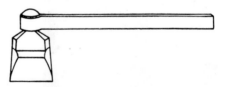

Fig. 5–3. Hatchet copper. (Electric Materials Co.)

23. What is the purpose of a soldering iron?

Ans. A soldering iron is used to melt the solder and heat the metals that are to be joined together.

24. How is a soldering iron heated?

Ans. A soldering iron is usually heated by a blowtorch (Fig. 5–4), or over a gas flame. Heating an iron in a coal fire is not advisable as this results in a dirty iron. Irons that are heated by electricity are also available (Fig. 5–5). The various parts of a blowtorch are shown in Fig. 5–6.

Fig. 5–4. Blowtorch. (Clayton & Lambert Mfg. Co.)

Fig. 5–5. Electric soldering iron. (Stanley Tools)

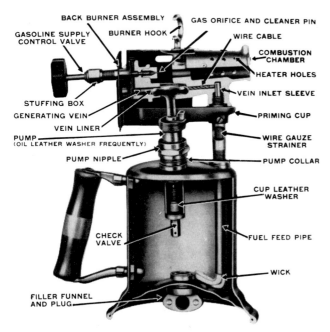

Fig. 5–6. Cut-away view of blowtorch. (Clayton & Lambert Mfg. Co.)

25. How is a soldering iron prepared for use?

Ans. In order to have solder cling to the iron, the tip of it must be tinned. To do this, first use a file to clean the copper back to the end of the beveled top, and then heat the copper a little more than is necessary to melt the solder. Rub the clean, heated copper with sal ammoniac and then apply the solder. To have a good clean point, rub over the soldered point with a rag immediately after it has been tinned. A soldering iron should not be overheated (red hot is too hot), as this will remove the solder from the point and it will have to be tinned again.

26. How should the surface of a piece of metal be prepared for soldering?

Ans. The surface of the metal must be cleaned. Use a file, scraper, or an acid cleaner.

27. What is the procedure for soldering a piece of metal to cast iron?

Ans. Prepare the surface of the cast iron by making it smooth and then cleaning it with raw muriatic acid. The surface of the cast iron should then be tinned, using zinc chloride as a flux. The piece of metal may then be soldered to the cast iron in the usual manner.

28. What is meant by sweating parts together?

Ans. Sweating parts together is done by first tinning the two surfaces to be joined. Flux is then applied to both surfaces after which they are clamped together and heated. When cool, the two parts will be soldered to each other. Split bushings are sometimes sweated together in this manner so that they may be machined as one unit. After machining, they may be separated by applying heat and pulling them apart.

29. What is the difference between soldering and brazing?

Ans. The difference lies in the kind of solder that is used and the amount of heat that is applied to the work. Hard solder, mentioned in question 3, requires the use of a blowtorch to melt it and also to heat the parts that are to be brazed together. Borax is often used as a flux for brazing. A brazed joint is much stronger than a soldered joint.

30. What can be done to prevent solder from running away from the surfaces to be joined?

Ans. For both soldering and brazing, it is a common practice to use clay to surround the area to be joined if the solder will otherwise run away from the surface to be soldered.

31. What is the correct design of the top of the square-point soldering iron, and how should it be applied to the work?

Ans. The point of a soldering iron should be rather stubby so that the heat will be retained at the point as long as possible. An included angle of 45 deg is suitable for medium and large irons. The iron at *A* in Fig. 5–7 is being correctly applied to the work so that the heat can be transmitted as rapidly as possible. The iron at *B* is shaped correctly, but it is being applied improperly to pass the heat to the work. The iron shown at *C* is too pointed, and the heat at the point is soon lost.

As solder will not flow upward, an attempt to solder the underside of a job by the method shown at *D* is not successful, because the solder will flow away from the joint. However, the following method can be used. Clean only one pointed side of the soldering iron, heat it, tin it, and then apply it to the work, as at *E*. Solder can be applied in this way because it will cling only to the clean side of the iron. Be sure that the other sides are left dirty so that the solder will not run off.

Whatever the type of soldering iron selected, it must have adequate capacity for the work it is to

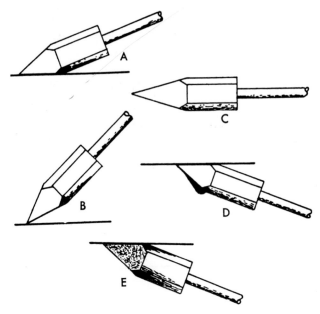

Fig. 5–7. Methods of applying a soldering iron.

do. A perfectly soldered connection can be obtained only when the surfaces to be joined have absorbed enough heat to melt the solder. For example, it is almost impossible to solder a large article with a small soldering iron, because the large article will absorb all the heat from the small iron and the part to be soldered will not be heated sufficiently to make a good fusion. As a large iron will carry more heat to the part being soldered, a large iron should be used on large jobs. A small iron should, of course, be used for small or intricate jobs.

Chapter 6 MEASURING TOOLS

One of the most important phases of manufacturing is measurement, accurate measurement. Many tools and devices have been designed for this purpose. Some of them are simple and inexpensive. Others are more intricate and cost a considerable amount of money. Each tool has its definite uses.

The most common measuring tool is a rule. There are many varieties. In the shop, rules are usually, although improperly, referred to as *scales*. The use of the proper name should be encouraged.

Before a student can read a rule or any of the precision measuring tools efficiently, he must be thoroughly familiar with common fractions and decimal fractions. Toolmakers and other skilled workers are often called upon to change decimal numbers to common fractions and common fractions to decimals in making measurements and in reading and checking blueprints and sketches.

When reading a rule, it is sometimes convenient to read either way from some large dimension line. For instance, in measuring 47/64 in., it is easier to find 3/4 (48/64) and subtract 1/64 from it than to count the divisions from the end of the rule.

To change a fraction to a decimal, it is customary to use a decimal-equivalent chart, but if a chart is not available, the method is to divide the numerator of the fraction by the denominator. For example, in changing 3/16 to a decimal, divide the 3 by 16, which equals 0.1875.

Precision measuring tools, such as micrometers and vernier tools, are read in thousandths and even in fractional parts of a thousandth of an inch. For example, 1/8 (0.125) is read as "one hundred and twenty-five thousandths," while 1/16 (0.0625) is read as "sixty-two and one-half thousandths"; 1/32 (0.03125) is read as "thirty-one and one-quarter thousandths"; etc. It will be noted that these readings give the full decimal values for the corresponding common fractions. However, since the

precision tools commonly used in the shop cannot be read closer than one-tenth of one-thousandth, it is customary for a mechanic to use only those figures up to and including the fourth decimal place. For example, the complete decimal value of 1/64 is 0.015625, which in the shop is commonly read as "fifteen and six-tenths thousandths," fifteen being the whole number of thousandths while six is six-tenths of one-thousandth, or a fractional part of a thousandth.

Table 6–1 contains the decimal equivalents of the common fractions that are most frequently used in the shop. They should be memorized.

Table 6–1. DECIMAL EQUIVALENTS OF FRACTIONS MOST FREQUENTLY USED IN THE SHOP

Fraction	64	32	16	8	4	Decimal	Fraction	64	32	16	8	4	Decimal
1/64	1					0.015625	7/16	28	14	7			0.4375
1/32	2	1				0.03125	1/2	32	16	8	4	2	0.5000
1/16	4	2	1			0.0625	9/16	36	18	9			0.5625
3/32	6	3				0.09375	5/8	40	20	10	5		0.6250
1/8	8	4	2	1		0.1250	11/16	44	22	11			0.6875
3/16	12	6	3			0.1875	3/4	48	24	12	6	3	0.7500
1/4	16	8	4	2	1	0.2500	13/16	52	26	13			0.8125
5/16	20	10	5			0.3125	7/8	56	28	14	7		0.8750
3/8	24	12	6	3		0.3750	15/16	60	30	15			0.9375

1. What is a rule?

Ans. A rule is a graduated measuring instrument, made of wood, metal, or other suitable material. It is usually graduated to indicate inches and fractions of an inch.

2. What is a scale?

Ans. A scale is similar in appearance to a rule, as its surface is graduated into regular spaces, but these spaces differ decidedly from those on a rule, being larger or smaller than the actual measurements indicated. A scale gives proportional meas-

Fig. 6–1. Flat boxwood scale.

Fig. 6–2. Triangular boxwood scale. (Post Frederick Co.)

urements. Figures 6–1 and 6–2 show two types of scales that are used by draftsmen. On each of these, one edge is graduated with full-sized inches and fractions of an inch; the other edges have graduations that are half-size, quarter-size, and so forth.

3. Are all rules graduated with the same divisions of an inch?

Ans. No. Most rules have four sets of graduations, one on each edge. Many combinations are available. Manufacturers have standard combinations which are identified by a number from 1 to 12, as shown in Table 6–2. No. 4 is the most popular, with eighths and sixteenths on one side, and thirty-seconds and sixty-fourths on the other side.

Table 6–2. BROWN AND SHARPE STANDARD GRADUATION OF RULES

No. of gradua-tion	First corner	Second corner	Third corner	Fourth corner
1	10, 20, 50, 100	12, 24, 48	14, 28	16, 32, 64
2	8	10, 20, 50, 100	12, 24, 48	16, 32, 64
3	10	50	32	64
4	8	16	32	64
7	16	32	64	100
10	32	64		
11	64	100		
12	50	100		

4. Describe a standard steel rule.

Ans. The most common steel rule used in a toolroom (Fig. 6–3) is made of tempered steel about 3/64 in. thick, 3/4 in. wide, and 6 in. long, with No. 4 graduations. The same style may be obtained in lengths from 1 to 48 in. and in a choice of gradu-

ations. The graduations on the end of the rule are handy for measuring a narrow space.

Fig. 6–3. Standard steel rule. (Brown & Sharpe Mfg. Co.)

5. What is a flexible steel rule?

Ans. A flexible steel rule is made of tempered spring steel about 1/64 in. thick, 1/2 in. wide, and 6 in. long. It is available in many graduations, Nos. 3 and 4 being most popular. It is also available in other lengths. This type of rule is for general use and for measuring work that is curved.

6. What is a narrow rule?

Ans. A narrow rule is made of tempered steel about 3/64 in. thick, 3/16 in. wide and in lengths from 4 to 12 in. It has a combination of either No. 10 or 11 graduations and is useful for measuring in small openings and spaces. It is similar in size and appearance to the narrow hook rule in Fig. 6–5.

7. What is a hook rule?

Ans. A hook rule, as shown in Fig. 6–4, has a hook attached to one end which makes it easy to take measurements from an inside edge when it is not convenient to see the end of the rule. Hook rules are made in many sizes. A narrow hook rule is made for measuring in holes as small as 3/8 in. in diameter (see Fig. 6–5).

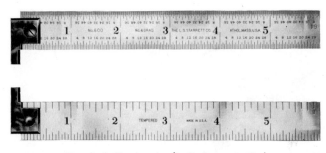

Fig. 6–4. Hook rule. (L. S. Starrett Co.)

Fig. 6–5. Narrow hook rule. (L. S. Starrett Co.)

8. What is a shrink rule?

Ans. A shrink rule (scale) (Fig. 6–6) is a tempered-steel rule similar in size and appearance to a standard rule. It has No. 4 graduations. It differs from other rules in that the inches are slightly longer than regular inches. It is used by patternmakers. Patterns for castings are deliberately made larger than the required castings to allow for the shrinkage of the molten metal as it cools to a solid. Since the amount of shrinkage is not the same for all metals, shrink rules are made from 1/10 to 7/16 in. per ft oversize.

Fig. 6–6. Shrink rule. (L. S. Starrett Co.)

9. What is a short rule?

Ans. A short rule is usually one of a set of small rules that are made for measuring in small spaces where it is inconvenient to use any other rule (see Fig. 6–7). The set of rules consists of a 1/4, 3/8, 1/2, 3/4, and 1 in. rule, together with a holder. The rule may be held at any angle. It is secured by turning the knurled nut at the end of the holder. The rules are available in No. 10 or 12 graduations.

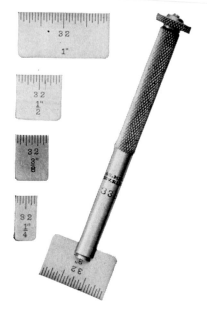

Fig. 6–7. Short rules. (Brown & Sharpe Mfg. Co.)

10. What is a caliper rule?

Ans. A caliper rule (Fig. 6–8) is made with a narrow rule that slides inside a groove in the side of a wider rule. It may be used to make internal and external measurements. It is provided with a screw that will lock the slide in place as required. The narrow nibs at the end of the jaws will enter a hole as small as 1/8 in. in diameter.

Fig. 6–8. Caliper rule. (L. S. Starrett Co.)

11. What is a rule depth gage?

Ans. A rule depth gage (Fig. 6–9) consists of a steel head which has a slot to receive a narrow rule. The rule is held in position by a knurled nut. It is designed to measure the depth of small holes and slots.

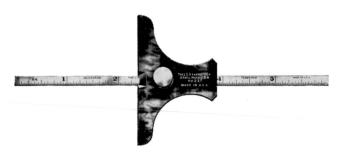

Fig. 6–9. Rule depth gage. (L. S. Starrett Co.)

12. Why are some graduations in common fractions of an inch and others in decimal fractions of an inch?

Ans. Most manufacturers in the United States design their products using common fractions for measurements of parts of an inch. For ordinary measurements, the rule is satisfactory, most mechanics being able to measure accurately as close as 1/64 in. When greater accuracy is required, dimensions are specified as decimal fractions. Such precision dimensions are usually given to the third or fourth decimal place as 0.375 or 0.5625.

A few manufacturers have adopted the decimal system for both ordinary and precision measurements. In this case, the inch is divided into tenths, hundredths, and thousandths. Measurements made with a rule may be read with accuracy to within twenty-thousandths (0.020) of an inch. For this reason, graduations are made in tenths of an inch (0.100) and in fiftieths (0.020) of an inch. The decimal system is preferred by some because it is simple. There is also little chance of error, as sometimes happens when common fractions have to be changed to decimal fractions for measuring with a precision instrument.

A drawing with dimensions specified in the decimal system and a rule graduated in tenths and fiftieths are shown in Fig. 6–10. Note that ordinary dimensions are either one- or two-place decimals, and that second-place decimals are even numbers.

14. *What is a steel-tape rule?*

Ans. A steel-tape rule (Fig. 6–13) is a flexible rule that when extended will support itself, but may also be used to measure curved or irregular surfaces. The blade is usually 1/2 in. wide and 72 in. long. The graduations are in sixteenths except for the first 6 in., which are graduated in thirty-seconds of an inch.

15. *What is a steel tape?*

Ans. A steel tape (Fig. 6–14) is similar to a steel-tape rule but differs in that it is entirely flexi-

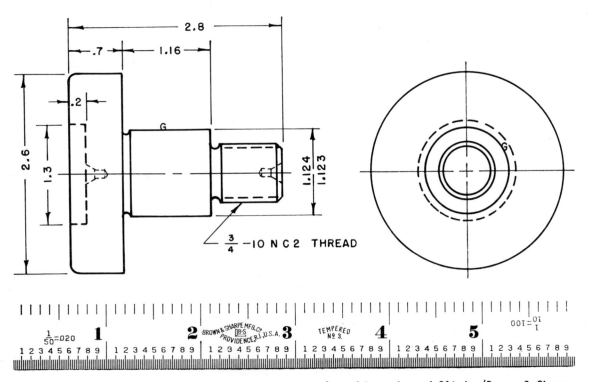

Fig. 6–10. Drawing with decimal dimensions and rule graduated in tenths and fiftieths. (Brown & Sharpe Mfg. Co.)

13. *What is a combination set?*

Ans. A combination set (Fig. 6–11) consists of a rule, a square, a center head, and a protractor. The rule is made of tempered steel with a groove cut the length of one side along which the other parts may slide. Each part is provided with a knurled nut for locking it into position. The rule has No. 4 or 7 graduations and is available in lengths of from 9 to 24 in. This tool may be used as a rule, a square, a depth gage, for marking miters, for locating the center on the end of round bars, and for measuring angles. Some applications of its use are shown in Fig. 6–12.

Fig. 6–11. Combination set. (L. S. Starrett Co.)

ble. It is mostly used for measuring long distances. The graduations are in eighths of an inch. The

Fig. 6–12. Some applications of the combination set: A, measuring the angle of a slide; B, measuring the depth of a job on a planer; C, locating the centerline of a bushing; D, other convenient uses. (Brown & Sharpe Mfg. Co. and L. S. Starrett Co.)

number of feet are marked on the tape. The tape is 3/8 in. wide and is available in lengths from 25 to 100 ft.

Two types of rules used by carpenters are shown in Figs. 6–15 and 6–16.

Many tools have been designed to make it more convenient for workmen to measure and lay out work with a rule, among which are dividers, calipers, surface gages, and trammels or beam compasses.

16. What is a divider?

Ans. A divider (Fig. 6–17) consists of a pair of steel legs adjusted by a screw and nut and held together by a circular spring at one end, in which

Fig. 6–13. Steel-tape rule. (Stanley Tools)

Fig. 6–14. Steel tape. (Lufkin Rule Co.)

Fig. 6–17. Spring divider. (Lufkin Rule Co.)

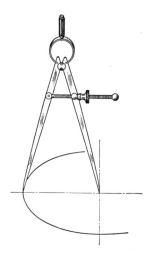

Fig. 6–18. Scribing a circle with dividers.

is inserted a handle. It is available in sizes from 2 to 8 in. The size is the length of the legs from the pivot to the point.

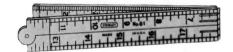

Fig. 6–15. Boxwood folding rule. (Stanley Tools)

Fig. 6–16. Zig-zag rule. (Lufkin Rule Co.)

17. For what purposes are dividers used?
Ans. Dividers are used for measuring the distance between points, for transferring a measurement directly from a rule, and for scribing circles and arcs on metal (see Fig. 6–18).

18. Describe the procedure for scribing a circle with dividers.

Ans. The center of the circle should first be located and marked with a prick punch. Adjust the legs of the divider to the required measurement (radius of the circle), as in Fig. 6–19. Set the point of one leg in the pricked center. Then, holding the handle between forefinger and thumb, scribe short arcs on opposite sides of center. Measure the distance between the arcs. If the distance is not equal to the required diameter, make the necessary adjustment of the divider before scribing the complete circle.

19. What is a trammel?
Ans. A trammel, also called a *beam compass* (Fig. 6–20) is a type of divider that is preferred for scribing large circles. It consists of a steel bar and two legs. In the end of each leg is a steel point. The legs are locked on the bar by tightening a knurled nut on the top of the leg. One of the legs

Fig. 6–19. Adjusting a divider to a required measurement.

has an adjusting screw attached to it. In setting the trammel to a required dimension, one leg is secured to one end of the bar, the other leg with the adjusting screw is moved from the first leg to approximately the correct distance. The adjusting screw is tightened to the bar, but the leg is not. By turning the adjusting screw, the loose leg is then adjusted for an accurate measurement, after which it, also, is locked on the bar. A V-shaped point may be used in one leg so that circles may be scribed from a hole. The bars are available in lengths of from 6 to 20 in.

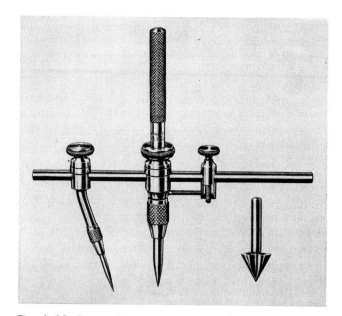

Fig. 6–20. Trammel or beam compass. (L. S. Starrett Co.)

20. *What is a caliper?*
Ans. A caliper is a tool that is designed for meas-

uring diameters. There are many kinds and sizes of calipers.

21. *What are some of the uses of outside calipers?*

Ans. Outside calipers (Fig. 6–21) are used to measure outside diameters. A rule may be used to measure the diameter of the end of a bar, but it is not practical to measure diameters in between the ends, as in the case of the detail in Fig. 6–22. To measure an outside diameter with calipers, they are first set to the approximate diameter of the stock. Then the calipers are held at right angles to the center line of the work, as in Fig. 6–23, and moved back and forth across the center line, while they are being adjusted, until the points bear lightly on the work. This is called "getting the feel." When the tool has been adjusted properly, the diameter may be read from a rule, as shown in Fig. 6–24.

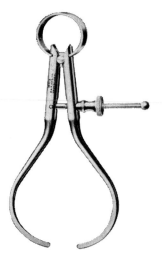

Fig. 6–21. Outside calipers. (Brown & Sharpe Mfg. Co.)

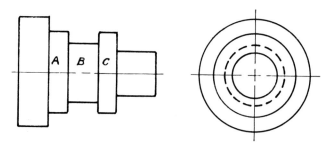

Fig. 6–22. Accurate measurement of diameters A, B, C are not possible with a rule.

22. *What are some of the uses of inside calipers?*
Ans. Inside calipers (Fig. 6–25) are used to

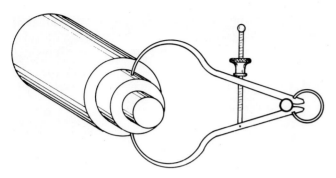

Fig. 6–23. Setting outside calipers to the size of the work.

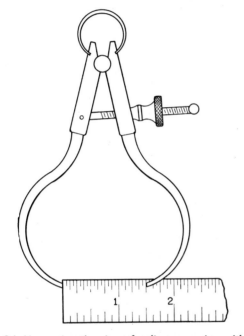

Fig. 6–24. Measuring the size of caliper opening with a rule.

measure inside diameters, widths of slots, and the like. To measure the diameter of a hole, open the calipers to the approximate size, then hold one leg

Fig. 6–25. Inside calipers.

of the calipers against the wall of the hole and turn the adjusting screw until the other leg just touches the opposite side. The calipers should be moved back and forth, as in Fig. 6–26, to feel the proper contact. The size of the opening is then read from a rule, as in Fig. 6–27, or from a micrometer, as in Fig. 6–28.

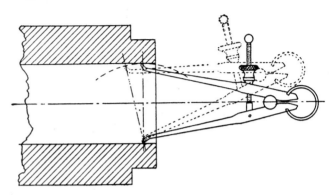

Fig. 6–26. Adjusting inside calipers to the size of a hole.

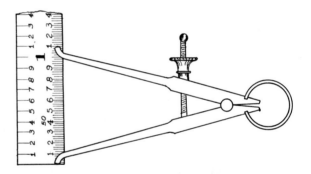

Fig. 6–27. Measuring opening of inside calipers with a rule.

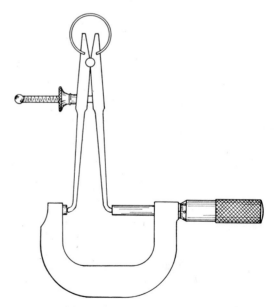

Fig. 6–28. Measuring opening of inside calipers with a micrometer.

23. Describe the transferring of a measurement from outside to inside calipers.

Ans. When a measurement has to be transferred from outside to inside calipers, both calipers are held so that they are in the position shown in Fig. 6–29. With the extreme point of one leg of the inside calipers placed on the extreme point of one leg of the outside calipers, adjust the inside calipers until the two extreme points touch lightly. Care must be taken not to force either pair of calipers, or a true reading will not be obtained.

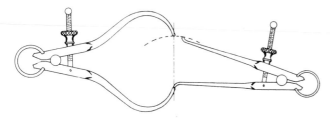

Fig. 6–29. Transferring a measurement from outside to inside calipers.

24. What is a telescoping gage?

Ans. A telescoping gage (Fig. 6–30) is a tool that is used in the same manner as inside calipers. It consists of a handle and two legs, the smaller one telescoping into the other. After being adjusted to fit a hole or slot, as in Fig. 6–31, the gage can be locked in position by turning a knurled screw in the handle. It may then be withdrawn from the hole and measured with a micrometer (see Fig. 6–32). Telescoping gages are made in many sizes to measure holes from 1/2 to 6 in. in diameter.

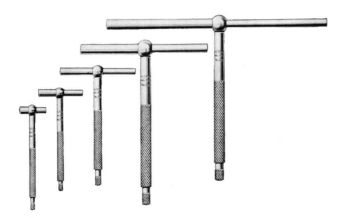

Fig. 6–30. Telescoping gages. (L. S. Starrett Co.)

25. What is a hermaphrodite caliper?

Ans. A hermaphrodite caliper has two legs which work on a hinge joint (Fig. 6–33). One leg

Fig. 6–31. Adjusting telescoping gage to the size of a hole. (L. S. Starrett Co.)

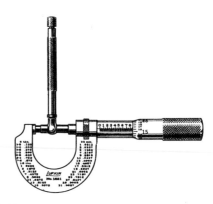

Fig. 6–32. Measuring a telescoping gage with a micrometer. (Lufkin Rule Co.)

is similar to a leg of a divider and the other is similar to a leg of an inside caliper. Hermaphrodite calipers may be used to scribe arcs, or as a marking gage in layout work. To set hermaphrodite calipers to a rule, adjust the scriber leg until it is slightly shorter than the curved leg. Then, with the curved leg set on the end of a rule, adjust the scriber leg to a point opposite the required line on the rule, as illustrated in Fig. 6–34.

26. What is a surface gage?

Ans. A surface gage (Fig. 6–35) is a tool consisting of a steel base with a rotating head which holds a steel spindle. On the spindle is clamped a scriber. The base has a V-shaped groove that makes it convenient for use on cylindrical work. A linear guide is provided by two gage pins that may be pushed down through the base. The spindle

Fig. 6–33. Hermaphrodite caliper. (Lufkin Rule Co.)

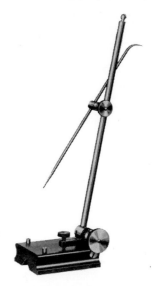

Fig. 6–35. Surface gage. (Lufkin Rule Co.)

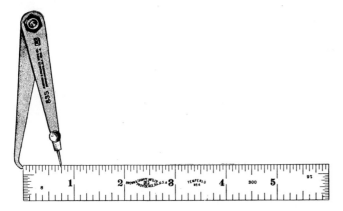

Fig. 6–34. Adjusting a hermaphrodite caliper to size with a rule. (Brown & Sharpe Mfg. Co.)

may be rotated to any required position, even below the flat surface of the base. A device is built into the base so that the spindle may be adjusted to the exact dimension required.

27. What are some of the uses of a surface gage?

Ans. A surface gage is used for scribing lines on layout work and for checking parallel surfaces. Preferred ways for setting the scriber to a definite dimension are shown. The combination square in Fig. 6–36 and the rule holder in Fig. 6–37 are used in preference to a rule alone because it may be held securely without wobbling. Set the square or rule holder on the layout table, being sure that the rule is resting on the table and clamped securely to the head of the square or rule holder. Then set the spindle of the gage at a convenient angle, place the scriber on the spindle at the approximate

height desired, and, finally, adjust the point of the scriber to the exact measurement by means of the adjusting screw on the base of the gage. Some of the many ways of using a surface gage are shown in Figs. 6–38 to 6–40.

Fig. 6–36. Setting surface gage to a combination square. (Brown & Sharpe Mfg. Co.)

The rule and the many measuring tools associated with it are used in the shop for measurements where a small variation in the size would not spoil the work. The term commonly used for such dimensions is *scale dimension*. Scale dimen-

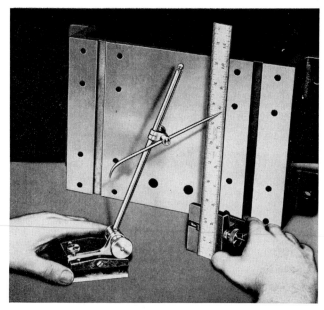

Fig. 6–37. Setting surface gage to a rule held in a rule holder. (L. S. Starrett Co.)

Fig. 6–39. Checking the location of a hole with a dial attachment on a surface gage. (Brown & Sharpe Mfg. Co.)

Fig. 6–38. Checking work on a planer with a surface gage. (Brown & Sharpe Mfg. Co.)

Fig. 6–40. Laying out work at the bench with a surface gage. (Lufkin Rule Co.)

sions are usually permitted to vary from the required size ten-thousandths (0.010) of an inch either way and still pass inspection. Skilled mechanics are able to measure within such limits with a rule. However, a good percentage of measurements made by toolmakers are for *precision dimensions*. This term is used for dimensions where

the amount of error permitted is less than 0.010 of an inch and may be as little as one ten-thousandth (0.0001) of an inch.

Special instruments have been invented and designed so that precision dimensions may be accurately measured. The most common precision instrument is the micrometer caliper. It was invented by Jean Palmer, a Frenchman, in 1848. It was introduced in the United States of America in 1867 when J. R. Brown and L. Sharpe brought back a Palmer micrometer caliper with them after a visit to the Paris Exposition (see Fig. 6–41). From this instrument they developed the predecessor of the modern micrometer which was offered to the public in 1877 (Fig. 6–42). In 1885, the same men introduced a new model (Fig. 6–43) which is almost identical with those in use today. Compared with the rule, the micrometer is a newcomer in the field of measurement. Figure 6–44 shows a modern 1-in. micrometer with identification of its parts. The regular micrometer, usually referred to in the shop as a *mike,* is used for measuring outside dimensions. It is available in many sizes. There are several other types of micrometers, but all are designed according to the same fundamental principle.

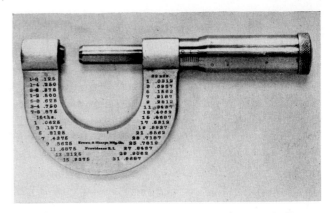

Fig. 6–43. Micrometer caliper of 1885. (Brown & Sharpe Mfg. Co.)

Fig. 6–41. Palmer micrometer of 1867. (Brown & Sharpe Mfg. Co.)

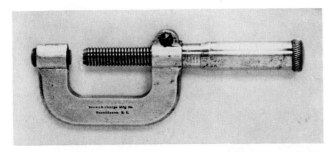

Fig. 6–42. Micrometer caliper of 1877. (Brown & Sharpe Mfg. Co.)

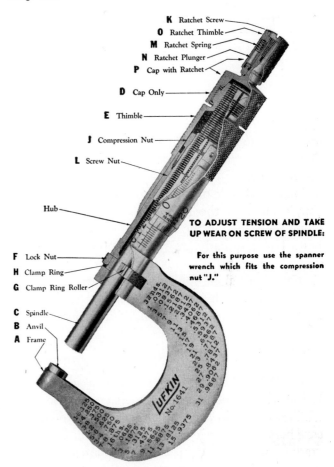

Fig. 6–44. Modern micrometer caliper with identification of its parts. (Lufkin Rule Co.)

28. What are the five principal parts of a micrometer?

Ans. The five principal parts are the frame, anvil, spindle, sleeve, and thimble (see Fig. 6–44).

29. What are the graduations of a micrometer?

Ans. The graduations on the sleeve of the micrometer are twenty-five-thousandths (0.025) of

an inch apart. Every fourth division on the sleeve is marked with a number from 0 to 10, thus identifying each one-tenth of an inch, or a hundred-thousandths (0.100). Each of the numbers is read as if two zeros were added to each one, as the 0.200 shown in Fig. 6–45.

The graduations on the thimble represent divisions of one-thousandth (0.001) of an inch. This is determined as follows: The edge of the thimble coincides with the zero on the sleeve when the micrometer is closed. Each time the thimble is revolved one revolution, it moves along the sleeve one graduation or 0.025 in. The circular edge of the thimble has 25 equal divisions scribed on it, so when the thimble is revolved just enough to equal one of the divisions, it has moved along the sleeve one twenty-fifth (1/25) of twenty-five thousandths, which is one-thousandth (0.001) of an inch. In order to make the counting of these divisions easier, every fifth one is numbered.

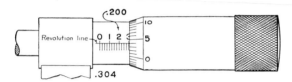

Fig. 6–45. Micrometer sleeve graduations.

30. *Why does the thimble of a micrometer move along the sleeve exactly twenty-five thousandths (0.025) of an inch for each complete revolution of the thimble?*

Ans. The inside of the micrometer is threaded so that each time the thimble is turned, it moves along the sleeve in the same manner as a nut on a bolt. These threads are made 40 to the inch, so when the thimble is revolved one complete revolution, it moves along the sleeve one-fortieth (1/40) of an inch, which equals the decimal fraction of twenty-five thousandths (0.025) of an inch.

31. *How are the graduations read on a micrometer?*

Ans. After the micrometer has been adjusted to fit the work to be measured, the size may be read while it is still on the work, or it may be removed, care being taken to avoid moving the thimble. The graduations exposed on the sleeve are read first, the numbers as hundreds, to which is added 25 for each of the remaining whole divisions, plus the actual number of divisions on the thimble which have passed the revolution line. The reading in Fig. 6–46 is 200 plus 25 plus 16, a total of 241 thousandths of an inch. In Fig. 6–47, the division on the sleeve past the figure 2 is not a complete division, so the reading is 200 on the sleeve plus 24 on the thimble, a total of 224 thousandths of an inch.

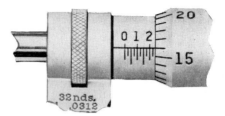

Fig. 6–46. A reading of 0.241 in. on a micrometer. (Brown & Sharpe Mfg. Co.)

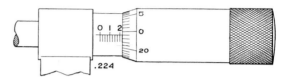

Fig. 6–47. A reading of 0.224 in. on a micrometer.

32. *Explain how a piece of work is measured with a micrometer.*

Ans. The work may be held in one hand and the micrometer in the other, as in Fig. 6–48. If the work is supported, as on the lathe in Fig. 6–49, it may be more convenient to use both hands. The thimble should be turned gently until the spindle and the anvil of the micrometer just touch the work. One should be able to feel the contact on both sides. Do not force the spindle against the work to grip it, as with a clamp. It is a common practice to revolve the micrometer back and forth a little around the work to make sure that a correct measurement is made.

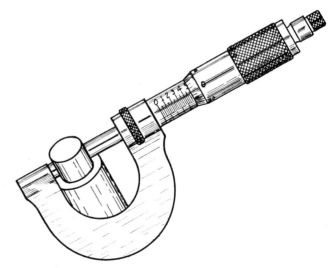

Fig. 6–48. Measuring the end of a round bar with a micrometer.

33. *What is a ratchet stop on a micrometer?*

Ans. A ratchet stop (Fig. 6–44) is a device that prevents the use of too much pressure when ad-

Fig. 6–49. Measuring turned work at the lathe with a micrometer. (Brown & Sharpe Mfg. Co.)

justing a micrometer around a part to be measured. The ratchet prevents further turning of the thimble, after the correct amount of pressure has been applied to the spindle to give an accurate measurement.

34. Can dimensions be accurately measured with a micrometer when the permissible variation is less than one-thousandth (0.001) of an inch?

Ans. Yes. With ordinary micrometers it is possible to estimate one-half of one-thousandth (0.0005) of an inch when the revolution line on the sleeve comes in between two division lines on the thimble. For accurate measurements of less than one-thousandth (0.001), a micrometer with a vernier scale on the sleeve should be used (Fig. 6–50).

Fig. 6–50. Vernier scale on the sleeve of a micrometer. (Brown & Sharpe Mfg. Co.)

35. Describe the vernier scale of a micrometer.

Ans. The vernier scale of a micrometer consists of 10 equal divisions that are scribed on the sleeve of the micrometer and numbered from 0 to 9. The 10 divisions equal in space 9 divisions of the thimble which represent nine-thousandths of an inch (0.009). By division it can be seen that each division on the vernier scale represents nine ten-thousandths of an inch (0.0009). The difference between one of the divisions on the thimble and one of those on the vernier scale is 0.0010 minus 0.0009, which equals 0.0001 or one ten-thousandth of an inch.

36. Explain how the vernier-scale graduations of a micrometer are read.

Ans. When the first and last lines on the vernier scale coincide with the lines on the thimble, as at *A* and *B* in Fig. 6–51, it indicates that the reading made in the ordinary way is accurate; in this case it is 0.250. If one of the other lines on the vernier scale coincides with one of the lines on the thimble, as at *C* in Fig. 6–51, then the number of the vernier line indicates how many ten-thousandths of an inch should be added to the original reading. In this case, line seven is the one that coincides with one of the lines on the thimble, so seven ten-thousandths (0.0007) should be added, making the correct reading 0.2507 of an inch.

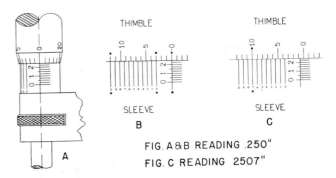

Fig. 6–51. Reading the vernier scale of a micrometer. (L. S. Starrett Co.)

37. What are some of the reasons why measurements made with a micrometer are not accurate?

Ans. The most common reason is failure to make sure that the work to be measured and the faces of the anvil and spindle of the micrometer are clean. Another reason is that the micrometer being used may be in need of adjustment due to wear or careless handling. A third reason is lack of care on the part of the workman in reading the graduations.

38. What is an inside micrometer?

Ans. An inside micrometer (Fig. 6–52) is designed with the same graduations as an outside micrometer and is adjusted by revolving the thimble in the same way. It is used for taking internal measurements where greater accuracy is required than can be obtained with inside calipers or telescoping gages. It is available in many sizes. Figure 6–53 shows an inside micrometer in use.

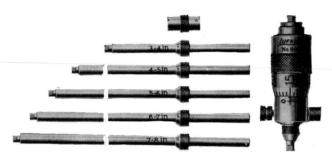

Fig. 6–52. Inside micrometer. (Lufkin Rule Co.)

Fig. 6–53. Measuring a bored hole with an inside micrometer. (South Bend Lathe Works)

39. What is a tube micrometer?

Ans. A tube micrometer (Fig. 6–54) is one that is specially designed to measure the thickness of the material of piping, tubing, and similar shapes.

40. What is a screw-thread micrometer?

Ans. A screw-thread micrometer (Fig. 6–55) is similar to an outside micrometer except that the spindle is pointed to fit between 60-deg V threads, and the anvil is shaped to fit over a 60-deg V

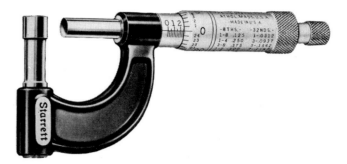

Fig. 6–54. Tube micrometer. (L. S. Starrett Co.)

thread. It is used to measure the pitch diameter of a thread. They are available in many sizes depending on the pitch of the thread to be measured.

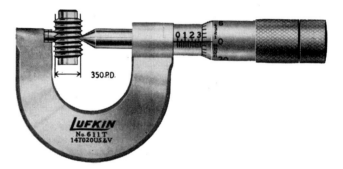

Fig. 6–55. Screw-thread micrometer. (Lufkin Rule Co.)

41. What is a depth micrometer?

Ans. A depth micrometer (Fig. 6–56) is a tool that is designed to measure accurately the depth of grooves, recesses, and holes. The graduations are read in the same manner as a regular micrometer.

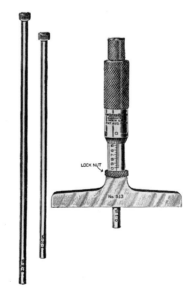

Fig. 6–56. Depth micrometer. (Lufkin Rule Co.)

42. What is an indicating micrometer?

Ans. An indicating micrometer (Fig. 6–57) combines the precision of the dial indicator, for uniform contact pressure, with the accuracy of the micrometer screw for measuring. The graduations on the sleeve and thimble are the same as on a regular micrometer. The indicator dial registers divisions of one ten-thousandth (0.0001) of an inch. In measuring with this type of micrometer, the size is noted on the sleeve in thousandths of an inch, and then the number of ten-thousandths shown on the dial by the indicator finger is added.

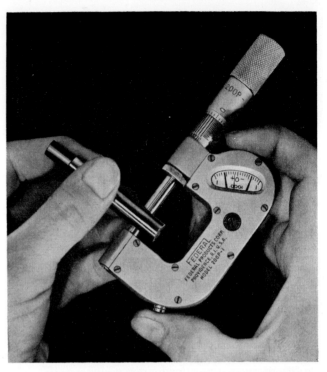

Fig. 6–58. Indicating micrometer may be used as a comparator. (Federal Products Corp.)

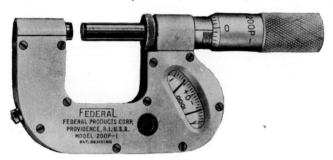

Fig. 6–57. Indicating micrometer. (Federal Products Corp.)

The indicating micrometer may also be used as a comparator. For this purpose, the spindle may be clamped in position to a required dimension by tightening the ring nut on the spindle. When it is to be used in this way, the two large hands of the indicator are adjusted on each side of zero, to indicate the amount of variation permitted above or below the required dimension. If the indicating finger is moved outside of the two hands, then the part being measured is too large or too small, depending upon which direction the finger moved. When measuring a number of parts of the same size, it is not necessary to turn the spindle, or to force the part between the anvil and spindle. Instead, the anvil may be retracted by pressing a button, as in Fig. 6–58. This saves wear on the ends of the anvil and spindle.

About 300 years ago, a Frenchman named Pierre Vernier invented a method for making accurate precision measurements with a rule. The method has been adapted for use with many measuring tools and bears the name of the inventor. One adaptation of this method has already been mentioned for the micrometer.

43. Explain the principle of the vernier scale used on a rule.

Ans. A vernier scale for a rule consists of a slide that fits over the rule. A distance on the slide of six-hundred thousandths (0.600) of an inch is graduated into 25 equal parts so that each division measures twenty-four thousandths (0.024) of an inch. The graduations on the rule itself are twenty-five thousandths (0.025) of an inch, so in a distance of 0.600 there are 24 divisions on the rule. The difference in the size of the divisions on the rule and those on the vernier scale is one-thousandth (0.001) of an inch.

44. How are measurements read on a vernier rule?

Ans. The zero mark on the vernier scale indicates the measurement to be read on the rule. In Fig. 6–59, this is seen to be 1.425 in. and a little more. The exact amount over 1.425 is found by examining the division lines of the vernier scale to see which one exactly coincides with one of the lines on the rule. In this case, it is line 11, so the full measurement is 1.425 plus 0.011, which equals 1.436 in.

45. The lines of a vernier scale are very fine and close together, so it is not easy to see which lines

Fig. 6–59. Vernier scale. (L. S. Starrett Co.)

coincide. *What precautions should be taken to ensure an accurate reading?*

Ans. Clean the vernier scale and the rule. Face the light with the vernier scale held in a horizontal position and tipped slightly, in order to look directly down the lines on the vernier plate. To make reading easier, it is a common practice to use a magnifying glass.

46. What is a vernier height gage?

Ans. A vernier height gage (Fig. 6–60) consists of an upright steel bar fastened to a steel base. On the bar is a movable jaw with a vernier scale. A clamp on the bar is connected to the movable jaw by a screw. This screw is used to adjust the vernier scale to a required position.

Fig. 6–60. Vernier height gage. (L. S. Starrett Co.)

47. Are both sides of the vernier height gage graduated in the same manner?

Ans. The size of the graduations is the same on both sides of the bar, but one side is for inside measurements with the graduations reading from zero. The other side of the bar has graduations for outside measurements which start at 1 in. For this reason, care should be taken to read the vernier from the correct side for the work that is being done.

48. What are some of the uses of a vernier height gage?

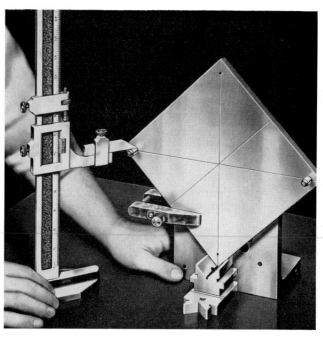

Fig. 6–61. Using vernier height gage with scriber for layout work. (L. S. Starrett Co.)

Ans. Many attachments may be used with a height gage. Figure 6–60 shows a flat scriber clamped to the movable jaw. This is standard equipment. The scriber is used for layout work, as in Fig. 6–61. An offset scriber (Fig. 6–62) is used when it is required to take measurements from the surface upon which the gage is standing to a lower

Fig. 6–62. Offset scribers. (L. S. Starrett Co.)

plane, as in Fig. 6–63. A rod may be attached, as in Fig. 6–64, so that the height gage may be used as a depth gage. For measuring between two points where extreme accuracy is required, an indicator may be attached to the movable jaw. Figure 6–65 shows how the location of a hole may be determined accurately with the aid of an indicator attached to a height gage.

Fig. 6–63. Using vernier height gage with offset scriber. (L. S. Starrett Co.)

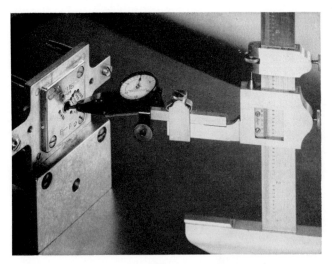

Fig. 6–65. Checking the location of a hole with a vernier height gage and dial attachment. (Federal Products Corp.)

49. What is a vernier caliper?

Ans. A vernier caliper (Fig. 6–66) is a tool for checking inside and outside measurements. Usually both sides of the bar are graduated. The jaws are hardened, ground, and lapped parallel with each other. With the jaws in contact, the vernier plate is set at zero on one side and at a point equal to the thickness of the measuring points or jaws on the other side. This is done to make it possible to check either outside or inside measurements without making any calculations. Points are provided on the bar and slide so that dividers may be set to transfer distances from the vernier caliper to a piece of work. Figure 6–67 shows outside measurements being taken with a vernier caliper. Figure 6–68 shows internal diameters being measured with the vernier caliper.

50. What is a gear-tooth vernier?

Ans. A gear-tooth vernier (Fig. 6–69) is an instrument with two vernier scales, for measuring the size of gear teeth. The thickness of the gear tooth is measured at a point where the pitch circle of the gear crosses the tooth. The vertical bar of

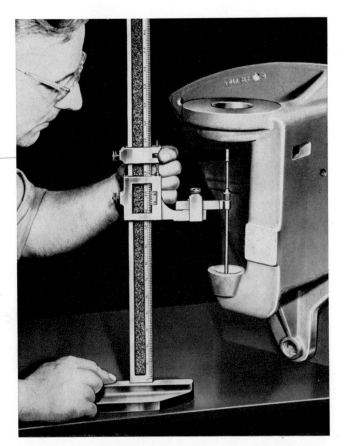

Fig. 6–64. Using vernier height gage as a depth gage. (L. S. Starrett Co.)

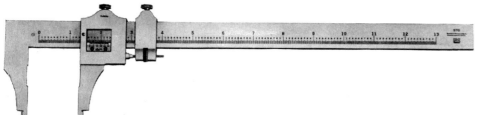

Fig. 6–66. Vernier caliper. (Brown & Sharpe Mfg. Co.)

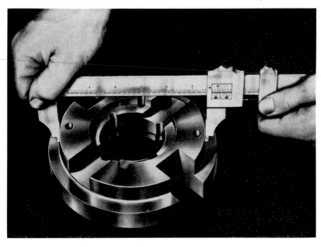

Fig. 6–67. Measuring outside diameter with a vernier caliper. (L. S. Starrett Co.)

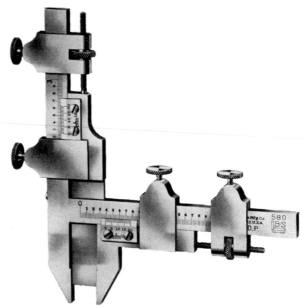

Fig. 6–69. Gear-tooth vernier. (Brown & Sharpe Mfg. Co.)

Fig. 6–68. Measuring inside diameter with a vernier caliper. (L. S. Starrett Co.)

Fig. 6–70. Vernier bevel protractor. (L. S. Starrett Co.)

the gear-tooth vernier is adjusted so that the jaws of the vernier will be at the pitch circle of the gear when the vernier rests on the tooth. The horizontal bar is then adjusted to measure the thickness of the gear tooth. These two measurements are known respectively as *corrected addendum* and *chordal thickness*. The graduations on the two bars

Fig. 6–71. Reading the size of an angle on a vernier bevel protractor. (L. S. Starrett Co.)

of the vernier are twenty-thousandths of an inch apart instead of twenty-five thousandths as on a height gage. This must be remembered when counting the divisions on the bar.

51. What is a vernier bevel protractor?

Ans. The vernier bevel protractor (Fig. 6–70) is an instrument having a dial graduated in degrees and a sliding blade which is usually about 1/16 in. thick. One side of the tool is flat, permitting it to be laid level upon the work. The disk of the bevel pro-

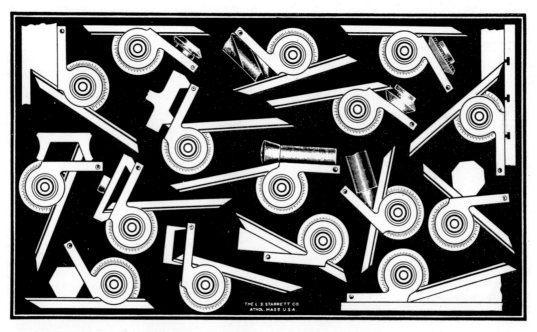

Fig. 6–72. Some applications of the use of the bevel protractor. (L. S. Starrett Co.)

Fig. 6–73. Using a vernier bevel protractor to measure the angle of a block. (L. S. Starrett Co.)

Fig. 6–74. Using a vernier bevel protractor to measure the angle of a slide. (Brown & Sharpe Mfg. Co.)

tractor is graduated in degrees throughout the entire circle. The vernier is graduated so that 12 divisions on the vernier occupy the same space as 23 deg on the disk. Each of the 12 divisions of the vernier is equal to one-twelfth of 23 deg (1,380 min), which amounts to 115 min. Each 2 deg on the protractor is equal to 120 min. The difference between 2 deg on the protractor and 1 division on the vernier equals 5 min.

52. How are measurements read on a vernier bevel protractor?

Ans. The vernier scale of the bevel protractor is double, so that readings may be taken from the left or from the right. In Fig. 6–71, a reading is to be made from the zero on the right side of the protractor. The zero on the vernier indicates the number of degrees, in this case 50, then continuing in the same direction from that point, it may be seen that the division lines of the protractor and those

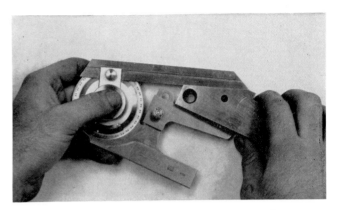

Fig. 6–75. Measuring the angle of a die section with a vernier bevel protractor with an acute-angle attachment. (Brown & Sharpe Mfg. Co.)

of the vernier coincide on the 20 line of the vernier. The full size of the angle being measured is therefore 50° 20′. Some of the ways in which a vernier bevel protractor is used are shown in Figs. 6–72 to 6–75.

Chapter 7 DRILLS AND DRILLING

OPERATIONS

The making of a hole in a piece of material can, in some instances, be a simple operation, but in a machine shop it is an important and precise job. A large number of different tools and machines have been designed so that holes may be made speedily, economically, and accurately in all kinds of material.

In order to be able to use these tools efficiently, it is well to become acquainted with them. The most common tool for making holes is the drill. It consists of a cylindrical piece of steel with spiral grooves. One end of the cylinder is pointed; the other end is shaped so that it may be attached to a portable or stationary drilling machine. The grooves, usually called *flutes*, may be cut into the steel cylinder, or the flutes may be formed by twisting a flat piece of steel into a cylindrical shape. Drills of this kind are sometimes referred to as *twist drills*.

1. What are the principal parts of a drill?

Ans. The principal parts of a drill are the body, which is the cutting unit, and the shank, which is gripped by the drilling machine. A straight-shank drill is shown in Fig. 7–1.

Fig. 7–1. Straight-shank drill. (Whitman & Barnes)

2. What is the dead center of a drill?

Ans. The dead center of a drill is the sharp edge at the extreme tip end of the drill (see Fig. 7–2). It is formed by the intersection of the cone-shaped surfaces of the point and should always be in the exact center of the axis of the drill.

3. Describe the point of a drill.

Ans. The point of the drill should not be confused with the dead center. The point is the entire cone-shaped surface at the cutting end of the drill.

4. What is the cutting edge of a drill?

Ans. The cutting edge of a drill (Fig. 7–2) is that part of the point that actually cuts away the material when drilling a hole. It is ordinarily as sharp as the edge of a knife. There is a cutting edge for each flute of the drill.

5. What is the lip clearance of a drill?

Ans. The lip clearance of a drill is the surface of the point that is ground away or relieved just back of the cutting edge of the drill (see Fig. 7–2).

6. What is the margin of a drill?

Ans. The margin of a drill is the narrow strip between A and B in Fig. 7–2. It is the full diameter of the drill and extends the entire length of the flute. Its surface is part of a cylinder which is interrupted by the flutes and by what is known as body clearance. The diameter of the margin at the shank end of the drill is 0.0005 to 0.002 in. smaller than the diameter at the point. This allows the drill to revolve without binding when drilling deep holes.

7. What is the body clearance of a drill?

Ans. The portion of the drill from B to C in Fig. 7–2 is smaller in diameter than the margin. This reduction in size, called *body clearance*, reduces the friction between the drill and the walls of the hole being drilled, while the margin ensures the hole being of accurate size.

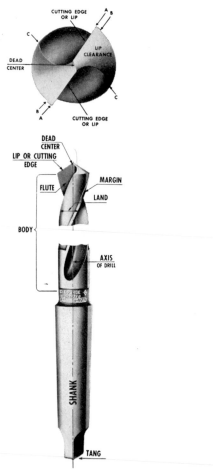

Fig. 7–2. Names of parts of a tapered-shank drill. (Cleveland Twist Drill Co.)

8. What is the tang of a drill?

Ans. A tang is found only on tapered-shank tools (see Fig. 7–2). It is designed to fit into a slot in the socket or spindle of a machine. It may bear a portion of the driving strain, but its principal use is to make it easy to remove the drill from the socket of the machine spindle with the aid of a drill drift (Fig. 7–3). A safety drill drift which is used without a hammer is shown in Fig. 7–4.

Fig. 7–3. Drill drift. (Armstrong Bros. Tool Co.)

Fig. 7–4. Safety drill drift. (Armstrong Bros. Tool Co.)

9. Explain how a tapered-shank drill is removed from the spindle of a drill press.

Ans. To remove a tapered-shank drill, place the drift in the slot of the spindle, as in Fig. 7–5, the sloping edge of the drift matching the slope on the end of the tang of the drill. A light tap on the wide end of the drift with a hammer is usually sufficient to loosen the shank from the spindle. Avoid having the drill drop on to the table of the machine as this may dull the point of the drill. Also, if it is necessary to tighten a shank in a spindle, use a mallet of rawhide or some equally soft material to tap the point of the drill.

Fig. 7–5. Removing a drill from the spindle of a drill press. (Armstrong Bros. Tool Co.)

10. What is the web of a drill?

Ans. The web of a drill is the metal column which separates the flutes. It runs the entire length of the drill between the flutes (see Fig. 7–6) and is the supporting section of the drill, the drill's backbone, in fact. It gradually increases in thickness toward the shank (see Fig. 7–7). This thickening of the web gives additional rigidity to the drill.

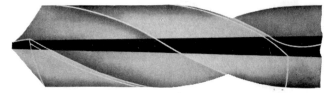

Fig. 7–6. Dark center section indicates the web of the drill. (Cleveland Twist Drill Co.)

Fig. 7–7. Drill section at left shows the thickness of the web near the point of a drill; section at right shows the thickness of the web near the shank end of the drill. (Cleveland Twist Drill Co.)

11. *What are the four most common shanks used on drills?*

Ans. The four most common shanks (Fig. 7–8) are the bit shank *A*, the straight shank *B*, the tapered shank *C*, and the ratchet shank *D*.

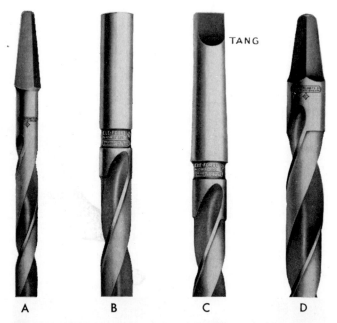

Fig. 7–8. Common drill shanks: (A) bit shank; (B) straight shank. (C) tapered shank; (D) ratchet shank. (Cleveland Twist Drill Co.)

12. *Why is the tapered shank used on drills?*

Ans. The tapered shank on a drill enables it to be quickly and accurately inserted into the spindle of a machine without the use of screws or clamps.

13. *What prevents a tapered-shank drill from falling out of the spindle?*

Ans. The hole in the spindle and the tapered shank match each other. When the drill is thrust into the spindle, they become wedged together. When drilling, the pressure of the work against the drill increases the wedgelike action.

14. *What should be done to ensure perfect contact between the socket in the spindle and the shank of the drill?*

Ans. Before inserting a drill into a socket, wipe the shank to make certain that it is smooth and free from grit. Also, inspect the inside of the socket to be sure that it is in the same good condition.

15. *Do all tapered-shank drills have shanks of the same size?*

Ans. No. When it is necessary to use a drill with a small shank, in a machine with a large socket, a sleeve is used (Fig. 7–9). Sleeves are made in several combinations of internal and external sizes.

Fig. 7–9. Sleeve for tapered shanks.

16. *How are straight-shank drills held in a drill press?*

Ans. Straight-shank drills are held in a drill press by a chuck. The jaws of the chuck are tightened around the drill by means of a key or wrench. Two varieties of drill chucks are shown in Fig. 7–10 and Fig. 7–11. Straight-shank drills are also used on most portable drilling machines such as the electric drill (Fig. 7–12) and the hand drill (Fig. 7–13).

17. *At what angle should the cutting edge be ground in relation to the axis of a drill?*

Ans. It has been found by experience that 59 deg (included angle equals 118 deg) is the best angle to grind a drill for work on steel or cast iron (see Fig. 7–14). However, for other materials, the size of the angle should be changed. A cutting angle up to 70 deg is best for extremely hard metals, whereas the angle may be as small as 40 deg for a soft material like fiber. It is customary to use a

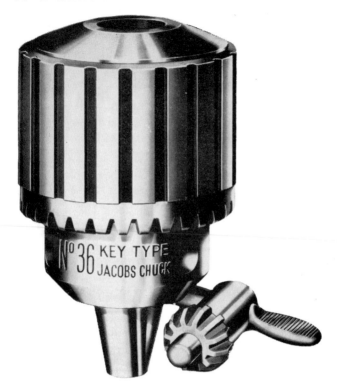

Fig. 7–10. Jacobs key-type drill chuck. (Jacobs Mfg. Co.)

Fig. 7–11. Two-jaw drill chuck.

Fig. 7–12. Portable electric drill. (Black & Decker Mfg.)

Fig. 7–13. Hand drill. (Stanley Tools)

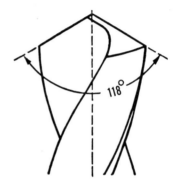

Fig. 7–14. Normal cutting angle of a drill. (Cleveland Twist Drill Co.)

drill-grinding gage (Fig. 7–15) to test the size of the angle.

NOTE: A drill made of high-speed steel should be ground on a dry grinding wheel of medium grain and soft grade. It must not be immersed in water after grinding as this will cause the point of the drill to crack.

Fig. 7–15. Drill grinding gage. (L. S. Starrett Co.)

18. If a drill is ground with its tip on center, but with the cutting edges at different angles, how will it affect the drilling operation?

Ans. The drill will bind on one side of the hole, as in Fig. 7–16. Only one lip or cutting edge will do the work, resulting in rapid wear on that edge, and the hole will be larger than the drill.

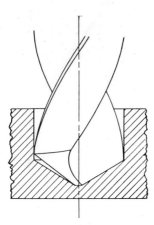

Fig. 7–16. Operation of drill with cutting edges ground at different angles. (Cleveland Twist Drill Co.)

19. What will be the result if the angles of the cutting edges of a drill are equal but the lips are of unequal lengths?

Ans. The result will be that both the point and the lip will be off center (Fig. 7–17). This will cause the hole to be larger than the drill. The effects of this condition are the same as the effects that would be obtained from a wheel with its axle placed at any point other than the exact center of the wheel. It will also place a strain on the drill press, the spindle will tend to weave and wobble, the drill will wear away rapidly, and, if continued, the machine will eventually break down because of the strains on the spindle bearings and other parts.

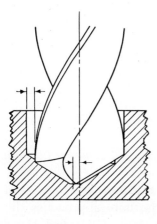

Fig. 7–17. Drill with lips of unequal length makes hole oversize. (Cleveland Twist Drill Co.)

20. What is the approximate angle to grind the lip clearance of a drill?

Ans. The heel (the surface of the point back of the cutting lip) should be ground away from the cutting lip at an angle of 8 to 12 deg, as shown in Figs. 7–18 and 7–19.

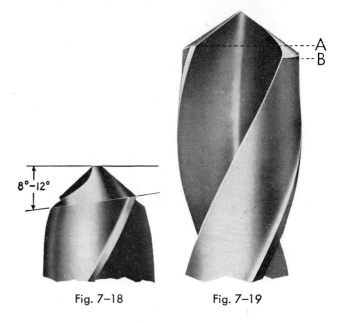

Fig. 7–18   Fig. 7–19

Fig. 7–18. Lip-clearance angle of a drill. (Cleveland Twist Drill Co.)
Fig. 7–19. View of drill showing proper lip clearance as indicated by the space between A and B. (Cleveland Twist Drill Co.)

21. What is liable to happen if the clearance angle is not correct?

Ans. If there is little or no clearance, as in Fig. 7–20, the cutting edge is lost. When pressure is applied, the drill will not cut, sometimes resulting in a cracked drill, as in Fig. 7–21. If the clearance angle is too large, the corners of the cutting edges may break away for lack of support, as in Fig. 7–22.

22. What is the rake angle of a drill?

Ans. The rake angle of a drill is the angle of the flute in relation to the work (Fig. 7–23). For ordinary drilling, the rake angle established by the manufacturer of the drill is correct and should remain untouched. If this angle was 90 deg or more, it would not give a good cutting edge. If the angle is ground too small, however, it makes the cutting edge so thin that it breaks down under the strain of the work.

CUTTING LIP

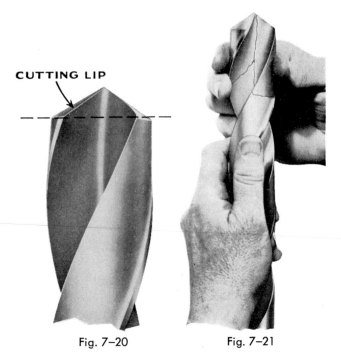

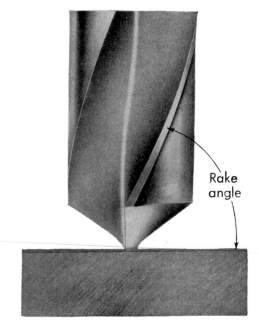

Fig. 7–20   Fig. 7–21

Fig. 7–23. Rake angle of a drill. (Cleveland Twist Drill Co).

Fig. 7–20. View of drill with no lip clearance. (Cleveland Twist Drill Co.)

Fig. 7–21. Drill cracked because of insufficient lip clearance. (Cleveland Twist Drill Co.)

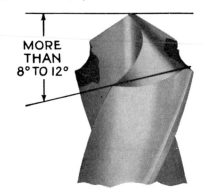

MORE THAN 8° TO 12°

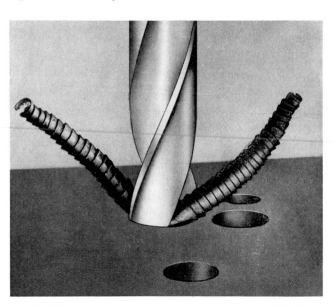

Fig. 7–22. Corners of drill broken because of too much lip clearance. (Cleveland Twist Drill Co.)

Fig. 7–24. Type of chip from a correctly ground drill. (Cleveland Twist Drill Co.)

The rake angle also partially governs the tightness with which the chips curl and hence the amount of space which the chips occupy. Other conditions being the same, a very large rake angle makes a tightly rolled chip, while a rather small rake angle makes a chip tend to curl into a more loosely rolled helix. Figure 7–24 shows how chips will be removed from the job by a correctly ground drill.

23. What will happen to a drill if the operating speed is too fast?

Ans. If a drill is operated at too fast a speed, the drill will become overheated and the temper will be drawn from the steel. This will cause the outer corners of the drill to wear away quickly (see the drill in Fig. 7–25).

24. Explain what is meant by thinning the point of a drill.

Ans. The thickness of the web of a drill is increased as the flute approaches the shank. After many sharpenings of the drill, the thicker part of the web thus exposed causes a corresponding in-

Fig. 7–25. Corners of drill worn because of excessive operating speed. (Cleveland Twist Drill Co.)

crease in the width of the dead center, making penetration into the work more difficult. This condition may be remedied by thinning the point, as in Fig. 7–26. The use of a convex grinding wheel (Fig. 7–27) is the most common method of thinning the point of a drill.

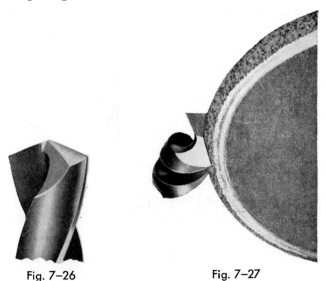

Fig. 7–26 Fig. 7–27

Fig. 7–26. Drill with thinned point. (Cleveland Twist Drill Co.)
Fig. 7–27. Thinning the point of a drill with a convex grinding wheel. (Cleveland Twist Drill Co.)

25. What are some of the indications of a dull drill?

Ans. Some of the indications of a dull drill are (1) the drill penetrates the work very slowly or not at all; (2) the drill becomes very hot; (3) a squealing noise is made by the drill; or (4) the finished hole has a rough surface.

26. What is an oil-hole drill?

Ans. An oil-hole drill is one which has holes through the body of the drill from the shank to the point, by means of which lubricant flows down to cool the point of the drill (see Fig. 7–28). This type of drill is generally used for deep-hole drilling.

Fig. 7–28. Oil-hole drills. (Whitman & Barnes)

27. What are some of the uses of a flat drill?

Ans. A flat drill (Fig. 7–29) is preferred by some for drilling a soft material such as brass, as it will not feed itself into the material more quickly than is desired. Another reason for its use is that, whereas hard spots in steel will cause an ordinary drill to slide off center, flat drills are not affected in this manner. Also, flat drills make fine chips instead of long coils. This is an advantage when samples of material are required for laboratory analysis.

Fig. 7–29. Flat drill. (Whitman & Barnes)

28. How should a job be laid out for drilling?

Ans. The laying out of the holes to be drilled is done from a sketch or blueprint. The surface of the material to be drilled is first coated with chalk or blue vitriol. The center lines of the holes are then scribed on the surface with a height gage or surface gage according to the dimensions specified on the blueprint. The intersection of the lines is marked with a center punch. To assist the machinist to see that the hole is being drilled on center, a circle the same size as the hole is scribed with dividers. The circle itself is then identified by making small indentations on it with a prick punch at short intervals (see Fig. 7–30).

29. Explain how a drill may be drawn back on center after it has moved away from center at the beginning of the drilling operation?

Ans. As a drill begins to cut, it forms a conical hole. If the hole is concentric with the layout, the drill has been started properly. However, a drill

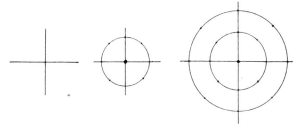

Fig. 7–30. Steps in laying out a hole for drilling.

may start off center, as in Fig. 7–31A. This may be due to improper center drilling, careless starting of the drill, improper grinding of the drill point, or hard spots in the metal.

To correct this condition, use a cape chisel which has been ground with a round nose (Fig. 7–31D), and cut a groove on the side of the hole toward which the center is to be drawn, as in Fig. 7–31B. The amount that the center has been moved may be judged by comparing the edge of the hole with the circular layout line. It may be necessary to move the center several times before the edge of the hole and the layout line are concentric, as in Fig. 7–31C. When the drill begins to cut its full diameter, the prick punch marks on the layout should be evenly cut at the center of the marks.

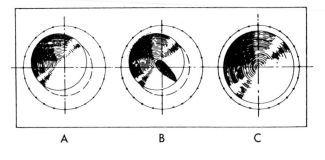

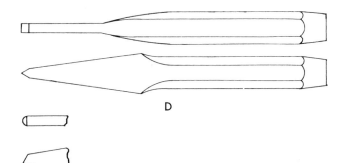

Fig. 7–31. Pulling an offside hole back on center by chipping a groove on one side.

30. When drilling a hole, why is soda water used for cooling a drill instead of plain water?

Ans. The addition of soda to plain water tends to reduce the amount of heat generated, improve the finish of the drilled hole, and overcome rusting of the material.

31. Describe the method used to drill glass.

Ans. Use a piece of copper or brass tubing as a drill. The tubing should be the same size as the outside diameter of the hole desired. A coarse grinding compound, or emery dust mixed with gasoline or light oil, makes a good abrasive to apply between the end of the tubing and the glass. Rest the glass on a rubber or felt pad, a little larger than the size of the hole to be drilled. Drill about halfway through the thickness of the glass and then invert the glass and finish drilling from the opposite side.

32. What is meant by the feed of a drill?

Ans. The feed of a drill is the distance that the drill enters the work on each revolution of the drill, measured in fractions of an inch. For example, a drill operated at 600 revolutions per minute (rpm) with a feed of 0.005 in. would make a hole 3 in. deep in 1 min. This is determined by multiplying the feed of one revolution by the number of revolutions made in 1 min: 0.005 times 600, which equals 3.000.

33. What is meant by the speed of a drill?

Ans. The speed of a drill is the speed of the circumference, called *peripheral speed*. It is the distance that a drill would roll if placed on its side and rolled for 1 min at a given rpm. The speed is expressed in feet per minute (fpm). For example, a 1/2-in. drill operating at 600 rpm would have a speed of the circumference of the drill expressed in feet (diameter $\times \pi \div 12$) multiplied by 600, or $1/2 \times 22/7 \times 1/12 \times 600$, which equals 78 fpm.

34. What speeds are recommended for drilling various materials?

Ans. The following speeds are recommended by the Cleveland Twist Drill Company when using drills made of high-speed steel. For drills made of carbon steel, the figures may be cut 50 percent.

Alloy steel	50– 70 fpm
Machine steel	70–100 fpm
Cast iron	100–150 fpm
Brass	200–300 fpm

35. If a toolmaker wanted to drill a 1/2-in. hole in a piece of machine steel at the recommended speed of 70 fpm, at what speed in rpm should he operate the drill press?

Ans. While the answer may be calculated mathematically, it is more practical to use a cutting-speed table similar to Table 7–1. By locating the diameter of the drill on the left side of Table 7–1 and then reading toward the right, we find that for a cutting speed of 70 fpm, the spindle of the drilling machine should revolve at 535 rpm.

Table 7–1. CUTTING SPEEDS*

(Fraction size drills)

Diameter, in.	Feet per minute												
	30	40	50	60	70	80	90	100	110	120	130	140	150
	Revolutions per minute												
1/16	1,833	2,445	3,056	3,667	4,278	4,889	5,500	6,111	6,722	7,334	7,945	8,556	9,167
1/8	917	1,222	1,528	1,833	2,139	2,445	2,750	3,056	3,361	3,667	3,973	4,278	4,584
3/16	611	815	1,019	1,222	1,426	1,630	1,833	2,037	2,241	2,445	2,648	2,852	3,056
1/4	458	611	764	917	1,070	1,222	1,375	1,528	1,681	1,833	1,986	2,139	2,292
5/16	367	489	611	733	856	978	1,100	1,222	1,345	1,467	1,589	1,711	1,833
3/8	306	407	509	611	713	815	917	1,019	1,120	1,222	1,324	1,426	1,528
7/16	262	349	437	524	611	698	786	873	960	1,048	1,135	1,222	1,310
1/2	229	306	382	458	535	611	688	764	840	917	993	1,070	1,146
5/8	183	244	306	367	428	489	550	611	672	733	794	856	917
3/4	153	203	255	306	357	407	458	509	560	611	662	713	764
7/8	131	175	218	262	306	349	393	436	480	524	568	611	655
1	115	153	191	229	267	306	344	382	420	458	497	535	573
1 1/8	102	136	170	204	238	272	306	340	373	407	441	475	509
1 1/4	92	122	153	183	214	244	275	306	336	367	397	428	458
1 3/8	83	111	139	167	194	222	250	278	306	333	361	389	417
1 1/2	76	102	127	153	178	204	229	255	280	306	331	357	382
1 5/8	70	94	117	141	165	188	212	235	259	282	306	329	353
1 3/4	65	87	109	131	153	175	196	218	240	262	284	306	327
1 7/8	61	81	102	122	143	163	183	204	224	244	265	285	306
2	57	76	95	115	134	153	172	191	210	229	248	267	287
2 1/4	51	68	85	102	119	136	153	170	187	204	221	238	255
2 1/2	46	61	76	92	107	122	137	153	168	183	199	214	229
2 3/4	42	56	69	83	97	111	125	139	153	167	181	194	208
3	38	51	64	76	89	102	115	127	140	153	166	178	191

* Cleveland Twist Drill Co.

36. Are drills made in sizes other than common fractions?

Ans. Yes. For many jobs in the shop, drill sizes in between the common fractional sizes are required. For this reason, drills are made in wire-gage sizes numbered from 1 to 80, ranging from 0.0135 in. for No. 80 to 0.228 in. for No. 1. There is also a series of letter-sized drills from A to Z rang-

ing from 0.234 in. for letter A to 0.413 in. for letter Z. A complete list of various drill sizes is given in Table 7–2.

37. In addition to the drilling of holes, what other operations are commonly performed on drilling machines?

Ans. Reaming, lapping, countersinking, counterboring, spot facing, and tapping.

38. Describe the operation of reaming.

Ans. A hole that has been made by drilling is seldom accurate in size. It is usually slightly oversize. This is quite satisfactory for holes in which bolts or rivets are placed. When greater accuracy and a smooth finish are required, the hole is first drilled undersize and then finished by reaming. The reamer (Fig. 7–32) is inserted into the spindle of the machine in the same manner as a drill. When a hole must be reamed to a size that is slightly under or over a standard size, an expansion reamer (Fig. 7–33) is used.

Fig. 7–32. Machine reamer. (Pratt & Whitney Co.)

Fig. 7–33. Expansion reamer. (Whitman & Barnes)

39. Describe the operation of lapping.

Ans. Lapping is a method of removing very small amounts of material by means of an abrasive. The abrasive material is kept in contact with the sides of a hole that is to be lapped, by the use of a lapping tool. There are many kinds of lapping tools. The copper-head laps in Fig. 7–34 are typical examples. In operation, the lap should just fit the hole. As the lap revolves in the hole, it should be constantly moved up and down so that the hole will be perfectly cylindrical.

Lapping is a long, tedious job. Usually only a few thousandths of an inch are removed by this method. It is a common practice to lap small holes —those less than 3/8 in. in diameter—when the material has been hardened, because grinding wheels are seldom so small. Before hardening,

Table 7–2. DECIMAL EQUIVALENTS OF DRILL SIZES

Inch	Mm	Wire gage	Decimals of an inch	Inch	Mm	Wire gage	Decimals of an inch	Inch	Mm	Wire gage	Decimals of an inch	Inch	Mm	Wire gage	Decimals of an inch	Inch	Mm	Letter sizes	Decimals of an inch	Inch	Mm	Letter sizes	Decimals of an inch
		80	0.0135		1.25		0.049212		2.5		0.098425		4.2		0.165354		5.9		0.232283		8		0.31496
		79	0.0145		1.3		0.051181			39	0.0995			19	0.166			A	0.234			O	0.316
1/64			0.015625			55	0.052			38	0.1015		4.25		0.167322	15/64			0.234375		8.1		0.318897
	0.4		0.015748		1.35		0.053149		2.6		0.102362		4.3		0.169291		6		0.23622		8.2		0.322834
		78	0.016			54	0.055			37	0.104			18	0.1695			B	0.238			P	0.323
		77	0.018		1.4		0.055118		2.7		0.106299			17	0.173		6.1		0.240157		8.25		0.324802
	0.5		0.019685		1.45		0.057086			36	0.1065		4.4		0.173228			C	0.242		8.3		0.326771
		76	0.02		1.5		0.059055		2.75		0.108267			16	0.177		6.2		0.244094	21/64			0.328125
		75	0.021			53	0.0595	7/64			0.109375		4.5		0.177165			D	0.246		8.4		0.330708
	0.55		0.021653		1.55		0.061023			35	0.11			15	0.18		6.25		0.246062			Q	0.332
		74	0.0225	1/16			0.0625		2.8		0.110236		4.6		0.181102		6.3		0.248031		8.5		0.334645
	0.6		0.023622		1.6		0.062992			34	0.111			14	0.182	1/4		E	0.25		8.6		0.338582
		73	0.024			52	0.0635			33	0.113			13	0.185		6.4		0.251968			R	0.339
		72	0.025		1.65		0.06496		2.9		0.114173		4.7		0.185039		6.5		0.255905		8.7		0.342519
	0.65		0.02559		1.7		0.066929			32	0.116		4.75		0.187007			F	0.257	11/32			0.34375
		71	0.026			51	0.067		3		0.11811	3/16			0.1875		6.6		0.259842		8.75		0.344487
	0.7		0.027559		1.75		0.068897			31	0.12		4.8		0.188976			G	0.261		8.8		0.346456
		70	0.028			50	0.07		3.1		0.122047			12	0.189		6.7		0.263779			S	0.348
		69	0.02925		1.8		0.070866	1/8			0.125			11	0.191	17/64			0.265625		8.9		0.350393
	0.75		0.029527		1.85		0.072834		3.2		0.125984		4.9		0.192913		6.75		0.265747		9		0.35433
		68	0.031			49	0.073		3.25		0.127952			10	0.1935			H	0.266			T	0.358
1/32			0.03125		1.9		0.074803			30	0.1285			9	0.196		6.8		0.267716		9.1		0.358267
	0.8		0.031496			48	0.076		3.3		0.129921		5		0.19685		6.9		0.271653	23/64			0.359375
		67	0.032		1.95		0.076771		3.4		0.133858			8	0.199			I	0.272		9.2		0.362204
		66	0.033	5/64			0.078125			29	0.136		5.1		0.200787		7		0.27559		9.25		0.364172
	0.85		0.033464			47	0.0785		3.5		0.137795			7	0.201			J	0.277		9.3		0.366141
		65	0.035		2		0.07874			28	0.1405	13/64			0.203125		7.1		0.279527			U	0.368
	0.9		0.035433		2.05		0.080708	9/64			0.140625			6	0.204			K	0.281		9.4		0.370078
		64	0.036			46	0.081		3.6		0.141732		5.2		0.204724	9/32			0.28125		9.5		0.374015
		63	0.037			45	0.082			27	0.144			5	0.2055		7.2		0.283464	3/8			0.375
	0.95		0.037401		2.1		0.082677		3.7		0.145669		5.25		0.206692		7.25		0.285432			V	0.377
		62	0.038		2.15		0.084645			26	0.147		5.3		0.208661		7.3		0.287401		9.6		0.377952
		61	0.039			44	0.086		3.75		0.147637			4	0.209			L	0.29		9.7		0.381889
	1		0.03937		2.2		0.086614			25	0.1495		5.4		0.212598		7.4		0.291338		9.75		0.383857
		60	0.04		2.25		0.088582		3.8		0.149606			3	0.213			M	0.295		9.8		0.385826
		59	0.041			43	0.089			24	0.152		5.5		0.216535		7.5		0.295275			W	0.386
	1.05		0.041338		2.3		0.090551		3.9		0.153543	7/32			0.21875	19/64			0.296875		9.9		0.389763
		58	0.042		2.35		0.092519			23	0.154		5.6		0.220472		7.6		0.299212	25/64			0.390625
		57	0.043			42	0.0935	5/32			0.15625			2	0.221			N	0.302		10.		0.3937
	1.1		0.043307	3/32			0.09375			22	0.157		5.7		0.224409		7.7		0.303149			X	0.397
	1.15		0.045275		2.4		0.094488		4		0.15748		5.75		0.226377		7.75		0.305117			Y	0.404
		56	0.0465			41	0.096			21	0.159			1	0.228		7.8		0.307086	13/32			0.40625
3/64			0.046875		2.45		0.096456			20	0.161		5.8		0.228346		7.9		0.311023			Z	0.413
	1.2		0.047244			40	0.098		4.1		0.161417		5.8		0.228346	5/16			0.3125		10.5		0.413385

small holes that are to be lapped are reamed with a lapping reamer. Lapping reamers are one- or two-thousandths of an inch less than standard-sized reamers.

Fig. 7–34. Copper-head laps. (Boyar-Schultz Corp.)

40. Describe the operation of countersinking.

Ans. Countersinking is the operation of beveling the mouth of a hole with a rotary tool called a *countersink* (Fig. 7–35). Countersinks are made in many sizes of diameter and angle. The size of the angle depends upon the reason for countersinking. Holes for flat-head screws are beveled at 82 deg, whereas holes for machine centers are beveled at 60 deg. Holes are sometimes drilled and countersunk in one operation with a tool known as a *com-

bined drill and countersink (Fig. 7–36). It is more commonly referred to as a *center drill*.

Fig. 7–35. Countersink. (Whitman & Barnes)

Fig. 7–36. Combined drill and countersink. (Whitman & Barnes)

41. Describe the operation of counterboring.

Ans. Counterboring is the operation of boring a second hole, larger in diameter than the first, but concentric with it. When this operation is done on a drilling machine, a tool known as a counterbore is used (Fig. 7–37). The small diameter on the end of the tool, known as a *pilot*, is for the purpose of keeping the counterbore concentric with the original hole. Pilots are interchangeable with others of different size to fit various sizes of holes.

The same type of tool is used for spot facing. In this operation, usually performed on castings, the objective is simply to remove enough material to provide a flat surface around a hole to accommodate the head of a bolt or a nut.

Fig. 7–37. Counterbore. (Pratt & Whitney Co.)

42. Describe the operation of tapping on a drill press.

Ans. Holes that are to be tapped (threaded) are first drilled to a specified size. In order to tap holes on a drilling machine, a special tapping chuck must be used. An example of such a chuck is shown in Fig. 7–38. This type of chuck accurately centers the tap on the round part of the tap shank, and floating jaws hold the tap on its square end in a firm, rigid grip which prevents the tap from pulling out of the chuck when reversing. It is not customary to tap holes on a drill press unless a large number of identical parts are required.

Fig. 7–38. Tapping chuck. (Ettco Tool Co., Inc.)

All the tools mentioned in this chapter are used in a drilling machine which is also called a *drill press*. It is the second oldest-known machine tool, having been invented shortly after the lathe, and is probably the most used of any machine in the shop. The drilling machine may be classified into three general divisions: vertical-spindle, multiple-spindle, and radial-spindle machines. The vertical-spindle drilling machine is available in three types: plain, sensitive, and heavy-duty.

The plain vertical-spindle drilling machine (Fig. 7–39) consists of a main column which is attached to a base. Clamped to the column is a bracket which supports a worktable. The bracket may be swung around the column 90 deg, right or left. It may also be moved up or down and may be firmly clamped in any of the above-mentioned positions. The worktable may be revolved to a desired position and then securely locked in place. The column also supports the operating mechanism which includes a variable-speed transmission, reversing mechanism, spindle support and spindle, and an automatic feed control. The spindle may be adjusted up or down on the column and locked at the desired height.

This type of drill press is a general-duty machine which may be used for all types of drilling, reaming, countersinking, counterboring, tapping, and lapping. Large pieces of work are usually fastened to the worktable with clamps and T bolts. Small parts are held in a vise which may be clamped to the table, although, for really small parts, the vise is sometimes kept stationary by holding it firmly by its handle.

Fig. 7–39. Plain, all-geared vertical-spindle drilling machine. (Cincinnati Bickford Tool Co.)

Fig. 7–40. Sensitive drilling machine. (Cincinnati Lathe & Tool Co.)

The sensitive drilling machine (Fig. 7–40) is a light machine which is more convenient than a large drill press for such operations as lapping and the drilling of small holes at a high speed. These machines do not have automatic feed mechanisms and so must be fed by hand. The lower table and the spindle may be adjusted to a required height. The square upper table can be rotated for angular drilling and may be swung out of the way when long pieces of work are to be drilled.

Another type of sensitive drilling machine is the bench model shown in Fig. 7–41. The head, together with the spindle, travels up or down the round column when the drill is being brought into contact with the work.

The heavy-duty drill press (Fig. 7–42) is a powerful machine that is designed for drilling large holes, although it may be used for any kind of drill-press work. It has an adjustable knee firmly gibbed to the front of the column and supported by an adjusting screw. It has 12 spindle speeds, from 60 to 1,000 rpm, and nine rates of power feed. Forward and reverse rotation and stop position of the spindle are controlled by the lever on the left side of

Fig. 7–41. Bench-model sensitive drilling machine. (Cincinnati Lathe & Tool Co.)

the machine. The spindle is bored for a No. 4 Morse taper.

Fig. 7–42. Heavy-duty drilling machine. (Cincinnati Bickford Tool Co.)

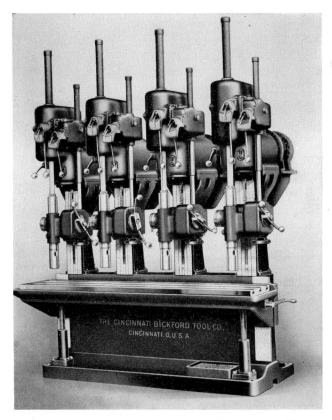

Fig. 7–43. Multiple-spindle or gang drilling machine. (Cincinnati Bickford Tool Co.)

The multiple-spindle or gang drilling machine consists of a large base supporting a long table. The back of the base is designed so that several spindles may be mounted on it, as in Fig. 7–43. Each spindle is driven by its individual direct-connected motor. The table has a groove around the outside for the return of the cutting lubricant and has T slots on its surface for ease in clamping work to the table. It is adjusted for height by means of a crank which actuates screws through worms and gears fitted with ball bearings.

This type of machine is generally preferred when the work is to be moved from spindle to spindle for successive operations. The spindles may be located on the base according to the particular nature of the work to be done.

The multiple-drill-head machine should not be confused with the multiple-spindle machine. The multiple-drill-head machine may have any number of spindles from 4 to 48, or more, all driven from the one spindle drive gear in one head. Multiple heads are specially designed for mass-production

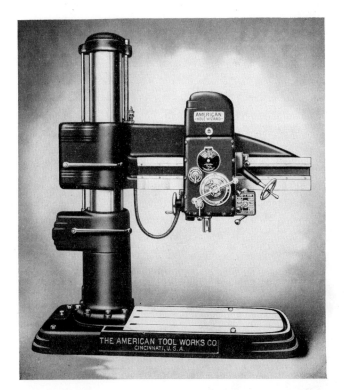

Fig. 7–44. Radial drilling machine. (American Tool Works Co.)

operations such as drilling, reaming, or tapping many holes at one time in a specific unit of work, like the motor block of an automobile. Sometimes, on one machine, there may be two or more drill heads, each with many spindles. This is necessary when holes are drilled from more than one direction, as, for instance, on the top, side, and end of a piece of work. Production units of this type are seldom used in a toolroom where custom work of a highly skilled nature is the normal situation.

The radial drill (Fig. 7–44) is a precision machine that is designed so that the entire mechanism may be adjusted to bring the spindle into the required position over the work, which is fastened securely to the stationary base. The large arm of the machine is raised or lowered by a motor-driven mechanism, which operates on a long, stationary elevating screw. The arm is automatically clamped on the vertical column when the elevating mechanism is stopped. The head, which contains the spindle and power-feeding mechanism, can be moved back and forth on the arm and clamped in place. The arm may be rotated around the column and clamped securely in the required location.

This type of drilling machine is used generally for work that is too large or too heavy to be placed on a vertical-spindle machine, but especially for jobs where accuracy of a high degree is required. It has a capacity for drilling or tapping holes up to 1 1/2 in. in diameter in steel, and up to 2 in. in diameter in cast iron, within very close limits.

Chapter 8 TAPERS

Most machines in the machine shop are provided with revolving spindles which have tapered holes into which the tapered shanks of drills, reamers, centers, and so forth, are fitted and securely held in place.

There are several standard tapers which have been adopted by industry. The principal ones are Brown and Sharpe, Jarno, Morse, and taper pin. In addition, many tools and machines are designed with tapered parts to suit particular situations (see Figs. 8–1 and 8–2). An understanding of the different kinds of tapers and the problems involved in machining and using them is of value to toolmakers and draftsmen.

Fig. 8–1. Tapered-face milling-cutter arbor. (Cincinnati Milling Machine Co.)

Fig. 8–2. Lathe center. (Whitman & Barnes)

1. Describe the Jarno taper.

Ans. The Jarno taper is a standard form of taper that was originally designed for use in lathes. The proportions of the taper are quite definite, and the dimensions for each one are few, inasmuch as there is no tang on the shank.

There are twenty sizes in the series of Jarno tapers, each one being identified by a number ranging from 1 to 20. The number of the taper is the key to its size as may be seen from the following formulas:

$$\text{Diameter of large end of Jarno taper} = \frac{\text{No. of taper}}{8}$$

$$\text{Diameter of small end of Jarno taper} = \frac{\text{No. of taper}}{10}$$

$$\text{Length of Jarno taper} = \frac{\text{No. of taper}}{2}$$

Accordingly, a No. 8 Jarno taper measures 8/8 or 1 in. at the large end; 8/10 or 0.8 at the small end; and 8/2 or 4 in. in length. The actual dimensions of Jarno tapers may be found in the Appendix in Table 11, page 312.

2. Describe the Brown and Sharpe taper.

Ans. The Brown and Sharpe is a standard form of taper that is used mostly on milling machines. There are 18 sizes in the series, numbered from 1 to 18. The number of the taper indicates its size only in a relative manner: the smallest is No. 1, and the largest is No. 18. The amount of taper, 1/2 in. per ft, is the same for all Brown and Sharpe tapers except No. 10, which has a taper of 0.5161 in. per ft. The Brown and Sharpe taper is designed with a tang at the small end. There are several dimensions that are used in the design and machining of Brown and Sharpe tapers, a complete list of which may be found in the Appendix in Table 10, page 311.

3. Describe the Morse taper.

Ans. The Morse taper is the most common of the standard tapers. It is used on drilling machines and on some lathes. Practically all tapered-shank drills, reamers, and special toolholders are made with

Morse tapered shanks. There are eight sizes in the Morse taper series, numbered from 0 to 7, 0 being the smallest and 7 the largest. There seems to be no uniformity in the proportion of the dimensions of each one. It seems probable that the original tapers of the Morse series were custom-made in matching units, that is, a shank was made to fit a particular socket. Finally, some well-matched pairs were measured, and the dimensions of those particular units were then adopted as standard dimensions. If so, this would account for the odd dimensions of the large and the small diameters and the variation in the amount of taper per foot (tpf) for each size. The small end of the tapered shank is designed with a tang. The dimensions for the design and machining of Morse tapers may be found in the Appendix in Table 9, page 310.

4. Describe the standard taper pin.

Ans. The taper pin most commonly used is the Pratt and Whitney standard taper pin. Taper pins are used as dowels for keeping units that are fastened together, in line with each other, and also as a means of joining parts together, such as a bushing or a collar on a shaft. It is used in preference to straight pins in situations where it is necessary to remove the pins from time to time. There are 14 pins in the series, numbered from 0 to 13. The smallest size is No. 0, the largest is No. 13. The amount of taper per foot is standard for all sizes. Complete dimensions for standard taper pins may be found in the Appendix in Table 12, page 313.

5. What is the procedure for machining a tapered hole?

Ans. A hole equal in size to the small diameter of the taper is first drilled or bored to the required depth. For example, a hole for a No. 3 Morse taper would be made 0.778 in. in diameter and 3 1/4 in. deep (see Table 9 of Appendix, page 310). The hole may then be tapered by reaming, boring, or grinding. Taper reamers are shown in Figs. 8–3 and 8–4.

Fig. 8–3. Morse taper reamer. (Whitman & Barnes)

6. How is the size of a standard tapered hole measured?

Fig. 8–4. Taper-pin reamer. (Whitman & Barnes)

Ans. When testing a tapered hole, two items are important: the diameter and the amount of taper. It is possible to measure the size of the diameters of each end of the taper with a rule and inside calipers, and also the depth of the hole. These being found accurate according to the standards of scale measurement, it may be presumed that the taper of the hole is also correct. However, this method of measuring a taper is not satisfactory in most cases. For an accurate measurement, a taper plug gage should be used (Fig. 8–5). To test the correctness of the taper, the gage is lightly covered with prussian blue and then carefully inserted into the hole. The gage should not be jammed tight in the hole but put in just far enough to make contact on the sides of the hole with the gage. When contact has been made, the gage should be rotated back and forth in the hole. When the gage is removed from the hole, the absence of blue from one end or the other of the gage will indicate that an adjustment is necessary in the amount of taper. When the amount of taper is correct, a certain amount of the blue will be absent all along the length of the taper gage. The diameter of the hole is tested for size by noting how far the gage enters the hole. A mark on the gage shows the correct diameter for the large end of the taper.

Fig. 8–5. Taper plug gage. (Morse Twist Drill & Machine Co.)

7. What is the procedure for machining a tapered shank?

Ans. The shank is first machined on a lathe to the required length and to the size of the diameter of the large end of the taper. The lathe is then adjusted to cut on a taper according to the specified taper per foot in the case of a standard taper, or according to the number of degrees of taper for special tapers (see Fig. 8–6). The size of the large and small diameters of the tapered shank may be measured with calipers or micrometer but it is difficult to be sure that the instruments are exactly on the correct spot. A taper ring gage (Fig. 8–7) is

Fig. 8–6. Cutting a taper on a lathe. (South Bend Lathe Works)

used when an accurate test is required of both the diameter and amount of taper. To do this, the gage is lightly smeared on the inside with prussian blue and then it is placed on the tapered shank, not tight, but just enough to make contact. The gage should be rotated forward and back around the shank and then removed. The presence of blue on the shank will indicate the accuracy of the taper. If it is uniformly distributed, then the amount of taper is correct. If one end is smeared with blue and the other is not, then an adjustment in the taper attachment for the amount of taper must be made. The correctness of the taper should be tested before the shank has been machined to its final size, because more than one adjustment may be necessary before an accurate setting is obtained.

In the case of special tapers, it is usually desirable to make the male member of a matching unit first and then to use it as a gage for machining the female part.

Fig. 8–7. Taper ring gage. (Morse Twist Drill & Machine Co.)

8. How may the accuracy and efficiency of tapers be preserved?

Ans. This may be done by keeping them free from dirt, chips, nicks, and burrs. They should be handled carefully and not dropped. If a tapered part is not to be used for any length of time, it should be oiled or greased, to prevent rusting.

There are many kinds of taper work to be done in the shop. Frequently the information given by the draftsman is not practical for use by the toolmaker. The ability to calculate dimensions that can be used, from those given, is expected from well-trained mechanics. Ratio and proportion is the method most frequently used.

9. The piece of work in Fig. 8–8 has dimensions for the diameter of each end and the length. Determine the amount of taper per foot.

Ans. In order to see the ratio between the taper of the work and the taper per foot, broken lines have been added to the side view of the drawing as in Fig. 8–9. It can now be seen that A or 3/8 equals the amount of taper in a distance of 2 in. and that T is the amount of taper in 12 in. or 1 ft.

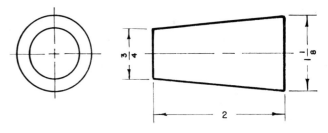

Fig. 8–8. Tapered plug.

A ratio and proportion problem can be made from this so that we can solve for T. The ratio between 2 and 12 is in proportion to the ratio between 3/8 and T. Therefore, we may state $2 : 12 :: 3/8 : T$. Solving the problem, we find that $2T = 12 \times 3/8$, $2T = 4.5$, $T = 2.25$, which is the taper per foot.

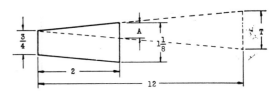

Fig. 8–9. Taper problem.

10. In the job shown in Fig. 8–10, the taper per foot is given, but before the toolmaker can use it, he must first turn the work to the size of the large end. Determine the size of the large end of the taper.

Ans. The size of the large end of the taper is equal to the size of the small end plus the amount of taper which is indicated by the dimension B. The ratio between the dimension B and the taper per foot, 0.602, is in proportion to the distance 3.0625 and 12 in. Therefore,

$$B:0.602 :: 3.0625:12$$
$$12B = 0.602 \times 3.0625$$
$$12B = 1.843625$$
$$B = 0.15363$$

The large end of the taper is equal to 0.92 plus 0.15363, or 1.07363.

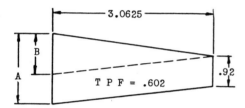

Fig. 8–10. Taper problem.

11. It is required to measure the diameter of the work in Fig. 8–11 marked A. Calculate the dimension.

Ans. The dimension A is equal to the diameter of the small end of the taper plus the amount of taper in a distance of 3/4 in. which is marked C. The amount of taper in the distance 4.250 is equal to the diameter of the large end of the taper minus the diameter of the small end, or 1.653 minus 0.938, which equals 0.715. The ratio between C and 0.715 is in proportion to the ratio of 3/4 and 4.250. Therefore,

$$C:0.715 :: 0.750:4.250$$
$$4.250C = 0.715 \times 0.750$$
$$4.250C = 0.53625$$
$$C = 0.12617$$

The distance A equals 0.938 plus 0.12617, or 1.06417.

12. In order to bore the tapered hole in Fig. 8–12, a straight hole must first be drilled or bored. Determine the size of the straight hole.

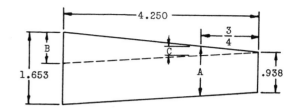

Fig. 8–11. Taper problem.

Ans. The diameter of the straight hole will equal the diameter of the large end of the taper minus the amount of taper. Let X equal the amount of taper in the hole. The ratio between X and the taper per foot, 0.625, is in proportion to the ratio between 10.8 and 12 in. Therefore,

$$X:0.625 :: 10.8:12$$
$$12X = 0.625 \times 10.8$$
$$12X = 6.750$$
$$X = 0.5625$$

The diameter of the straight hole equals 1.5 minus 0.5625, or 0.9375.

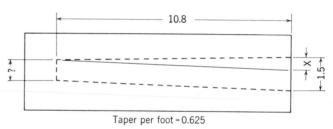

Fig. 8–12. Taper problem.

13. The problem in Fig. 8–13 is to determine how deep to bore the 1.4-diameter hole before cutting the taper.

Ans. The ratio between the taper of the hole and the taper per foot is in proportion to the depth of the hole and 12 in. The amount of taper in the hole is equal to 1.7 minus 1.4, or 0.3 in. Therefore,

$$0.3:0.750 :: X:12$$
$$0.750X = 0.3 \times 12$$
$$0.750X = 3.6$$
$$X = 4.8 \quad \text{Depth of hole}$$

14. Determine the spacing of the parallels in Fig. 8–14 so that the upper surface of the work will be paralleled with the base line.

Ans. The ratio between the taper of the work and the difference in the height of the parallels is in proportion to the length of the work and the distance X. The taper of the work equals 15/16 minus

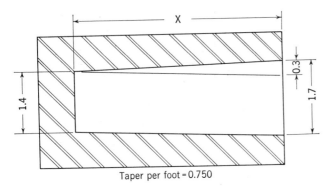

Taper per foot = 0.750

Fig. 8–13. Taper problem.

3/8, or 9/16. The difference in the height of the parallels equals 7/8 minus 1/2, or 3/8. Therefore,

$$\frac{9}{16} : \frac{3}{8} :: 12 : X$$
$$\frac{9}{16} \times X = \frac{3}{8} \times 12$$
$$\frac{9}{16} \times X = 4.5$$
$$9X = 72$$
$$X = 8 \quad \text{Spacing of parallels}$$

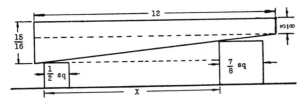

Fig. 8–14. Taper problem.

15. To what size of diameter and length should a bar of stock be turned before cutting the taper on a No. 4 Morse tapered shank?

Ans. Refer to the chart in the Appendix. The diameter of the large end of the taper is 1.231. The length including the tang is 4 7/8. Note the clearance between the edge of the socket and the large end of the shank. This is purposely designed to ensure a tight fit and to allow for regrinding when the shank becomes worn. For this reason, the actual diameter of the large end of the taper is larger than the diameter of the socket. In this case, the clearance is 1/4 in., so according to the amount of taper per foot, the full diameter should be 1.231 plus 0.013, or 1.244.

16. What size and depth of hole should be bored before cutting the taper for a No. 8 Brown and Sharpe socket?

Ans. Refer to Table 10 of Appendix, page 311. The size of hole to be bored is that of the small end of the taper, 0.750. The depth of the hole is 3 9/16 in.

17. A socket for a No. 6 Jarno taper is to be ground after it has been hardened. The lathe operator wishes to leave 0.015 in. of stock for grinding. How far should the plug gage extend outside of the hole when the diameter of the hole is 0.015 in. undersize?

Ans. Jarno tapers have 0.600 taper per foot. The ratio between the 0.015 of grinding stock and the taper per foot is in proportion to the amount that the plug should extend past the hole and 12 in. Therefore,

$$0.015 : 0.600 :: X : 12$$
$$0.600X = 0.015 \times 12$$
$$0.600X = 0.180$$
$$X = 0.3 \quad \text{Amount plug gage}$$
$$\text{should extend past}$$
$$\text{hole}$$

18. What is the usual operation for cutting the taper in a hole for a standard taper pin?

Ans. The hole is first drilled and then reamed with a standard-taper-pin reamer.

19. What size of hole should be drilled for a No. 5 standard taper pin?

Ans. This information may be found in the standard-taper-pin chart in the Appendix. The size of the hole should be 1/4 in.

20. How far must a boring tool be fed into the work to allow a 0.750 taper per foot plug gage to advance 0.062 into a tapered hole?

Ans. Solve for the amount of taper in the distance of 0.062 and divide the answer by 2.

$$X : 0.750 :: 0.062 : 12$$
$$12X = 0.750 \times 0.062$$
$$12X = 0.186$$
$$X = 0.003875$$

Required distance equals 0.003875 divided by 2 or 0.00194 in.

Chapter 9 THREADS

Threads and screws play an important part in toolroom work. Most of the screws and nuts that are used in the assembling of tools and machines are manufactured on a mass-production basis, but the toolmaker is frequently required to make both standard and special screws and matching parts. There are many varieties of screw threads, each one designed for a specific type of work.

TERMS RELATING TO SCREW THREADS

1. Screw thread. A ridge of uniform section in the form of a helix on the surface of a cylinder or cone.

2. External and internal threads. An external thread is a thread on the outside of a member. EXAMPLE: A threaded plug. An internal thread is a thread on the inside of a member. EXAMPLE: A threaded hole

3. Major diameter (formerly known as outside diameter). The largest diameter of the thread of the screw or nut. The term *major diameter* replaces the term *outside diameter* as applied to the thread of a screw and also the term *full diameter* as applied to the thread of a nut.

4. Minor diameter (formerly known as core diameter or root diameter). The smallest diameter of the thread of the screw or nut. The term *minor diameter* replaces the term *core diameter* as applied to the thread of a screw and also the term *inside diameter* as applied to the thread of a nut.

5. Pitch diameter. On a straight screw thread, it is the diameter of an imaginary cylinder, the surface of which would pass through the threads at such points as to make equal the width of the threads and the width of the spaces cut by the surface of the cylinder. On a tapered screw thread, it is the diameter, at a given distance from a reference plane perpendicular to the axis, of an imag-

inary cone, the surface of which would pass through the threads at such points as to make equal the width of the threads and the width of the spaces cut by the surface of the cone.

6. Pitch. The distance from a point on a screw thread to a corresponding point on the next thread, measured parallel to the axis.

$$\text{Pitch, in.} = \frac{1.0000}{\text{No. of threads per inch}}$$

7. Lead. The distance a screw thread advances axially in one turn. On a single-thread screw, the lead and pitch are identical; on a double-thread screw the lead is twice the pitch; on a triple-thread screw, the lead is three times the pitch, and so forth.

8. Angle of thread. The angle included between the sides of the thread measured in an axial plane.

9. Helix angle. The angle made by the helix of the thread at the pitch diameter with a plane perpendicular to the axis.

10. Crest. The top surface joining the two sides of a thread.

11. Root. The bottom surface joining the sides of two adjacent threads.

12. Side. The surface of the threads which connect the crest with the root.

13. Axis of a screw. The longitudinal center line through the screw.

14. Base of thread. The bottom section of the thread, the greatest section between the two adjacent roots.

15. Depth of thread. The distance between the crest and the base of the thread, measured normal to the axis.

16. Number of threads. Number of threads in 1 in. of length.

17. Length of engagement. The length of contact between two mating parts, measured axially.

18. Depth of engagement. The depth of thread contact of two mating parts, measured radially.

19. Pitch line. An element of the imaginary cylinder or cone specified in definition 5.

20. Thickness of thread. The distance between the adjacent sides of the thread measured along or parallel to the pitch line.

21. Allowance. An intentional difference in the dimensions of mating parts. It is the minimum clearance or the maximum interference which is intended between mating parts. It represents the condition of the tightest permissible fit, or the largest internal member mated with the smallest external member. This is illustrated by the two following examples:

EXAMPLE 1: One-half inch, class 1, loose fit, American National coarse thread series:

Minimum pitch diameter of nut	0.4500
Maximum pitch diameter of screw	0.4478
Allowance (positive)	0.0022

EXAMPLE 2: One-half inch, class 4, close fit, American National coarse thread series:

Minimum pitch diameter of nut	0.4500
Maximum pitch diameter of screw	0.4504
Allowance (negative)	0.0004

22. Tolerance. The amount of variation permitted in the size of a part. EXAMPLE: One-half-inch screw, class 1, loose fit, American National coarse thread series:

Maximum pitch diameter	0.4478
Minimum pitch diameter	0.4404
Tolerance	0.0074

23. Basic size. The theoretical or nominal standard size from which all variations are made.

24. Crest allowance. Defined on a screw form as the space between the crest of a thread and the root of its mating thread.

25. Finish. The character of the surface of a screw thread or other product.

26. Fit. The relation between two mating parts with reference to the conditions of assembly, as wrench fit, close fit, medium fit, free fit, and loose fit. The quality of fit depends upon both the relative size and finish of the mating parts.

27. Neutral zone. A positive allowance (see Allowance).

28. Limits. The extreme permissible dimensions of a part. EXAMPLE: One-half-inch screw, class 1, loose fit, American National coarse thread series:

Maximum pitch diameter	0.4478	These are
Minimum pitch diameter	0.4404	the limits.

The most common type of thread in use today is the American National form of thread of which there are two series: coarse thread series and fine thread series. However, according to an agreement between Canada, the United Kingdom, and the United States, made on Nov. 18, 1948, to standardize threads on a universal basis, these threads are now known as the Unified and American screw threads. The form of this thread and the formulas for determining the dimensions of each part of the thread are shown in Fig. 9–1. An illustration of some general screw-thread symbols is shown in Fig. 9–2.

1. Describe the difference between the lead and the pitch of a screw.

Ans. The pitch is the distance between a point on one thread and the corresponding point on the next thread, measured parallel to the axis. The lead is the distance a nut will advance on a screw, parallel to its axis, in one revolution. On a single-thread screw the lead equals the pitch. On a double-thread screw it equals twice the pitch, on a triple-thread screw, three times the pitch, and so on (see Fig. 9–3).

2. What are some of the methods of producing threads?

Ans. Threads may be produced (1) by hand with taps or dies; (2) on a lathe with specially shaped cutting tools; (3) on special machines using rotary cutters; (4) by rolling on special machines, using dies; and (5) on thread-grinding machines.

3. What is a tap?

Ans. A tap (Fig. 9–4) is a cylindrical bar of steel with threads formed around it and grooves or flutes running lengthwise in it, intersecting with the threads to form cutting edges. It is used to cut internal threads.

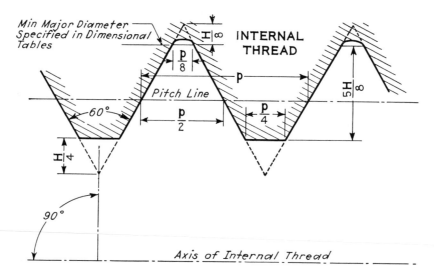

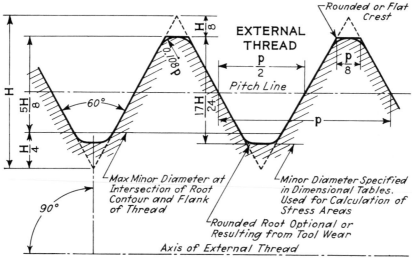

Fig. 9–1. Unified and American internal and external screw-thread design forms and formulas. (American Society of Mechanical Engineers)

Angle of thread $\quad 2\alpha = 60°$

Half angle of thread $\quad \alpha = 30°$

Number of threads per inch $\quad n = \dfrac{1}{p}$

Pitch of thread $\quad p = \dfrac{1}{n}$

Height of sharp $\quad H = 0.86603p$

V thread $\quad = \dfrac{0.86603}{n}$

Height of external thread $\quad h_s = 0.61343p$

$\quad = \dfrac{0.61343}{n}$

$\quad = \dfrac{17}{24}H$

Height of internal thread $\quad h_n = 0.54127p$

$\quad = \dfrac{0.54127}{n}$

$\quad = \dfrac{5}{8}H$

Major diameter of external thread (nominal diameter) $\quad D_s$

Pitch diameter of external thread $\quad E_s = D - 2h_{as}$

$\quad = D - 0.64952p$

$\quad = D - \dfrac{0.64952}{n}$

Minor diameter of external thread $\quad K_s = D_s - 2h_s$

$\quad = D_s - 1.22687p$

$\quad = D_s - \dfrac{1.22687}{n}$

Major diameter of internal thread $\quad D_n$

Pitch diameter of internal thread $\quad E_n$

Minor diameter of internal thread $\quad K_n = D_n - 2h_n$

$\quad = D_n - 1.08253p$

$\quad = D_n - \dfrac{1.08253}{n}$

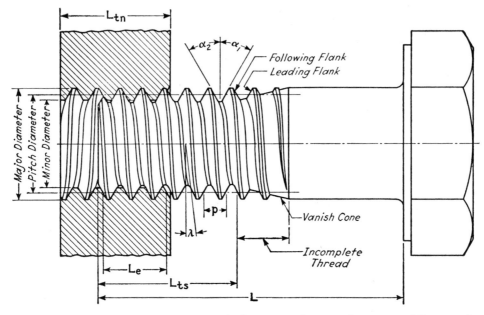

Fig. 9–2. General screw-thread symbols. (American Society of Mechanical Engineers)

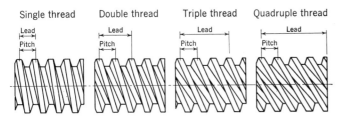

Fig. 9–3. Relation of lead and pitch of multiple threads.

Fig. 9–4. Hand tap. (Pratt & Whitney Co.)

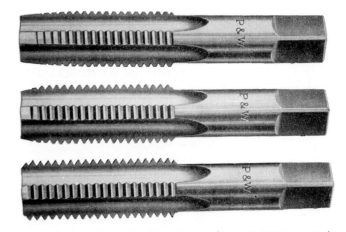

Fig. 9–5. Set of standard hand taps. (Pratt & Whitney Co.)

4. What is a set of taps?

Ans. A set of taps (Fig. 9–5) consists of three taps known as taper, plug, and bottoming taps. The taper tap is used to start the cutting of the threads, and if the hole is open at both ends, no other tap is required. If the hole is blind, then a plug tap is used after the taper tap to complete the cutting of the threads near the bottom of the hole. When it is necessary for the threads at the bottom of a hole to be fully cut, then a bottoming tap is used.

5. What is a tap wrench?

Ans. A tap wrench (Fig. 9–6) is a tool for gripping and holding a tap securely. For large sizes of taps, the type of wrench shown in Fig. 9–7 is preferred.

Fig. 9–6. T-handle tap wrench. (Greenfield Tap & Die Corp.)

6. What is an extension tap?

Ans. An extension tap (Fig. 9–8) is one that is much longer than the ordinary tap. It is used for

Fig. 9–7. Hand-tap wrench. (Greenfield Tap & Die Corp.)

cutting threads in deep holes and for tapping nuts by machine.

Fig. 9–8. Extension tap. (Pratt & Whitney Co.)

7. *How may a tapped hole be checked for being perpendicular to the surface of the work?*

Ans. It may be tested with a steel square. The vertical edge of the square should touch the solid body of the tap. The hole should be tested before all the threads have been cut, as well as after the job is done.

8. *Describe the technique of tapping a hole.*

Ans. After the location of the hole has been properly laid out, a hole is drilled. The correct size of the drill to use is usually determined by consulting a table similar to Table 9–1. For example, a

27/64 drill would be used for a 1/2—13 tap and a 29/64 drill for a 1/2—20 tap. The hole is usually drilled 1/8 to 1/4 in. deeper than the required depth of the thread (see Fig. 9–9). In starting the tap into the hole, care must be used to keep the tap perpendicular to the work. The tap should be revolved only one-half a revolution at a time, after which it should be reversed in order to break the chips of metal before revolving forward again.

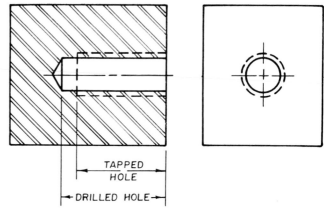

TAPPED HOLE

DRILLED HOLE

Fig. 9–9. Cross section of tapped hole.

Table 9–1. AMERICAN NATIONAL THREAD DIMENSIONS AND TAP DRILL SIZES *

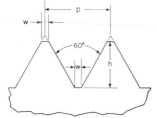

$$p = \text{pitch} = \frac{1}{\text{No. of threads per inch}}$$

n = number of threads per inch

$$h = \text{depth} = \text{pitch} \times 0.649519 \text{ or } \frac{0.649519}{n}$$

$$w = \text{flat} = \frac{\text{pitch}}{8}$$

Numbered Sizes

Nominal size	Outside dia, in.	Pitch dia, in.	Root dia, in.	Tap drill, in.	Decimal equivalent of tap drill, in.	Nominal size	Outside dia, in.	Pitch dia, in.	Root dia, in.	Tap drill, in.	Decimal equivalent of tap drill, in.
†0–80	0.0600	0.0519	0.0438	3/64	0.0469	†10–24	0.1900	0.1629	0.1359	25	0.1495
†1–56	0.0730	0.0614	0.0498	54	0.0550	28	0.1900	0.1668	0.1436	23	0.1540
64	0.0730	0.0629	0.0527	53	0.0595	30	0.1900	0.1684	0.1467	22	0.1570
72	0.0730	0.0640	0.0550	53	0.0595	32	0.1900	0.1697	0.1494	21	0.1590
†2–56	0.0860	0.0744	0.0628	50	0.0700	†12–24	0.2160	0.1889	0.1619	16	0.1770
64	0.0860	0.0759	0.0657	50	0.0700	28	0.2160	0.1928	0.1696	14	0.1820
†3–48	0.0990	0.0855	0.0719	47	0.0785	32	0.2160	0.1957	0.1754	13	0.1850
56	0.0990	0.0874	0.0758	45	0.0820	†14–20	0.2420	0.2095	0.1770	10	0.1935
†4–32	0.1120	0.0917	0.0714	45	0.0820	24	0.2420	0.2149	0.1879	7	0.2010
36	0.1120	0.0940	0.0759	44	0.0860	†16–18	0.2680	0.2319	0.1958	3	0.2130
40	0.1120	0.0958	0.0795	43	0.0890	20	0.2680	0.2355	0.2030	7/32	0.2187
48	0.1120	0.0985	0.0849	42	0.0935	22	0.2680	0.2385	0.2090	2	0.2210
†5–36	0.1250	0.1070	0.0889	40	0.0980	†18–18	0.2940	0.2579	0.2218	B	0.2380
40	0.1250	0.1088	0.0925	38	0.1015	20	0.2940	0.2615	0.2290	D	0.2460
44	0.1250	0.1102	0.0955	37	0.1040	†20–16	0.3200	0.2794	0.2388	G	0.2610
†6–32	0.1380	0.1177	0.0974	36	0.1065	18	0.3200	0.2839	0.2478	17/64	0.2656
36	0.1380	0.1200	0.1019	34	0.1110	20	0.3200	0.2875	0.2550	I	0.2720
40	0.1380	0.1218	0.1055	33	0.1130	22–16	0.3460	0.3054	0.2648	9/32	0.2812
†7–30	0.1510	0.1294	0.1077	31	0.1200	18	0.3460	0.3099	0.2738	L	0.2900
32	0.1510	0.1307	0.1104	31	0.1200	†24–16	0.3720	0.3314	0.2908	5/16	0.3125
36	0.1510	0.1330	0.1149	1/8	0.1250	18	0.3720	0.3359	0.2998	O	0.3160
†8–30	0.1640	0.1423	0.1207	30	0.1285	26–14	0.3980	0.3516	0.3052	21/64	0.3281
32	0.1640	0.1437	0.1234	29	0.1360	16	0.3980	0.3574	0.3168	R	0.3390
36	0.1640	0.1460	0.1279	29	0.1360	28–14	0.4240	0.3776	0.3312	T	0.3580
40	0.1640	0.1478	0.1315	28	0.1405	16	0.4240	0.3834	0.3428	23/64	0.3594
†9–24	0.1770	0.1499	0.1229	29	0.1360	30–14	0.4500	0.4036	0.3572	V	0.3770
30	0.1770	0.1553	0.1337	27	0.1440	16	0.4500	0.4094	0.3688	25/64	0.3906
32	0.1770	0.1567	0.1364	26	0.1470						

* Brown & Sharpe Manufacturing Co.
† American National Standard wood screws are made in same numbers and corresponding body diameters (outside diameter).

Fractional Sizes

Nominal size	Outside dia, in.	Pitch dia, in.	Root dia, in.	Tap drill, in.	Decimal equivalent of tap drill, in.	Nominal size	Outside dia, in.	Pitch dia, in.	Root dia, in.	Tap drill, in.	Decimal equivalent of tap drill, in.
1/16–64	0.0625	0.0524	0.0422	3/64	0.0469	5/8–18	0.6250	0.5889	0.5528	37/64	0.5781
72	0.0625	0.0535	0.0445	3/64	0.0469	27	0.6250	0.6009	0.5769	19/32	0 5937
5/64–60	0.0781	0.0673	0.0563	1/16	0.0625	11/16–11	0.6875	0.6285	0.5694	19/32	0.5937
72	0.0781	0.0691	0.0601	52	0.0635	16	0.6875	0.6469	0.6063	5/8	0.6250
3/32–48	0.0938	0.0803	0.0667	49	0.0730	3/4–10	0.7500	0.6850	0.6201	21/32	0.6562
50	0.0938	0.0808	0.0678	49	0.0730	12	0.7500	0.6959	0.6418	43/64	0.6719
7/64–48	0.1094	0.0959	0.0823	43	0.0890	16	0.7500	0.7094	0.6688	11/16	0.6875
1/8–32	0.1250	0.1047	0.0844	3/32	0.0937	27	0.7500	0.7259	0.7019	23/32	0.7187
40	0.1250	0.1088	0.0925	38	0.1015	13/16–10	0.8125	0.7476	0.6826	23/32	0.7187
9/64–40	0.1406	0.1244	0.1081	32	0.1160	7/8–9	0.8750	0.8028	0.7307	49/64	0.7656
5/32–32	0.1563	0.1360	0.1157	1/8	0.1250	12	0.8750	0.8209	0.7668	51/64	0.7969
36	0.1563	0.1382	0.1202	30	0.1285	14	0.8750	0.8286	0.7822	13/16	0.8125
11/64–32	0.1719	0.1516	0.1313	9/64	0.1406	18	0.8750	0.8389	0.8028	53/64	0.8281
3/16–24	0.1875	0.1604	0.1334	26	0.1470	27	0.8750	0.8509	0.8269	27/32	0.8437
32	0.1875	0.1672	0.1469	22	0.1570	15/16–9	0.9375	0.8654	0.7932	53/64	0.8281
13/64–24	0.2031	0.1760	0.1490	20	0.1610	1–8	1.0000	0.9188	0.8376	7/8	0.8750
7/32–24	0.2188	0.1917	0.1646	16	0.1770	12	1.0000	0.9459	0.8918	59/64	0.9219
32	0.2188	0.1985	0.1782	12	0.1890	14	1.0000	0.9536	0.9072	15/16	0.9375
15/64–24	0.2344	0.2073	0.1806	10	0.1935	27	1.0000	0.9759	0.9519	31/32	0.9687
1/4–20	0.2500	0.2175	0.1850	7	0.2010	1 1/8–7	1.1250	1.0322	0.9394	63/64	0.9844
24	0.2500	0.2229	0.1959	4	0.2090	12	1.1250	1.0709	1.0168	1 3/64	1.0469
27	0.2500	0.2260	0.2019	3	0.2130	1 1/4–7	1.2500	1.1572	1.0644	1 7/64	1.1094
28	0.250)	0.2268	0.2036	3	0.2130	12	1.2500	1.1959	1.1418	1 11/64	1.1719
32	0.2500	0.2297	0.2094	7/32	0.2188	1 3/8–6	1.3750	1.2667	1.1585	1 7/32	1.2187
5/16–18	0.3125	0.2764	0.2403	F	0.2570	12	1.3750	1.3209	1.2668	1 19/64	1.2969
20	0.3125	0.2800	0.2476	17/64	0.2656	1 1/2–6	1.5000	1.3917	1.2835	1 11/32	1.3437
24	0.3125	0.2854	0.2584	I	0.2720	12	1.5000	1.4459	1.3918	1 27/64	1.4219
27	0.3125	0.2884	0.2644	J	0.2770	1 5/8–5 1/2	1.6250	1.5069	1.3888	1 29/64	1.4531
32	0.3125	0.2922	0.2719	9/32	0.2812	1 3/4–5	1.7500	1.6201	1.4902	1 9/16	1.5625
3/8–16	0.3750	0.3344	0.2938	5/16	0.3125	1 7/8–5	1.8750	1.7451	1.6152	1 11/16	1.6875
20	0.3750	0.3425	0.3100	21/64	0.3281	2–4 1/2	2.0000	1.8557	1.7113	1 25/32	1.7812
24	0.3750	0.3479	0.3209	Q	0.3320	2 1/8–4 1/2	2.1250	1.9807	1.8363	1 29/32	1.9062
27	0.3750	0.3509	0.3269	R	0.3390	2 1/4–4 1/2	2.2500	2.1057	1.9613	2 1/32	2.0312
7/16–14	0.4375	0.3911	0.3447	U	0.3680	2 3/8–4	2.3750	2.2126	2.0502	2 1/8	2.1250
20	0.4375	0.4050	0.3726	25/64	0.3906	2 1/2–4	2.5000	2.3376	2.1752	2 1/4	2.2500
24	0.4375	0.4104	0.3834	X	0.3970	2 3/4–4	2.7500	2.5876	2.4252	2 1/2	2.5000
27	0.4375	0.4134	0.3894	Y	0.4040	3–4	3.0000	2.8376	2.6752	2 3/4	2.7500
1/2–12	0.5000	0.4459	0.3918	27/64	0.4219	3 1/4–4	3.2500	3.0876	2.9252	3	3.0000
13	0.5000	0.4500	0.4001	27/64	0.4219	3 1/2–4	3.5000	3.3376	3.1752	3 1/4	3.2500
20	0.5000	0.4675	0.4351	29/64	0.4531	3 3/4–4	3.7500	3.5876	3.4252	3 1/2	3.5000
24	0.5000	0.4729	0.4459	29/64	0.4531	4–4	4.0000	3.8376	3.6752	3 3/4	3.7500
27	0.5000	0.4759	0.4519	15/32	0.4687						
9/16–12	0.5625	0.5084	0.4542	31/64	0.4844						
18	0.5625	0.5264	0.4903	33/64	0.5156						
27	0.5625	0.5384	0.5144	17/32	0.5312						
5/8–11	0.6250	0.5660	0.5069	17/32	0.5312						
12	0.6250	0.5709	0.5168	35/64	0.5469						

This procedure helps to avoid breaking the tap. The tap should also be lubricated.

9. What kind of lubricant should be used for general threading?

Ans. Mineral lard oil is a very good lubricant for threading. It is made of white lead, graphite, and fatty oil. The Geometric Tool Company advises the use of the following compound for screw-thread cutting: 40 gal of water mixed with 10 gal of mineral lard oil and 2 1/2 lb of soda.

10. How should a tapped hole be checked for accuracy?

Fig. 9–10. Plug thread gage. (Taft-Pierce Mfg. Co.)

Ans. A plug thread gage (Fig. 9–10) is used to test the quality of the threads according to the fit specified on the blueprint.

11. How are the specifications for a thread given on a blueprint?

Ans. The specifications for a thread are given on a blueprint in a definite, abbreviated form. For example, the specifications may read 1/2—13NC—3 tap, 4 holes. The workman who reads these specifications is informed that the major diameter of the thread is 1/2 in., the number of threads per inch is 13, the kind of thread is the National form, it is a standard member of the coarse series of threads, the thread gage is to have a medium fit (3), the operation is to tap, and four such holes are required.

12. Describe the ways in which a thread gage may fit a thread.

Ans. Four distinct classes of screw-thread fits have been established by the National Screw

Thread Commission for the purpose of ensuring the interchangeable manufacture of screw-thread parts throughout the country. The numbers and corresponding fits are as follows:

No. 1. Loose fit. Usually specified for small tapped holes such as the numbered sizes made by mass-production methods.

No. 2. Free fit. The fit usually found on bolts and nuts of medium size in hardware stores. A thread gage should rotate freely in such a fit, without being loose.

No. 3. Medium fit. For most threads made in the toolroom for some particular use in special machines and fixtures. For this class of fit, a thread gage should rotate with little effort, but not freely, nor should it be tight.

No. 4. Close fit. Usually specified only for the larger sizes of custom-made threads and for aircraft work. There should be perfect contact between each thread and the gage.

13. How may a broken tap be removed from a tapped hole?

Ans. If there is not enough of the tap protruding above the hole so that it may be gripped with pliers, a tap extractor should be used (Fig. 9–11). The extractor is held in a tap wrench. The steel prongs are pushed down each flute of the tap as far as possible and held in place by the long bushing. The extractor must be turned carefully to avoid breaking its prongs.

Fig. 9–11. Tap extractor. (Walton Co.)

14. How may a broken screw be removed from a tapped hole?

Ans. A broken screw may be removed with an Ezy-out (Fig. 9–12). A hole is first drilled into the broken screw. It should be a little smaller than the minor diameter of the thread. An Ezy-out of the proper size is then inserted in the hole. The left-hand spirals of the Ezy-out will grip the sides of the hole, and as it is turned counterclockwise, the screw will be backed out.

Fig. 9–12. Ezy-outs. (Whitman & Barnes)

15. What is a threading die?

Ans. A threading die is a flat piece of hardened steel, internally threaded, with grooves or flutes intersecting the threads to form cutting edges. It is used for cutting external threads on round bars of metal. The die is split on one side. The purpose of this split is to permit turning a setscrew on the side

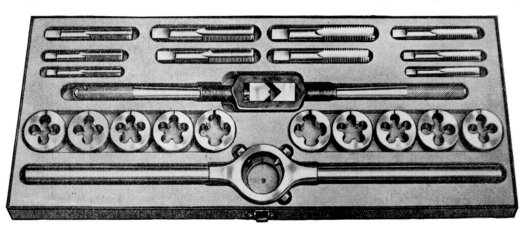

Fig. 9–13. Threading tools. (Morse Twist Drill & Machine Co.)

of the die. This expands the die so that the first cut may be more easily made. A set of threading tools, taps, tap holder, dies, and die holder (diestock) is shown in Fig. 9–13.

16. *What is a diestock?*

Ans. A diestock is a tool for holding threading dies. An example of its use is shown in Fig. 9–14. The bar to be threaded is held in a vise, and the threading die, held in the diestock, is worked around the bar clockwise. It is customary to reverse the movement occasionally in order to break the metal chips which might clog the die.

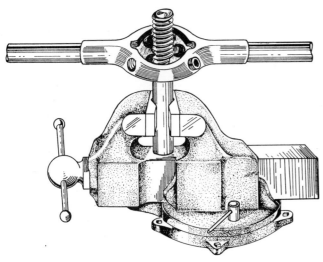

Fig. 9–14. Cutting external threads with a die held in a diestock.

17. *Are both sides of a threading die the same?*

Ans. No. On one side, the hole in the die is chamfered more than on the other side. The deep chamfer helps to get the die started on the work.

18. *How are external threads tested for accuracy?*

Ans. The most common way to test the accuracy of an external thread is with a ring thread gage (Fig. 9–15) according to the fit specified on the

Fig. 9–15. Ring thread gage. (Taft-Pierce Mfg. Co.)

blueprint, as explained in the answer to question 12. Threads may also be checked with a screw-pitch gage, a thread micrometer, the three-wire system, or various types of thread comparators.

19. *What is a screw-pitch gage?*

Ans. A screw-pitch gage (Fig. 9–16) is a tool for measuring the number of threads per inch of internal and external threads. It has a series of blades which are accurately notched and numbered. To test a thread to determine the number of threads per inch, one blade at a time is placed on the threads until one is found that is a perfect match.

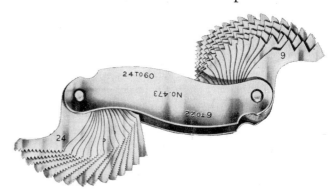

Fig. 9–16. Screw-pitch gage. (L. S. Starrett Co.)

20. *What part of a thread is checked with a thread micrometer?*

Ans. The thread micrometer (Fig. 9–17) is used to measure the pitch diameter of threads. The spindle has a 60-deg conical point and the anvil has a matching groove. The size of pitch diameters of National threads is given in Table 9–1.

Fig. 9–17. Thread micrometer. (Lufkin Rule Co.)

21. *What is the three-wire system for measuring the size of threads?*

Ans. The three-wire system for measuring the pitch diameter of threads is considered more accurate than the direct reading obtained with a thread micrometer, although the latter method is more simple. In practice, two wires are laid in adjacent grooves on one side of a thread and one wire is placed in a groove on the opposite side (see Fig. 9–18). A regular micrometer is then used to measure over the three wires.

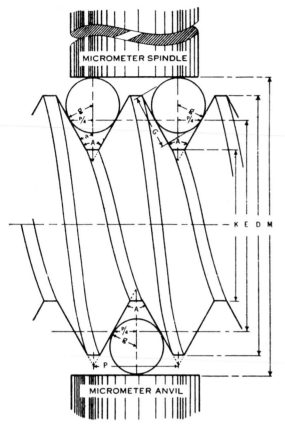

Fig. 9–18. Three-wire system of measuring pitch diameter of a thread.

22. How are the size of the wire and the measurement over the wires, used in measuring threads, determined?

Ans. The best size of wire to use is equal to 0.57735 divided by the number of threads per inch. However, it is customary to use a table giving the diameters of best-size wires (see Table 9–2). The measurement over the wires must equal a predetermined size if the pitch diameter of the thread is the correct size. The symbol used to designate the size of the wire is G; for the measurement over three wires, it is M. The formula for determining the size of M for the National form of thread is

$$M = D + 3G - \frac{1.5155}{N}$$

23. Calculate the micrometer reading over three wires to check the pitch diameter of a 3/4—10 NC thread.

Table 9–2. DIAMETERS OF BEST-SIZE WIRES

Threads per inch	Pitch	Diameter of best-size wires	Single depth National form thread	Width of flat on crest and root NC and NF	Single depth V thread
4	0.250000	0.1443375	0.162379	0.0312	0.216506
4½	0.222222	0.1282998	0.144337	0.0278	0.192449
5	0.200000	0.1154700	0.129903	0.0250	0.173205
5½	0.181818	0.1049726	0.118094	0.0227	0.157458
6	0.166666	0.0962246	0.108253	0.0208	0.144336
7	0.142857	0.0824784	0.092788	0.0179	0.123717
8	0.125000	0.0721687	0.081189	0.0156	0.108253
9	0.111111	0.0641499	0.072168	0.0139	0.096224
10	0.100000	0.0577350	0.064951	0.0125	0.086602
11	0.090909	0.0524863	0.059047	0.0114	0.078729
11½	0.086956	0.0502040	0.056479	0.0108	0.075306
12	0.083333	0.0481123	0.054126	0.0104	0.072168
13	0.076923	0.0444114	0.049963	0.0096	0.066617
14	0.071428	0.0412389	0.046394	0.0089	0.061858
16	0.062500	0.0360843	0.040594	0.0078	0.054126
18	0.055555	0.0320746	0.036084	0.0069	0.048112
19	0.052631	0.0303865	0.034185	0.0065	0.045579
20	0.050000	0.0288675	0.032475	0.0062	0.043301
22	0.045454	0.0262428	0.029523	0.0057	0.039364
24	0.041666	0.0240558	0.027063	0.0052	0.036083
27	0.037037	0.0213833	0.024056	0.0046	0.032074
28	0.035714	0.0206194	0.023197	0.0045	0.030929
30	0.033333	0.0192448	0.021650	0.0042	0.028867
32	0.031250	0.0180421	0.020297	0.0039	0.027063
34	0.029411	0.0169804	0.019103	0.0037	0.025470
36	0.027777	0.0160370	0.018042	0.0035	0.024055
40	0.025000	0.0144337	0.016237	0.0031	0.021650
44	0.022727	0.0131214	0.014761	0.0028	0.019682
48	0.020833	0.0120279	0.013531	0.0026	0.018041
50	0.020000	0.0115470	0.012990	0.0025	0.017320
56	0.017857	0.0103097	0.011598	0.0022	0.015464
64	0.015625	0.0090210	0.010148	0.0020	0.013531
72	0.013888	0.0080182	0.009021	0.0017	0.012027
80	0.012500	0.0072168	0.008118	0.0016	0.010825

Ans. First determine the wire size to use by referring to Table 9–2. Read down the column marked "Threads per inch" to the required number of threads, then follow horizontally to the number in the column marked "Diameter of best-size wires." The number is 0.057735. Next, use the formula given in the answer to question 22.

$$M = 0.750 + (3 \times 0.057735) - \frac{1.5155}{10}$$
$$= 0.750 + 0.1732 - 0.15155$$
$$= 0.7717 \quad \text{Measurement over three wires}$$

24. When the size of wire required to gage the thread on the pitch diameter cannot be obtained, state the method of finding the commercial size of wire that can be successfully used to check threads by the three-wire system.

Ans. The minimum diameter of the wire must be such that the wires extend beyond the top of the screw to prevent the micrometer from bearing on the threads instead of on the wires, and the maximum limit must be such that the wires bear on the sides of the thread and not on the crest. The following formulas do not give the extreme theoretical limits, but they do give the smallest and the largest sizes that are practicable.

The smallest diameter of wire to use is equal to 0.56 divided by the number of threads per inch.

The largest diameter of wire to use is equal to 0.90 divided by the number of threads per inch.

25. What is a comparator?

Ans. A comparator (Fig. 9–19) is an instrument for checking the accuracy of machined parts by comparing the magnified picture of the part with a master gage. This method is sometimes used to check the accuracy of threads.

The comparator in Fig. 9–20 has two lines drawn at right angles to each other, intersecting at the center of the screen. Around the edge of the screen

Fig. 9–20. Comparator with angle-measuring attachment. (Jones & Lamson Machine Co.)

is a vernier protractor. This is used to measure accurately the angle of a thread. The screen is rotated until the lines on the screen exactly match the edge of the enlarged shadow of the thread being checked. The thread being measured in the illustration is a 29-deg acme thread.

Another type of comparator is shown in Fig. 9–21. The two sections of the anvil are similar to a ring gage. When a threaded part is placed within the anvil, the dial indicator shows the amount of

Fig. 9–19. Bench optical comparator. (Jones & Lamson Machine Co.)

error, if any, of the lead, thread angle, and pitch diameter. Each size of thread requires a corresponding size of anvil.

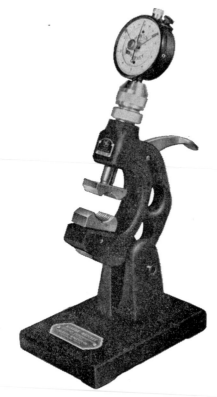

Fig. 9–21. Thread comparator. (Hanson-Whitney Co.)

Some gages are designed to inspect only one element of a thread. The device in Fig. 9–22 is a thread-lead gage which is used to test the accuracy of the lead of a thread within 0.0001 in. The thread

Fig. 9–22. Thread-lead gage. (Federal Products Corp.)

to be tested is placed on the horizontal table and brought into contact with the contact points. Any variation of lead is shown on the indicating dial. A gage for testing the pitch diameter of threads is shown in Fig. 9–23. The thread to be measured is placed between the upper and lower rollers. Any variation from the required pitch diameter is shown on the indicating dial.

Fig. 9–23. Pitch-diameter thread gage. (Federal Products Corp.)

26. Describe the procedure for cutting external National form threads on a lathe.

Ans. After the material has been set up in the lathe, the machining operations are as follows: (1) The part of the material to be threaded is turned to the major diameter of the thread. (2) A tool bit is then ground to the shape of the thread and

Fig. 9–24. Center gage. (Brown & Sharpe Mfg. Co.)

checked for accuracy with a center gage (Fig. 9–24). (3) The lathe compound is adjusted to an angle of 30 deg, as in Fig. 9–25. (4) The lead screw of the lathe is adjusted to the required number of threads per inch. (5) The cutting tool is set square with the work, using a center gage, as in Fig. 9–26. A typical setup for thread cutting is shown in Fig. 9–27.

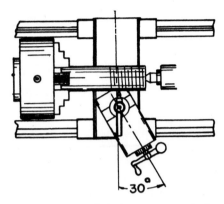

Fig. 9–25. Adjustment of lathe compound for external threading.

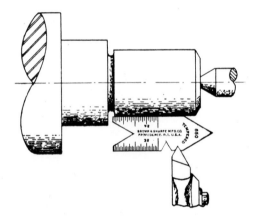

Fig. 9–26. Setting the cutting tool for external threading.

Fig. 9–27. Cutting an external thread on the lathe. (South Bend Lathe Works)

27. *When cutting a thread on a lathe, what precaution should be made to check the setting of the lead screw?*

Ans. A very light cut should be made, just deep enough to make a thin line. The number of threads per inch may then be measured by placing a rule on the work and counting the number of spaces in 1 in.

28. *How is the accuracy of the thread determined?*

Ans. The thread is checked for accuracy with a ring thread gage according to the fit specified on the blueprint.

NOTE: For free fits (No. 2) a standard nut is sometimes used as a gage.

29. *Explain the difference between the minor diameter of a screw and of a nut.*

Ans. The minor diameter of a nut is made larger than the minor diameter of a screw. This is done to provide a working clearance between the two parts (see Fig. 9–28). For many jobs, the recommended size of tap drill will make a hole with a reasonable clearance. For more precise work, the actual size of hole to be bored may be calculated

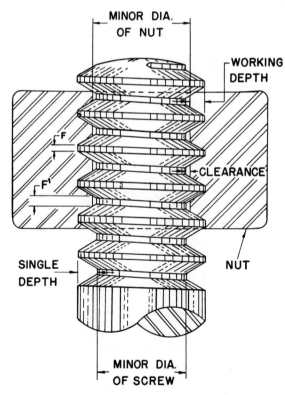

Fig. 9–28. Comparison between the minor diameter of a nut and a screw.

by the following formula: minor diameter of nut equals major diameter minus 1.0825/N.

30. Describe the procedure for cutting internal National form threads on a lathe.

Ans. After the material has been set up in the lathe, the machining operations are as follows: (1) The part of the material to be threaded is bored to the required minor diameter of the thread. (2) A tool bit is then ground to the shape of the thread

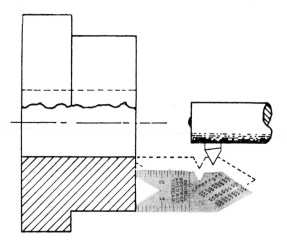

Fig. 9–29. Setting the cutting tool for internal threading.

Fig. 9–32. Thread-rolling attachment. (Reed Rolled Thread Die Co.)

Fig. 9–30. Flat thread-rolling dies. (Reed Rolled Thread Die Co.)

Fig. 9–33. Cylindrical thread-rolling dies. (Reed Rolled Thread Die Co.)

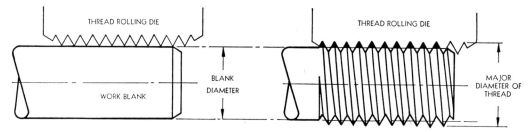

Fig. 9–31. Displacement of material by thread rolling. (Reed Rolled Thread Die Co.)

and checked for accuracy with a center gage. (3) The lathe compound is adjusted to an angle of 30 deg. (4) The lead screw of the lathe is adjusted to the required number of threads per inch. (5) The cutting tool is set square with the work, using a center gage, as in Fig. 9–29. (6) Check accuracy of finished thread with a plug thread gage.

31. *What is the process of producing rolled threads?*

Ans. Rolled threads are produced by passing cylindrical material through flat-grooved dies (Fig. 9–30). As the material is rolled through the dies, the top of the grooves of the die is forced into the surface of the material. The material displaced by the die in this manner is compressed into the bottom of the grooves to form the top of the finished thread, as in Fig. 9–31.

Cylindrical dies are also used for rolling threads. They are held in a thread-rolling attachment (Fig.

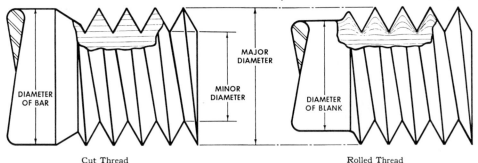

Fig. 9–34. Comparison between the size of material required for cut threads and rolled threads. (Reed Rolled Thread Die Co.)

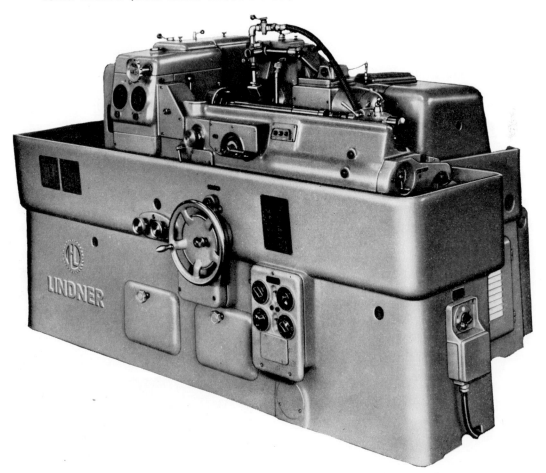

Fig. 9–35. External thread grinder. (Kurt Orban Co., Inc.)

9–32) which is attached to the tool post of a turret lathe or to an automatic screw machine. A variety of cylindrical thread-rolling dies is shown in Fig. 9–33.

32. What size of material should be used for rolled threads?

Ans. The outside diameter of material for rolled threads should equal approximately the pitch diameter of the required thread. After the threads

have been rolled, the outside diameter of the threaded material will equal the major diameter of the thread. Figure 9–34 shows a comparison between the size of material required for cut threads and rolled threads.

33. What is the process of grinding threads?

Ans. The production of threads by the grinding process is comparatively new. During the last 30 years, this method for producing threads has been developed to a high degree of perfection, so that it is being accepted and used throughout industry. Special machines are required for this purpose. Figure 9–35 shows an external-thread grinder and Fig. 9–36 an internal-thread grinder.

There are two main types of thread grinding, single rib and multiple rib. Single-rib grinding involves the use of a narrow grinding wheel which

Fig. 9–36. Internal thread grinder. (Ex-Cell-O Corp.)

A. Work-drive housing
B. Work-head slide
C. Thread and index control
D. Workpiece
E. Grinding wheel
F. Controls and lights
G. Electrical compartment
H. Wheel slide
J. Size-control wheel
K. Operator's control panel
L. Lead and backlash control

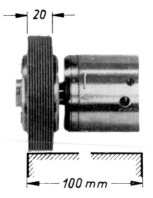

Fig. 9–38. Multiple-rib thread-grinding wheel. (Kurt Orban Co., Inc.)

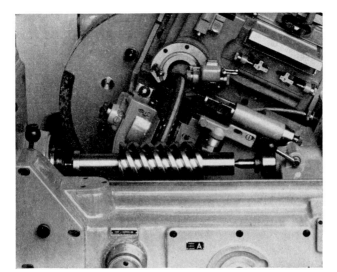

Fig. 9–37. Grinding an external thread with a single-rib wheel. (Kurt Orban Co., Inc.)

Fig. 9–39. Grinding an external thread with a multiple-rib wheel. (Kurt Orban Co., Inc.)

is shaped to the form of the required thread. An example of this type of thread grinding is shown in Fig. 9–37.

Multiple-rib grinding is done with a grinding wheel with many grooves on its face, as in Fig. 9–38. This type of wheel grinds many threads at one time, as on the shaft shown in Fig. 9–39. Internal threads may also be ground with a multiple-rib grinding wheel. An example of internal-thread grinding is shown in Fig. 9–40.

Single-rib wheels are kept true to shape with a diamond wheel dresser. Multiple-rib wheels are shaped with crushing rollers (see Fig. 9–41). These rollers are mounted behind the grinding wheel and may be forced against the wheel to keep it true to shape as occasion may require.

34. What is a sharp V thread?

Ans. The sharp V thread (Fig. 9–42) is similar to the National form of thread. Because the sharp point of the thread is easily damaged, this type of thread is becoming obsolete. It was favored by watchmakers for very small screws.

35. What is a square thread?

Ans. A square thread (Fig. 9–42) is one in which the width of the thread, the depth of the thread, and the space between threads are all equal. This type of thread is very strong. It is preferred for use on the lead screws of lathes and other machine tools, and for heavy-duty jacks. It is rather difficult to machine square threads accurately.

36. What size of hole should be bored before cutting a 2-in. internal square thread having four threads per inch?

Ans. The diameter of the hole to be bored is equal to the major diameter of the thread minus the double depth of the thread. In this case,

$$2 - 2\left(\frac{0.500}{4}\right) = 2 - 0.250 = 1.750$$

37. What is an acme thread?

Ans. An acme thread (Fig. 9–42) is a modification of the square thread. Although it is not quite as strong as the square thread, it is preferred for many jobs because it is fairly easy to machine. An acme thread gage (Fig. 9–43) is used when grinding the cutting tool and also for adjusting the tool square with the work. The notches around the edge of the gage are for checking the correct width

Fig. 9–40. Grinding an internal thread with a multiple-rib wheel. (Kurt Orban Co., Inc.)

Fig. 9–41. Crushing rollers for dressing multiple-rib grinding wheels. (Kurt Orban Co., Inc.)

of the point of the tool according to the number of threads per inch specified for the acme thread.

38. What size of hole should be bored before cutting a 2 1/2-in. internal acme thread having three threads per inch?

Ans. The diameter of the hole to be bored is equal to the major diameter of the required thread minus the double depth of the thread. In this case,

$$2.5 - 2\left(\frac{0.500}{3}\right) = 2.5 - 0.3333 = 2.1667$$

39. What is a Brown and Sharpe worm thread?

Ans. The Brown and Sharpe worm thread (Fig. 9–42) is another modification of the square thread. It is similar to the acme thread in shape but is cut deeper. The circular gage in Fig. 9–44 is used to grind the cutting tool to the required shape and size. The tool-setting gage is used for setting the cutting tool square with the work.

40. What is the minor diameter of a Brown and Sharpe worm thread that has a major diameter of 3 in., with two threads per inch?

Ans. The minor diameter of the thread is equal to the major diameter minus the double depth of the thread. In this case,

$$3 - 2\left(\frac{0.6866}{2}\right) = 3 - 0.6866 = 2.3134$$

41. What is a buttress thread?

Ans. A buttress thread is cut square on one side and slanting on the other side, as in Fig. 9–42. It is used where a thread requiring great strength in

Sharp V Thread

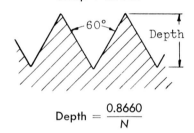

$$\text{Depth} = \frac{0.8660}{N}$$

Brown & Sharpe Worm Thread

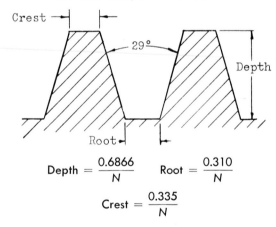

$$\text{Depth} = \frac{0.6866}{N} \qquad \text{Root} = \frac{0.310}{N}$$

$$\text{Crest} = \frac{0.335}{N}$$

Acme Thread

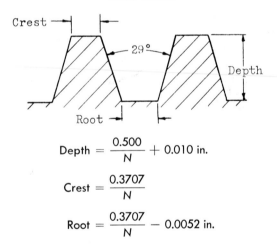

$$\text{Depth} = \frac{0.500}{N} + 0.010 \text{ in.}$$

$$\text{Crest} = \frac{0.3707}{N}$$

$$\text{Root} = \frac{0.3707}{N} - 0.0052 \text{ in.}$$

Square Thread

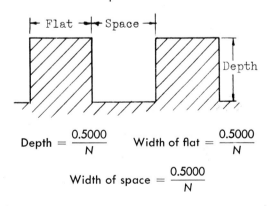

$$\text{Depth} = \frac{0.5000}{N} \qquad \text{Width of flat} = \frac{0.5000}{N}$$

$$\text{Width of space} = \frac{0.5000}{N}$$

Buttress Thread

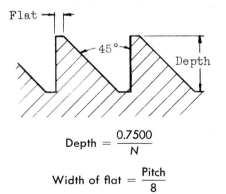

$$\text{Depth} = \frac{0.7500}{N}$$

$$\text{Width of flat} = \frac{\text{Pitch}}{8}$$

Fig. 9–42. Standard forms of threads.

one direction is required, as in certain types of vises, gun breeches, and ratchets.

42. What information is required on a blueprint for cutting square, acme, Brown and Sharpe, and buttress threads?

Ans. The specifications for all such threads should include (1) major diameter, (2) number of threads per inch, (3) kind of thread, and (4) operation to be performed.

EXAMPLE: 1 1/2—3 acme thread

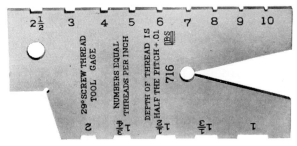

Fig. 9–43. Acme thread gage. (Brown & Sharpe Mfg. Co.)

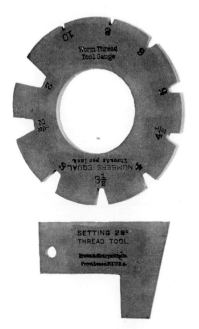

Fig. 9–44. Brown & Sharpe worm-thread gage and setting tool. (Brown & Sharpe Mfg. Co.)

43. How are square, acme, Brown and Sharpe, and buttress threads tested for accuracy?

Ans. Threads of this kind are usually expected to have close fits. If gages are available, they are used in the same manner as other thread gages. When gages are not available, it is customary to match the mating parts. The external thread is made first and then it is used as a gage for checking the matching thread.

44. Are all threads cut right-handed?

Ans. No. Threads are cut right-handed unless otherwise specified. When a left-hand thread is required, it is indicated in the specifications as 3/4—10NC—3 LH thread.

45. What is a pipe thread?

Ans. A pipe thread is similar in shape to the National form of thread (Fig. 9–45). The threads are cut on a taper to ensure a watertight fit between a pipe and pipe fittings.

46. What specifications are required for cutting pipe threads?

Ans. The only specifications required for cutting pipe threads are (1) nominal size of the pipe, (2) kind of thread, and (3) operation to be performed.

EXAMPLE: 1/2 pipe tap

47. Is the nominal size of pipe equal to the inside or outside diameter of pipe?

Ans. Neither. At one time, the nominal size of pipe equalled the inside diameter. Today, the inside diameter of a pipe is larger than the nominal size. The quality of material used in making pipe today is superior to that used many years ago, so the thickness of the material is less than it was originally. The size of the outside of the pipe has not been changed, as this would cause trouble in fitting pipes together. The basic measurements and formulas of pipe threads are given in Fig. 9–45 (*a*) and (*b*). Numerical values for these dimensions can be found in any standard handbook for machinists.

48. How are pipe threads usually cut?

Ans. Pipe threads are usually cut with threading dies or taps. They may also be cut on a lathe in much the same manner as other threads. A tap for cutting pipe threads is shown in Fig. 9–46.

49. When cutting pipe threads on a lathe, should the cutting tool be set at 90 deg with the center line of the work or at 90 deg with the taper?

Ans. The tool should be set at 90 deg with the center line of the work.

50. Describe the gaging of external pipe threads.

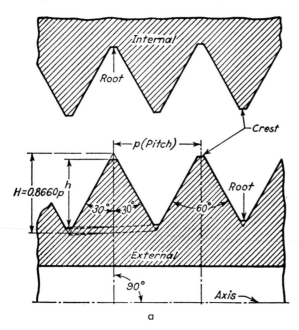

$$\text{Pitch in inches } (p) = \frac{1}{\text{threads per inch } (n)}$$

Depth sharp V thread $(H) = 0.8660p$

Basic maximum depth $(h) = 0.800p$

D = outside diameter of pipe

E_0 = pitch diameter at beginning of external thread

L_1 = length, hand-tight engagement

E_1 = diameter, hand-tight engagement

L_2 = length, effective thread, external

E_2 = diameter, effective thread, external

L_3 = length, wrench make-up, internal thread

E_3 = diameter, wrench make-up, internal thread

V = vanish threads

L_4 = over-all length, external thread

L_5 = length, nominal perfect external threads

E_5 = diameter, nominal perfect external threads

$$E_0 = D - (0.050D + 1.1)\frac{1}{n}$$

$$E_1 = E_0 + 0.0625L_1$$

$$L_2 = (0.80D + 6.8)\frac{1}{n}$$

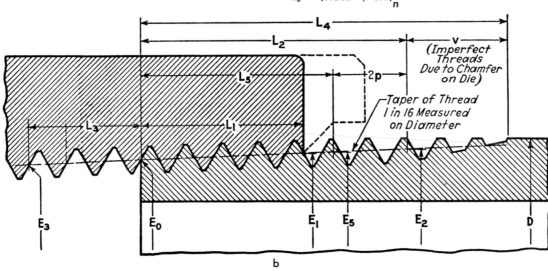

Fig. 9–45. (a) Basic form of American standard taper pipe thread. (b) Basic dimensions of American standard taper pipe thread. (American Standard Association)

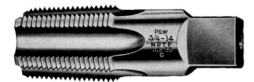

Fig. 9–46. Standard-taper pipe tap. (Pratt & Whitney Co.)

Ans. In gaging external, or male, pipe threads, the ring gage (Fig. 9–47) should be screwed tight, by hand, on the pipe, or male, thread until the end of the gage is flush with the end of the thread.

51. Describe the gaging of internal pipe threads.
Ans. In gaging internal, or female, pipe threads,

Fig. 9–47. Ring gage for standard-taper pipe threads. (John Bath & Co.)

the plug thread gage (Fig. 9–48) should be screwed tight, by hand, into the fitting or coupling

Table 9–3. SUGGESTED DIAMETERS OF TWIST DRILLS FOR TAPPED HOLES FOR PIPE THREADS*

1	2	3	4
	Taper thread		
Nominal pipe size	With use of reamer	Without use of reamer	Straight pipe thread
$\frac{1}{16}$	... 0.240†	... 0.246†	$\frac{1}{4}$ 0.250†
$\frac{1}{8}$	$\frac{21}{64}$ 0.328†	... 0.332†	$\frac{11}{32}$ 0.344†
$\frac{1}{4}$	$\frac{27}{64}$ 0.422	$\frac{7}{16}$ 0.438†	$\frac{7}{16}$ 0.438†
$\frac{3}{8}$	$\frac{9}{16}$ 0.562	$\frac{9}{16}$ 0.562	$\frac{37}{64}$ 0.578
$\frac{1}{2}$	$\frac{11}{16}$ 0.688	$\frac{45}{64}$ 0.703	$\frac{23}{32}$ 0.719
$\frac{3}{4}$	$\frac{57}{64}$ 0.891	$\frac{29}{32}$ 0.906	$\frac{59}{64}$ 0.922
1	$1\frac{1}{8}$ 1.125	$1\frac{9}{64}$ 1.141	$1\frac{5}{32}$ 1.156
$1\frac{1}{4}$	$1\frac{15}{32}$ 1.469	$1\frac{31}{64}$ 1.484	$1\frac{1}{2}$ 1.500
$1\frac{1}{2}$	$1\frac{23}{32}$ 1.719	$1\frac{47}{64}$ 1.734	$1\frac{3}{4}$ 1.750
2	$2\frac{3}{16}$ 2.188	$2\frac{13}{64}$ 2.203	$2\frac{7}{32}$ 2.219
$2\frac{1}{2}$	$2\frac{19}{32}$ 2.594	$2\frac{5}{8}$ 2.625	$2\frac{21}{32}$ 2.656

* 1. All dimensions are given in inches.
  2. American Society of Mechanical Engineers.
† American Standard twist drill sizes.

Fig. 9–48. Plug gage for standard-taper pipe threads. (John Bath & Co.)

until the notch on the gage is flush with the face. When the thread is chamfered, the notch should be flush with the bottom of the chamfer.

52. What size of hole should be drilled to accommodate a 3/4-in. pipe tap?

Ans. The correct size of drill to use is usually obtained from a table similar to Table 9–3. In this case, the correct size to use is 29/32 in., unless the hole is to be reamed after drilling, in which case the hole would be made 1/64 smaller, or 57/64 in.

53. What material is used between the threads of pipe and pipe fittings to prevent leakage at the joints?

Ans. Either red lead or white lead spread over the threads before screwing the parts together will effectively seal the joints.

Chapter 10   GEARING

A gear is a toothed wheel which when meshed with other gears transmits motion from one part of a mechanism to another. The design of the gears determines whether the speed, or the direction, of the motion will be maintained or changed.

SPUR GEARS

Of the many different types of gears, the most common type is the spur gear.

Fig. 10–1. Spur gear.

1. What is a spur gear?
Ans. A spur gear (Fig. 10–1) is a wheel with teeth cut parallel with the axis of rotation.

2. What are spur gears used for?
Ans. Spur gears are used to transmit motion from one shaft to another shaft that is parallel to it.
There are many definitions that are commonly used when discussing spur gears. A knowledge of these definitions is essential to those who expect to design or make such gears (see Fig. 10–2).

3. What is the pitch circle of a gear?
Ans. The pitch circle of a gear is an imaginary circle located about halfway down the teeth, where the teeth of both gears contact each other.

4. What is the pitch diameter of a gear?
Ans. The pitch diameter is the diameter of the pitch circle.

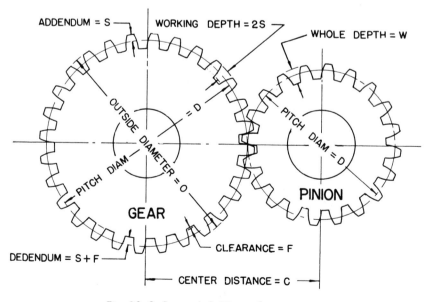

Fig. 10–2. Some definitions of spur gears.

5. What is diametral pitch?

Ans. The diametral pitch is a number that indicates the size of gear teeth. This pitch number corresponds to the number of teeth in 3.1416 (π), measured on the pitch circle of a gear.

6. What is the circular pitch of a gear?

Ans. The circular pitch is the distance from the center of one tooth to the center of the next consecutive tooth, measured on the pitch circle.

7. What is the addendum of a gear tooth?

Ans. The addendum is that portion of the tooth which projects above, or outside of, the pitch circle.

8. What is the dedendum of a gear tooth?

Ans. The dedendum is that portion of the tooth between the pitch circle and the root circle and is equal to one addendum plus the clearance.

9. What is the root circle of a gear?

Ans. The root circle is the circle formed by the bottoms of the teeth.

10. What is the outside diameter of a spur gear?

Ans. The outside diameter of a spur gear is the size to which the material for making the gear must be turned before cutting the teeth. It is equal to the pitch diameter plus two addendums.

11. What is the whole depth of a gear tooth?

Ans. The whole depth is the distance from the top of the tooth to the bottom and consists of addendum plus dedendum.

12. What is meant by the clearance on a gear?

Ans. Gear teeth are designed so that there will be a small space or clearance between the end of a tooth and the root circle of the meshing gear. This eliminates some of the friction and provides space for lubrication.

13. What is the center distance between gears?

Ans. The center distance is the measurement from the center of one gear to the center of a meshing gear. It is equal to half of the pitch diameter of one gear plus half of the pitch diameter of the meshing gear.

14. What form of tooth is commonly used for spur gears?

Ans. The common form of gear tooth is known as the involute.

15. What is the pressure angle of involute gear teeth?

Ans. The pressure angle is the angle at which the pressure of one tooth upon another is applied and distributed. The size of the angle is 14 1/2 deg (see Fig. 10–3).

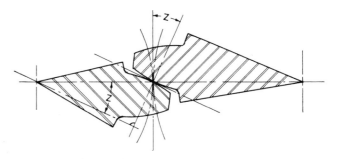

Fig. 10–3. Pressure angle of meshing gear teeth is shown at Z.

16. What is a stub tooth?

Ans. A stub tooth is one that is thicker in proportion to its length than the involute tooth. It is not as smooth in operation as the involute but is preferred where strength is more important.

17. What are the proportions of a stub tooth?

Ans. A stub tooth is designed by combining two sizes of teeth, that is, two diametral pitch numbers. One size is used to determine the thickness of the tooth, the other for the length of the tooth. For example, a 4/6-pitch tooth would have the thickness of 4-pitch teeth and the length of 6-pitch teeth. The pressure angle of stub gear teeth is 20 deg.

18. What is the chordal thickness of a gear tooth?

Ans. The chordal thickness of a gear tooth is the distance in a straight line (chord) from one side of a tooth to the other side at points where the pitch circle passes through the tooth (see Fig. 10–4).

19. What is the corrected addendum of a gear tooth?

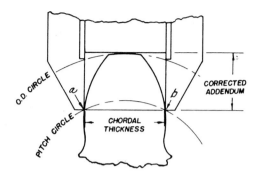

Fig. 10–4. Chordal thickness and corrected addendum of a gear tooth.

Ans. The corrected addendum of a gear tooth is the distance from the top of a tooth to the chord across the tooth at the pitch circle (see Fig. 10–4).

20. For what purpose are the chordal thickness and corrected addendum dimensions used?

Ans. The chordal thickness and corrected addendum dimensions are used to measure the size

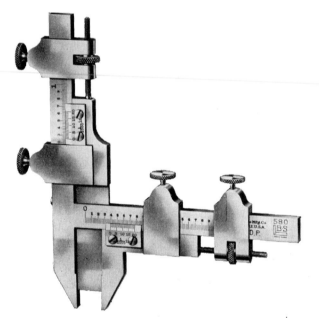

Fig. 10–5. Gear-tooth vernier caliper. (Brown & Sharpe Mfg. Co.)

of gear teeth. The thickness of the tooth varies from the top to the bottom of the tooth. The thickness at the pitch line has been selected for measuring because the location and thickness may be accurately calculated and measured.

21. How is the chordal thickness of a gear tooth measured?

Ans. The chordal thickness is measured with a gear-tooth vernier caliper as shown in Fig. 10–5. The vertical bar is adjusted to the corrected addendum measurement and then the caliper is placed on the tooth. The chordal thickness is measured with the horizontal bar of the caliper.

22. How are the chordal thickness and corrected addendum dimensions determined?

Ans. The dimensions may be calculated as shown in Fig. 10–6. However, it is customary to use a table similar to Table 10–1.

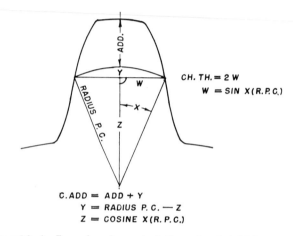

$$CH. TH. = 2 W$$
$$W = SIN \; X(R.P.C.)$$

$$C. ADD = ADD + Y$$
$$Y = RADIUS \; P.C. — Z$$
$$Z = COSINE \; X(R.P.C.)$$

Fig. 10–6. Formulas for calculating chordal-thickness and corrected-addendum dimensions.

GEAR RACK

23. What is a gear rack?

Ans. A gear rack is a piece of material with teeth cut on a flat surface (Fig. 10–7). Rectangular stock is the kind commonly used, but round stock may be used, as on the side of a shaft.

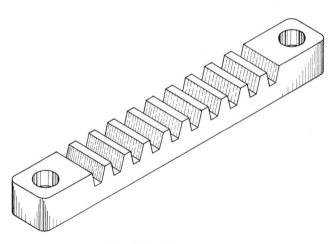

Fig. 10–7. Gear rack.

Table 10–1. DIMENSIONS FOR CORRECTED ADDENDUM AND CHORDAL THICKNESS

Pitch	Part of gear tooth to be measured	Number of cutter and corresponding number of teeth in a gear							
		No. 1 135 T	No. 2 55 T	No. 3 35 T	No. 4 26 T	No. 5 21 T	No. 6 17 T	No. 7 14 T	No. 8 12 T
1	Corrected addendum	1.0047	1.0112	1.0176	1.0237	1.0294	1.0362	1.0440	1.0514
	Chordal thickness	1.5707	1.5706	1.5702	1.5698	1.5694	1.5686	1.5675	1.5663
2	Corrected addendum	0.5023	0.5056	0.5088	0.5118	0.5147	0.5181	0.5220	0.5257
	Chordal thickness	0.7853	0.7853	0.7851	0.7849	0.7847	0.7843	0.7837	0.7831
3	Corrected addendum	0.3349	0.3370	0.3392	0.3412	0.3431	0.3454	0.3480	0.3504
	Chordal thickness	0.5235	0.5235	0.5234	0.5232	0.5231	0.5228	0.5225	0.5221
4	Corrected addendum	0.2511	0.2528	0.2544	0.2559	0.2573	0.2590	0.2610	0.2628
	Chordal thickness	0.3926	0.3926	0.3926	0.3924	0.3923	0.3921	0.3919	0.3915
5	Corrected addendum	0.2009	0.2022	0.2035	0.2047	0.2058	0.2072	0.2088	0.2102
	Chordal thickness	0.3141	0.3141	0.3140	0.3139	0.3138	0.3137	0.3135	0.3132
6	Corrected addendum	0.1674	0.1685	0.1696	0.1706	0.1715	0.1727	0.1740	0.1752
	Chordal thickness	0.2618	0.2617	0.2617	0.2616	0.2615	0.2614	0.2612	0.2612
7	Corrected addendum	0.1435	0.1444	0.1453	0.1462	0.1470	0.1480	0.1491	0.1502
	Chordal thickness	0.2244	0.2243	0.2243	0.2242	0.2242	0.2240	0.2239	0.2237
8	Corrected addendum	0.1255	0.1264	0.1272	0.1279	0.1286	0.1295	0.1305	0.1314
	Chordal thickness	0.1963	0.1963	0.1962	0.1962	0.1961	0.1960	0.1959	0.1957
10	Corrected addendum	0.1004	0.1011	0.1017	0.1023	0.1029	0.1036	0.1044	0.1051
	Chordal thickness	0.1570	0.1570	0.1570	0.1569	0.1569	0.1568	0.1567	0.1566
12	Corrected addendum	0.0837	0.0842	0.0848	0.0853	0.0857	0.0863	0.0870	0.0876
	Chordal thickness	0.1309	0.1309	0.1308	0.1308	0.1308	0.1307	0.1306	0.1305
14	Corrected addendum	0.0717	0.0722	0.0726	0.0731	0.0735	0.0740	0.0745	0.0751
	Chordal thickness	0.1122	0.1122	0.1121	0.1121	0.1121	0.1120	0.1119	0.1118
16	Corrected addendum	0.0628	0.0632	0.0636	0.0639	0.0643	0.0647	0.0652	0.0657
	Chordal thickness	0.0981	0.0981	0.0981	0.0981	0.0980	0.0980	0.0979	0.0979

24. What is the purpose of a gear rack?

Ans. A gear rack, when meshed with a gear, is used to change rotary motion to reciprocating motion.

25. What definitions used for gears are identical for gear racks?

Ans. Diametral pitch, addendum, dedendum, whole depth, clearance, and pressure angle.

26. What is the pitch line of a rack?

Ans. The pitch line of a rack (Fig. 10–8) is an imaginary line that passes through the teeth, separating the addendum from the dedendum. It corresponds to the pitch circle of a gear.

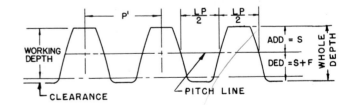

Fig. 10–8. Some definitions of a gear rack.

27. *What is the linear pitch of a rack?*

Ans. The linear pitch of a rack is the distance from the center of one tooth to the center of the next tooth. It corresponds to the circular pitch of a gear.

28. *What dimensions are used to measure the size of a rack tooth?*

Ans. The thickness of a tooth and the space between two teeth are equal on the pitch circle or pitch line. The pitch line being straight, it is not necessary to calculate the length of a chord, but only to divide the linear pitch by two. The dimensions required to measure a rack tooth are addendum and one half of the linear pitch. A gear-tooth vernier caliper is used for measuring rack teeth in the same manner as for measuring gear teeth.

INTERNAL GEAR

29. *What is an internal gear?*

Ans. An internal gear (Fig. 10–9) is one in

Fig. 10–9. Internal gear. (Philadelphia Gear Works)

which teeth are cut on the inner surface of a ring, instead of being cut on the outside of a wheel.

30. *What is the inside diameter of an internal gear?*

Ans. The inside diameter of an internal gear is the size of the hole to be bored before the teeth are cut. It is equal to the pitch diameter minus two addendums.

GENERAL

31. *What is a gear sector?*

Ans. A gear sector (Fig. 10–10) is a wheel that has teeth on a part of its periphery only. It is used to transmit power in an intermittent manner; that is, each time the sector revolves, it will cause the

meshing gear to revolve only while the teeth of each one are in contact, and to remain idle until the sector teeth again come in contact with the gear. The sector illustrated has 20 out of a possible 40 teeth. If it is meshed with a gear having 60 teeth, the latter will be revolved only one-third of a revolution (after which it will be idle during a corresponding period of time) each time the sector makes one complete revolution. Intermittent straight-line motion may also be obtained by meshing a gear sector with a gear rack.

Fig. 10–10. Gear sector. (Boston Gear Works)

32. *Do gears that mesh together always have teeth identical in shape?*

Ans. No. Meshing gears always have teeth of the same size (pitch number), but while they are similar in appearance, the teeth are identical only when the meshing gears are the same size. The curved shape of the teeth varies according to the number of teeth in each gear.

33. *Why are not all gear teeth of a given size identical in shape?*

Ans. For efficient operation, the curvature on the side of a gear tooth is made in proportion to the curvature of the segment of the pitch circle containing one tooth. When only a few teeth are cut on a gear, the curvature of the segment is quite large compared to that of a gear with many teeth (see Fig. 10–11).

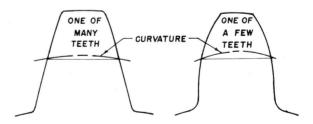

Fig. 10–11. Variations in curvature of gear teeth.

CUTTING GEAR TEETH

34. Are differently shaped cutters used for cutting gear teeth of a given size?

Ans. Yes. For example, when cutting gear teeth on a milling machine with an involute gear cutter (Fig. 10–12), any one of eight different cutters may be used for one size of teeth. The selection of cutter to be used depends on the number of teeth in the gear (see Table 10–2) as well as the size of the gear tooth. Figure 10–13 shows the profile of each of the eight cutters, and, underneath each one, the shape of the corresponding tooth. When requisitioning an involute gear cutter from the tool crib, be sure to ask for the correct number of cutter as well as the correct size.

35. What are some of the methods for cutting spur-gear teeth?

Ans. Spur-gear teeth may be cut one tooth at a time on a milling machine (Fig. 10–14), using an involute gear cutter of the type shown in Fig. 10–12. Another method is to cut the teeth with a multi-

Fig. 10–12. Involute gear cutter. (Pratt & Whitney Co.)

Table 10–2. SELECTION OF CUTTER
FOR GEAR TEETH

Cutter No.	No. of gear teeth
1	135 to a rack
2	55 to 134
3	35 to 54
4	26 to 34
5	21 to 25
6	17 to 20
7	14 to 16
8	12 to 13

Fig. 10–14. Cutting gear teeth on a milling machine. (Cincinnati Milling Machine Co.)

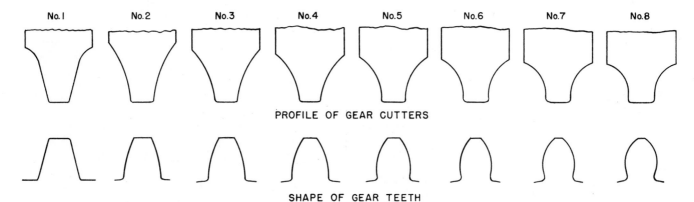

No.1   No.2   No.3   No.4   No.5   No.6   No.7   No.8

PROFILE OF GEAR CUTTERS

SHAPE OF GEAR TEETH

Fig. 10–13. The shape of gear teeth varies according to the number of the gear cutter.

ple cutter called a *hob* (Fig. 10–15). It is used on a special gear-cutting machine known as a *gear hobber* (Fig. 10–16). The gear blanks are held on a vertical arbor as in Fig. 10–27. A close-up view of a hob cutting several gears at one time is shown in Fig. 10–17.

A third method is to cut the teeth, one at a time, on a gear shaper (Fig. 10–18). This machine uses

a cutter that looks like a gear (Fig. 10–19). The cutter is given a reciprocating motion similar to that of a planing or shaping tool. In Fig. 10–20,

Fig. 10–15. Hob for cutting gear teeth. (Pratt & Whitney Co.)

Fig. 10–18. Gear shaper. (Fellows Gear Shaper Co.)

Fig. 10–16. Gear-hobbing Machine. (Gould & Eberhardt, Inc.)

Fig. 10–17. Cutting eight gears at one time on a hobbing machine. (Gould & Eberhardt, Inc.)

Fig. 10–19. The gear-shaping cutter looks like a gear. (Fellows Gear Shaper Co.)

the cutter and work are shown rotating together in the direction of the arrows. The outlines show the various positions which the cutting edge will occupy for each successive stroke of the cutter. The distance between any two adjacent outlines at any point represents the thickness of the chip at that point.

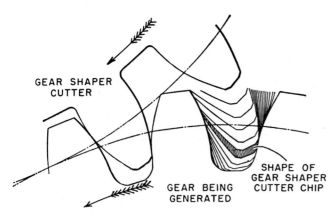

GEAR SHAPER CUTTER

GEAR BEING GENERATED

SHAPE OF GEAR SHAPER CUTTER CHIP

Fig. 10–20. Cutting action of a gear-shaping cutter. (Fellows Gear Shaper Co.)

ABBREVIATIONS AND FORMULAS

36. What abbreviations are used in spur-gear formulas?
Ans.

S = addendum
C = center distance
T = chordal thickness
CP = circular pitch
F = clearance
H = corrected addendum
$S + F$ = dedendum
P = diametral pitch
I = inside diameter
L = length of rack
LP = linear pitch
Ng = number of teeth in the gear
Np = number of teeth in the pinion
OD = outside diameter
PD = pitch diameter
Z = pressure angle
W = whole depth

37. What formulas are used in calculating the dimensions of spur gears?
Ans.

Addendum^x $\qquad S = \dfrac{1}{P}$

Center distance	$C = \dfrac{Ng + Np}{2P}$
Circular pitch^x	$CP = \dfrac{3.1416}{P}$
*Clearance^x	$F = \dfrac{0.157}{P}$
*Dedendum^x	$S + F = \dfrac{1.157}{P}$
Diametral pitch^x	$P = \dfrac{3.1416}{CP}$
Diametral pitch	$P = \dfrac{N + 2}{OD}$
Diametral pitch^x	$P = \dfrac{N}{PD}$
Number of teeth^x	$N = P \times PD$
Outside diameter	$OD = \dfrac{N + 2}{P}$
Outside diameter	$OD = PD + 2S$
Pitch diameter^x	$PD = \dfrac{N}{P}$
Pitch diameter	$PD = OD - 2S$
*Whole depth^x	$W = \dfrac{2.157}{P}$
*Whole depth^x	$W = 0.6866 \times CP$

38. What formulas, in addition to those marked with an asterisk in question 37 are used in calculating the dimensions of gear racks?
Ans.

Diametral pitch	$P = \dfrac{3.1416}{LP}$
Length of rack	$L = N \times LP$
Linear pitch	$LP = \dfrac{3.1416}{P}$

39. What formulas, in addition to those marked with a superior x in question 37 are used in calculating the dimensions of internal gears?
Ans.

Center distance	$C = \dfrac{Ng - Np}{2P}$
Diametral pitch	$P = \dfrac{Ng - Np}{2C}$
Inside diameter	$I = \dfrac{N - 2}{P}$

40. What dimensions are necessary for drawing and machining spur gears?

Ans.

1. Pitch diameter
2. Addendum
3. Dedendum
4. Diameter of hole
5. Keyway
6. Face
7. Outside diameter
8. Pitch
9. Number of teeth
10. Chordal thickness
11. Corrected addendum

41. Calculate the dimensions required for drawing and machining two meshing spur gears. The center distance is 3.9 in. The ratio is 2:1. The size of the hole, face, and pitch may be chosen.

Ans. The sum of the two pitch diameters is equal to twice the center distance, 3.9 times 2 equals 7.8. The pitch diameter of the large gear equals 2/3 of 7.8, or 15.6 divided by 3, which equals 5.2. The pitch diameter of the small gear or pinion equals 1/3 of 7.8, or 2.6.

The size of the tooth or pitch depends upon the pinion. In order to avoid having fractional parts of a tooth in a gear, the first choice of a pitch number is the denominator of the fraction in the pitch diameter; in this case it is 10.

Using the formulas, the addendum equals 1/10 or 0.100, the dedendum equals 1.157 divided by 10, or 0.1157.

After selecting the size of the hole, for instance, 1.250 for the gear and 0.750 for the pinion, the size of the keyways may be found in the Appendix in Table 6, page 304.

Meshing gears have the same face measurement. A reasonable size is 0.7 in.

The outside diameter and the number of teeth for each gear may be calculated from the formulas.

The chordal thickness and corrected addendum for each gear may be obtained from Table 10–1.

The complete list of dimensions is given in Table 10–3.

SPUR-GEAR PROBLEMS

For additional experience in calculating spur gears, the following problems may be solved.

1. Calculate the dimensions required for drawing and machining two meshing spur gears having a 2.1 ratio and a 3-in. center distance. The size of the teeth, face, and hole may be chosen.
2. Calculate the dimensions required for drawing and machining two meshing spur gears having a 2:1 ratio and a 2 17/32-in. center distance. The size of the teeth, face, and hole may be chosen.
3. A rack measures approximately 29 1/32-in. over 37 teeth. Calculate all the dimensions for a gear that will move the rack 25 1/8 in. when the gear makes one revolution.
4. A spur gear having a 1-in. face, 2.083 in. outside diameter, and 23 teeth is mounted on a pump shaft which is run at 300 rpm. This gear is driving a second gear running at 100 rpm. Calculate the dimensions necessary for both gears.
5. Calculate the dimensions for a pair of stub-tooth gears, 4/6 pitch, 2:1 ratio, with a center distance of 4.5 in.
6. A gear revolving through an angle of 112 1/2 deg causes a rack to move 4 11/64 in. Calculate the dimensions for the gear.
7. A gear having 75 teeth and an outside diameter of 9.625 in. runs at 100 rpm. The pinion runs at 312.5 rpm. Calculate the dimensions for both gears.
8. An internal gear with a pitch diameter of 6 in. and 48 teeth is driven by a pinion. The center distance is 2 1/8 in. Calculate the dimensions for both gears.

BEVEL GEARS

42. What is a bevel gear?

Ans. A bevel gear (Fig. 10–21) is one in which the teeth are cut so that they radiate from the apex of a cone and lie on the conical surface.

Table 10–3. GEAR AND PINION DIMENSIONS

Gear		Pinion
5.200	Pitch diameter	2.600
0.100	Addendum	0.100
0.1157	Dedendum	0.1157
1.250	Diameter of hole	0.750
$\frac{5}{16} \times \frac{5}{32}$	Keyway	$\frac{3}{16} \times \frac{3}{32}$
0.7	Face	0.7
5.400	Outside diameter	2.800
10	Pitch	10
52	Number of teeth	26
0.1570	Chordal thickness	0.1569
0.1011	Corrected addendum	0.1023

Fig. 10–21. Bevel gear and pinion. (Philadelphia Gear Works)

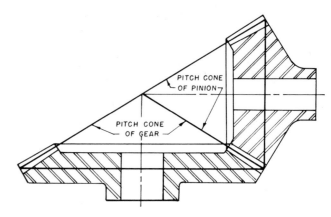

Fig. 10–23. Pitch cones of bevel gear and pinion.

43. What are bevel gears used for?

Ans. Bevel gears are used to transmit motion from one shaft to another shaft at an angle to the first.

The terms used for spur gears have the same meaning for bevel gears. However, there are some additional terms that are peculiar to bevel gears (see Fig. 10–22).

44. What is the vertex distance of a bevel gear?

Ans. The vertex distance of a bevel gear is equal to the altitude of the pitch cone.

45. What is the cutting angle of a bevel gear?

Ans. The cutting angle of a bevel gear is the angle at which the gear blank is held while cutting the teeth on a milling machine. Bevel gears are also cut on special machines.

46. What is the pitch cone angle of a bevel gear?

Ans. The pitch cone angle is the angle between the conical surface of the pitch cone and the center line.

47. What is the face angle of a bevel gear?

Ans. The face angle is the angle to which the gear blank is machined before cutting the teeth.

48. What are miter gears?

Ans. Miter gears is the name given to mating bevel gears having the same number of teeth and pitch cone angles of 45 deg.

49. What are the formulas for calculating the dimensions that are peculiar to bevel gears with shafts intersecting at 90 deg?

Ans.

Vertex distance = pitch diameter of meshing gear ÷ 2

Pitch cone angle of gear = tangent of *PD* of gear ÷ *PD* of pinion

Pitch cone angle of pinion = 90 deg − pitch cone angle of gear

Outside diameter = pitch diameter + 2(cos *PC* angle × addendum)

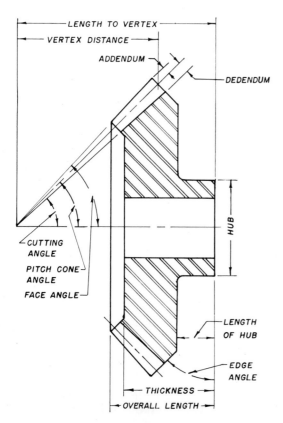

Fig. 10–22. Some definitions of bevel gears.

A set of bevel gears is developed on adjacent cones that have a common vertex, as in Fig. 10–23. These are called *pitch cones.*

Pitch cone radius = cosecant, pitch cone angle $\times$ $PD \div 2$

Cutting angle = pitch cone angle $-$

$$\left(\text{tangent of } \frac{\text{dedendum}}{\text{PC radius}} \right)$$

Face angle = pitch cone angle $+$

$$\left(\text{tangent of } \frac{\text{addendum}}{\text{PC radius}} \right)$$

50. What dimensions are necessary for drawing and machining bevel gears?

Ans.

1. Pitch diameter	12. Face angle
2. Vertex distance	13. Outside diameter
3. Addendum	14. Diameter of hole
4. Dedendum	15. Keyway
5. Pitch	16. Diameter of hub
6. Number of teeth	17. Length of hub
7. Chordal thickness	18. Face
8. Corrected addendum	19. Length to vertex
9. Pitch cone angle	20. Thickness
10. Pitch cone radius	21. Edge angle
11. Cutting angle	22. Over-all length

HELICAL GEARS

51. What is a helical gear?

Ans. A helical gear (Fig. 10–24) is one having teeth cut on a cylinder and at an angle with the axis of rotation of the gear body.

Fig. 10–24. Helical gears on parallel shafts. (Boston Gear Works)

52. What are helical gears used for?

Ans. Helical gears are used to transmit motion from one shaft to another shaft that is parallel with it, as with spur gears (see Fig. 10–24), and also to another shaft that is not parallel to it, as in Fig. 10–25.

Fig. 10–25. Helical gears on shafts at an angle from each other. (Boston Gear Works)

53. What are the advantages of helical gears?

Ans. Helical gears operate more quietly and smoothly than spur gears. The reason for this is that the teeth of helical gears do not hit each other, as in spur gears, but slide one across the other. Also, when helical gears are meshed together, several teeth of each gear are in contact at one time and the load is spread, resulting in greater strength than if only one tooth of each is in contact at a time.

54. What is the undesirable factor of helical gears?

Ans. Because of the sliding action of one tooth on another, the friction, and consequent heat and wear, is high. To offset this condition, helical gears are usually designed to run in an oil bath, as in an automobile transmission.

55. What is the helix angle of a helical gear?

Ans. The helix angle is the angle at which the teeth of a helical gear are slanted across the face of the gear.

56. What is the lead of a helical gear, and for what is it used?

Ans. The lead of a helical gear is the distance that the gear, if thought of as a multiple thread, would advance in one complete revolution of the gear. It is used to select the proper gears to be used in connection with the dividing head on the milling machine, so that the gear blank will rotate properly while the teeth are being cut (see Fig. 10–26). Helical gears are also cut on special gear-hobbing machines, as in Fig. 10–27.

Fig. 10–26. Cutting a helical gear on a milling machine. (Brown & Sharpe Mfg. Co.)

Fig. 10–27. Cutting helical gears on a gear hobber. (Gould & Eberhardt, Inc.)

57. The spur gears in question 41 are to be replaced with helical gears. The center distance of the shafts and the size of the teeth are not to be changed. Calculate the dimensions for the helical gears.

Ans. The center distance and pitch remaining as before, several dimensions will be the same as in the original spur gears, namely, pitch diameter, addendum, dedendum, diameter of hole, keyway, face, outside diameter, pitch, chordal thickness, and corrected addendum.

When the teeth are slanted across the face of the gear, the distance between each one on the edge of the gear is greater than the circular pitch (see Fig. 10–28). It is obvious, then, that the

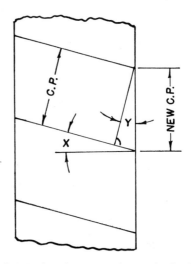

Fig. 10–28. Original and new circular pitch of a helical gear.

helical gears will have fewer teeth than the spur gears. In order to maintain the ratio between the gears, we may decide to use 50 teeth in the gear and 25 in the pinion. The helix angle may now be determined by using the formula

$$\text{Cosine of helix angle} = \frac{N \text{ of helical gear}}{N \text{ of spur gear}} = \frac{50}{52} = 15° 56'$$

The lead of the gear is equal to the circumference of the pitch circle multiplied by the cotangent of the helix angle.

$$5.200 \times 3.1416 \times 3.50279 = 57.222$$

The pinion being one-half the size of the gear, the lead of the pinion will be one-half of the lead of the gear, or 28.611.

The complete list of dimensions for a set of helical gears is given in Table 10–4.

Table 10–4. HELICAL GEAR AND PINION DIMENSIONS

Gear		Pinion
5.200	Pitch diameter	2.600
0.100	Addendum	0.100
0.1157	Dedendum	0.1157
1.250	Diameter of hole	0.750
$\frac{5}{16} \times \frac{5}{32}$	Keyway	$\frac{3}{16} \times \frac{3}{32}$
0.7	Face	0.7
5.400	Outside diameter	2.800
10	Pitch	10
50	Number of teeth	25
0.1570	Chordal thickness	0.1569
0.1011	Corrected addendum	0.1023
15° 56'	Helix angle	15° 56'
57.222	Lead	28.611

NOTE: When shafts are parallel, one gear is cut right-handed, the other one left-handed.

HERRINGBONE GEARS

58. What is a herringbone gear?

Ans. Originally, a herringbone gear (Fig. 10–29) consisted of two helical gears of equal size but of opposite hand joined together. Today, most herringbone gears are produced as a single unit on special machines which cut the teeth in two directions at one time.

Fig. 10–29. Herringbone gears. (Philadelphia Gear Works)

59. What are some of the advantages of herringbone gears?

Ans. (1) The sliding action of helical gear teeth exerts pressure of one gear toward the other which has to be compensated for by the use of thrust bearings. The thrust is equalized when herringbone gears are used. (2) Herringbone gears have a greater bearing surface than other gears of like size, which gives them exceptional tooth strength and heavy load-carrying capacity. (3) They are more satisfactory than other gears where a large ratio between gears is necessary. (4) They stand up under continuous high-speed operation better than other gears.

WORM AND WORM GEARS

60. What is a worm gear?

Ans. A worm gear (Fig. 10–30) is a wheel having teeth cut angular with the axis of rotation and radially in the gear face.

Fig. 10–30. Worm gear. (Boston Gear Works)

61. What is a worm?

Ans. A worm (Fig. 10–31) is a cylinder with teeth resembling those of an acme thread. The worm is mounted on a shaft that is perpendicular to the shaft of the worm gear.

Fig. 10–31. Worm. (Boston Gear Works)

62. What are worm gears used for?

Ans. Worm gears are used for heavy-duty work where a large ratio of speed is required. They are used extensively in speed reducers.

There are several terms used in worm gearing that are not used for other types of gears (see Fig. 10–32).

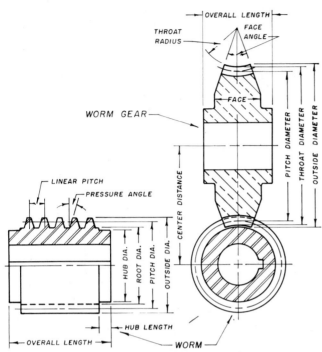

Fig. 10–32. Some definitions of worms and worm gears.

63. What is the normal pitch of a worm?

Ans. The normal pitch of a worm is the distance between the center of one tooth and the center of an adjacent tooth, measured perpendicular to the teeth.

64. What is the throat of a worm gear?

Ans. The throat of a worm gear is the concave surface of the gear tooth.

65. What is the throat radius of a worm gear?

Ans. The throat radius of a worm gear is the radius of the concave surface of the throat.

66. What is the throat diameter of a worm gear?

Ans. The throat diameter of a worm gear is the diameter of the gear, measured at the center of the throat.

67. What is the face angle of a worm gear?

Ans. The face angle of a worm gear is the angle to which the face of the gear is cut.

68. What formulas are used for calculating worm gears?

Ans.

$$\text{Pitch diameter} = 0.3183 \times N \times CP$$
$$\text{Center distance} = \frac{PD \text{ of gear} + PD \text{ of worm}}{2}$$
$$\text{Addendum} = 0.3183 \times CP$$
$$\text{Dedendum} = 0.3677 \times CP$$
$$\text{Face} = 0.25 + (CP \times 2.38)$$
$$\text{Throat diameter} = PD + 2 \times \text{addendum}$$
$$\text{Throat radius} = 0.55 + (CP \times 0.882)$$

69. What formulas are necessary for calculating worms?

Ans.

$$\text{Pitch diameter} = 1.1 + (LP \times 2.4)$$
$$\text{Addendum} = 0.3183 \times LP$$
$$\text{Dedendum} = 0.3677 \times LP$$
$$\text{Root diameter} = PD - 2 \times \text{dedendum}$$
$$\text{Outside diameter} = PD + 2 \times \text{addendum}$$
$$\text{Lead} = LP \times \text{number of threads}$$
$$\text{Helix angle} = PD \times 3.1416 \div \text{lead} = \text{cotangent}$$
$$\text{Normal pitch} = LP \times \text{cosine of helix angle}$$

The complete list of dimensions for drawing and machining a worm and a worm gear is given in Table 10–5.

Table 10–5. WORM AND WORM GEAR

Worm	Worm gear
Pitch diameter	Pitch diameter
Addendum	Addendum
Dedendum	Dedendum
Diameter of hub	Diameter of hub
Diameter of hole	Diameter of hole
Keyway	Keyway
Over-all length	Over-all length
Length of hub	Face
Linear pitch	Circular pitch
Pressure angle	Pressure angle
Outside diameter	Outside diameter
Root diameter	Throat diameter
Number of threads	Number of teeth
Lead	Center distance
Helix angle	Helix angle
Normal pitch	Face angle
	Throat radius

Chapter 11 CUTTING TOOLS

The successful operation of a lathe, shaper, or planer depends to a great extent on the operator's knowledge of cutting tools and his skill in preparing them for specific machining operations.

Custom work, such as is done by toolmakers, involves the use of single, interchangeable cutting tools which are fastened securely to a toolholder (Fig. 11–1).

Fig. 11–1. Toolholder. (Armstrong Bros. Tool Co.)

1. What is a cutting tool?

Ans. A cutting tool, commonly known as a tool bit (Fig. 11–2), is a piece of steel or an alloy, usually square in shape and of various sizes and lengths.

Fig. 11–2. Tool bit. (Armstrong Bros. Tool Co.)

2. How is the cutting edge of a tool bit prepared for use?

Ans. The cutting edge is prepared by grinding. In most cases, it is ground in four directions or angles.

3. What are the grinding angles that are required on a tool bit that is to be used for lathe work?

Ans. The angles are shown in Fig. 11–3. Angle *A* is the top rake angle, angle *B* is the side rake angle, angle *C* is the front clearance angle, and angle *D* is the side clearance angle.

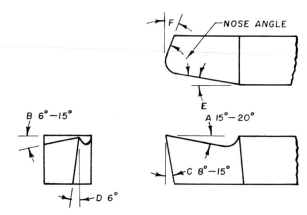

Fig. 11–3. Angles of a tool bit.

4. What is the purpose of the top rake angle?

Ans. The top rake angle is not always ground, but is often taken care of by the design of the toolholder. The slot in the toolholder, into which the tool bit is inserted, is made at an angle of 15 to 20 deg, as in Fig. 11–4. This angle is intended to aim the cutting edge toward the work so that it shears the material with an upward, rather than a forward, thrust, as in Fig. 11–5. The size of the angle

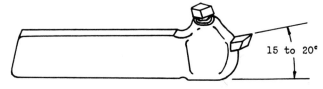

Fig. 11–4. Slot in toolholder is made at an angle.

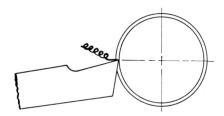

Fig. 11–5. The top rake angle gives the tool bit an upward thrust against the material.

106

depends upon the material to be machined. As a general principle, the harder the material, the greater the angle. A large top rake angle tends to make the tool dig in, when turning soft materials.

5. What is the purpose of the side rake angle and the side clearance angle?

Ans. The side rake angle is usually from 6 to 15 deg and performs a similar function to that of the top rake angle. This angle, together with the side clearance angle, shapes the cutting edge so that a shearing action occurs as the tool moves sideways against the material (Fig. 11–6). The side clearance angle also keeps the vertical edge of the tool from rubbing against the work. The size of the side rake angle is made less for soft material than for hard material.

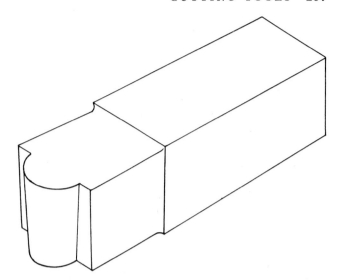

Fig. 11–7. Tool bit ground to cut concave grooves of a particular size.

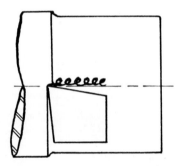

Fig. 11–6. Cutting action of tool bit is helped by the side-rake and side clearance angles.

6. What is the purpose of the front clearance angle?

Ans. The front clearance angle is designed to prevent the work from rubbing against the tool. The size of the angle may vary from 8 to 15 deg. It should be made as small as possible. When the angle is too large, the cutting edge of the tool is quickly worn.

7. What is the correct shape of a tool bit?

Ans. The shape of a tool bit depends upon the work to be done. In all cases, it must be remembered that, regardless of the shape, cutting edges with suitable clearances must be provided. The direction of the cut must always be considered. A tool bit may be ground to almost any shape to suit a particular design, as in Fig. 11–7. Some of the more common examples of tool bits used in lathe operations are shown in Fig. 11–8.

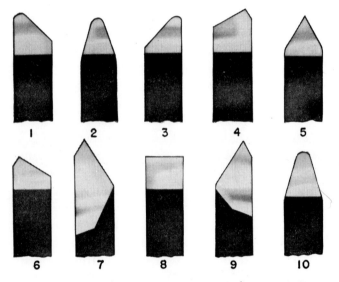

Fig. 11–8. Tool bits ground for lathe work. (Armstrong Bros. Tool Co.)

1. Left-hand turning tool
2. Roundnose turning tool
3. Right-hand turning tool
4. Left-hand corner tool
5. Threading tool
6. Right-hand corner tool
7. Left-hand side tool
8. Squarenose tool
9. Right-hand side tool
10. Brass tool

8. How does a cutting-off tool differ from other cutting tools?

Ans. A cutting-off tool cuts in one direction only, straight forward. For this reason the side rake angle is omitted and clearance angles are made on both of the sides and the front. Grinding a lip on the upper surface back of the cutting edge, as in Fig. 11–9, improves the effectiveness of the cutting operation.

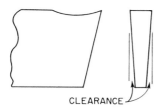

Fig. 11–9. Cutting-off tool.

9. What care must be used when grinding tool bits?

Ans. All cutting tools should be prevented from becoming overheated, which may burn or soften the cutting edge. A wet grinding wheel is preferred, but if ground on a dry wheel, the tool should be cooled frequently by dipping it in water.

10. What is meant by honing a tool bit?

Ans. Honing a tool bit means smoothing the cutting edges with an oilstone. This is desirable for a light cut, when a good finish is required. It is not considered practical for heavy work, as the edge produced by honing would soon be worn away.

11. What is a carbide-tipped tool?

Ans. A carbide-tipped tool is one which has a piece of carbide brazed on it, to form the cutting edges. Figure 11–10. Carbide is a name for several different alloys of carbon and some metallic element such as tungsten, titanium, or tantalum. It is exceptionally hard, almost as hard as a diamond, and will maintain a sharp cutting edge under conditions that would cause ordinary cutting tools to burn away. It is available under a variety of trade names.

12. What is a boring tool?

Ans. A boring tool (Fig. 11–11) is one that is designed to enlarge the size of a hole. This particular style is suitable for light work. If heavy cuts are attempted, the tool, being somewhat flexible, will be forced away from the work. This usually results in the hole being tapered. The cutting edges of the tool are sharpened in a similar manner, and for the same reasons, as other cutting tools. It is held in a special type of toolholder.

Tool bits are also used for boring. They are held in boring toolholders similar to the one shown in Fig. 11–12. This style of boring tool is less flexible than the one in Fig. 11–11, so heavier cuts and

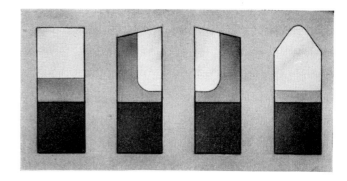

Fig. 11–10. Carbide-tipped tool bits. (J. H. Williams & Co.)

Fig. 11–11. Boring tool and holder. (Armstrong Bros. Tool Co.)

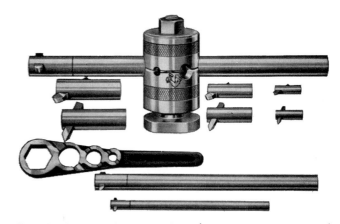

Fig. 11–12. Boring bar and holder. (Armstrong Bros. Tool Co.)

faster feeds are possible. The slots in the bars for the tool bits are made 45, 60, or 90 deg to the length of the bar.

13. In what respects do shaper and planer tool bits differ from those used on a lathe?

Ans. Shaper and planer tools cut in one direction only. For this reason, a side rake angle is seldom ground on them. Because the tool is fed, or is moved into position to cut, on the return stroke of the machine only, the side clearance angle may be less than on lathe tools. The front clearance angle should be 3 to 4 deg when the tool is in the cutting position (see Fig. 11–13). Some examples of tool bits ground for use on shapers and planers are shown in Fig. 11–14.

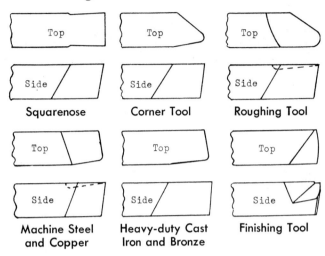

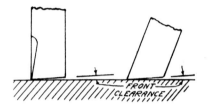

Fig. 11–13. Front clearance angle of shaper and planer tools.

Fig. 11–14. Common types of shaper and planer tool bits.

Chapter 12 SHAPER

Among the many machines used in a toolroom is the shaper. This machine removes stock from a piece of metal in much the same manner as a woodworker's plane cuts shavings from a piece of

Fig. 12–1. Nomenclature of shaper. (Gould & Eberhardt, Inc.)

A. Base
B. Frame
C. Ram
D. Toolhead
E. Table
F. Clutch control for starting and stopping; operates brake when stopping machine
G. Back-gear selector used in conjunction with L
H. Feed selector
J. Power rapid-traverse control for moving table horizontally in direction opposite to feed set
K. Stroke-length control (under the cover); automatically locked; positions crankpin in crank plate to obtain stroke lengths
L. Transmission-speed selector for obtaining eight ram speeds

M. Ram clamp to clamp ram to link and lever after positioning
N. Ram-positioning control
P. Toolhead lock for clamping head in adjusted position
R. Toolhead slide control for positioning slide vertically
S. Toolslide lock for clamping slide in vertically adjusted position
T. Tool post
U. Vise
V. Rail clamp for locking crossrail in adjusted position
W. Feed-direction control; neutral position disengages feed
X. Table-support clamp and lock
Y. Table horizontal-position control for positioning and feeding table manually
Z. Table vertical-position control for raising and lowering worktable

110

wood. Many types of work may be machined on a shaper, depending upon the tools used and the manner of adjusting the various parts of the machine. Figure 12–1 shows a shaper with an identification list of its parts.

1. What are the five principal parts of a shaper?
Ans. The five principal parts of a shaper are (1) the base, (2) the frame, (3) the ram, (4) the toolhead, (5) the table.

2. What is the purpose of the base?
Ans. The base is a hollow casting upon which the other parts of the shaper are mounted. It is also a reservoir for a supply of oil which is circulated to the moving parts of the machine.

3. What is the function of the frame?
Ans. The frame is a large casting that rests upon the base. It houses the mechanism and supports the ram and the table.

4. What is the ram, and how does it operate?
Ans. The ram is the main moving part of a shaper. It holds and drives a cutting tool back and forth across the work. It is attached to a rocker

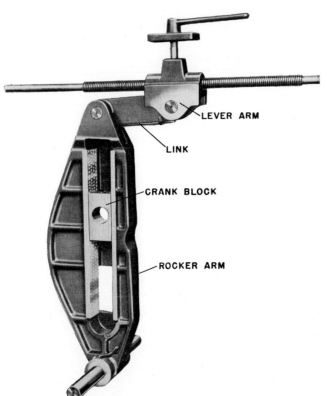

Fig. 12–2. Rocker-arm assembly. (Gould & Eberhardt, Inc.)

arm (Fig. 12–2), which is given an oscillating motion by the turning of a large drive wheel to which is attached a wheel which acts as a crank (Fig. 12–3). The length of the stroke of the ram and its speed are adjustable.

Fig. 12–3. Crank plate and driving gears. (Gould & Eberhardt, Inc.)

5. What is the purpose of the toolhead?
Ans. The toolhead (Fig. 12–4) is designed to hold the cutting tools. It is attached to the front of the ram. It may be swiveled to a required angle to the left or to the right and locked in place. It may also be adjusted vertically and locked in position. The tool post is fastened to a clapper block, which is hinged at the top to permit the tool to ride over the work on the return stroke.

6. What is the purpose of the table?
Ans. The table (Fig. 12–5) is a metal box that is attached to the frame of the shaper. It has T slots on the top and sides, which are used for clamping work or a vise to the table. It may be adjusted vertically and locked in position. It is supported in front by a bracket attached to the base. The bolts connecting the bracket to the crossarm on which the table rests must be loosened while the vertical adjustment is being made.

7. How is the horizontal adjustment of the table made?

Fig. 12–4. Toolhead. (Gould & Eberhardt, Inc.)

Ans. The table is moved horizontally by means of a hand crank or by power. Under power, the table may be moved a required distance, or it may

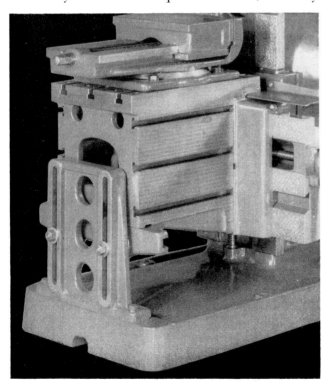

Fig. 12–5. Table. (Cincinnati Shaper Co.)

be moved a definite amount during each return stroke of the ram. This is known as an *automatic power feed.*

8. *What is a universal table?*

Ans. A universal table (Fig. 12–6) is one that can be operated in the same manner as a standard table. In addition, it may be swiveled to the left or to the right and, if need be, rotated a full circle.

Fig. 12–6. Universal table. (Gould & Eberhardt, Inc.)

A dial plate, graduated in degrees, indicates the angular setting. The top surface may be tilted up to 15 deg forward or back. It, too, has graduations in degrees on its curved edge. All rotating and tilting movements are manually controlled. Examples of the use of the universal table are shown in Figs. 12–7 and 12–8.

9. *How is the size of a shaper determined?*

Ans. The size of a shaper is determined by the length of the stroke of the ram.

Fig. 12–7. Universal table is rotated while shaping a curved contour. (Cincinnati Shaper Co.)

Fig. 12–8. Top of universal table is tilted forward for shaping a beveled edge. (Cincinnati Shaper Co.)

10. What safety rules apply to shaper work?

Ans. (1) Always wear goggles (Fig. 12–9) to protect the eyes from flying particles of metal. (2) Do not pass the hands between the tool and the work while the machine is in operation. Use a brush to remove chips from the work. (3) Do not start the ram in motion until you are sure that the work is securely fastened to the vise or to the table, that the tool is secure in the tool post, and that the tool has been adjusted for height. (4) Keep tools away from the moving parts of the machine. (5) Do not wear long sleeves or neckties. (6) Make sure that you understand what you have to do, regarding the operations to be performed, the dimensions, and the specifications. (7) Check the size of the rough stock. (8) Keep the machine well oiled. (9) Keep your mind on your work at all times.

11. Explain how to set the stroke of the ram for length and position.

Ans. To set the ram for the length of the stroke, bring the ram to the extreme back position and set for the length of work plus about 5/8 in., as shown

Fig. 12–9. Goggles. (Willson Products, Inc.)

on the graduated scale on the machine. This will allow for about 1/8 in. clearance in the front of the work and 1/2 in. in the back. For the position of the stroke, bring the ram to the extreme forward position and adjust it so that the front of the tool bit will clear the front of the job by about 1/8 in.

12. How should the toolholder be set in the tool post?

Ans. Set the toolholder so that the tool bit does not extend farther than 2 in. from the tool post.

13. How much clearance should there be between the work in the vise and the ram?

Ans. There should be about 2 in. clearance, or enough to clear one's hand (see Fig. 12–10).

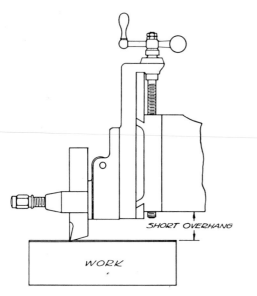

Fig. 12–10. Tool bit and tool post adjusted for minimum clearance. (Cincinnati Shaper Co.)

14. What are the most common causes of chattering on a shaper?

Ans. Chattering may be caused by the following: (1) the tool being suspended too far from the toolholder, as in Fig. 12–11; (2) the work not be-

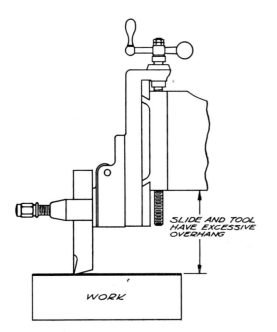

Fig. 12–11. Tool bit and slide are too far from the work. This causes tool to chatter. (Cincinnati Shaper Co.)

ing held rigidly in the vise; and (3) the ram gibs not being in proper adjustment.

15. How can chattering on a shaper be eliminated?

Ans. Chattering may be eliminated by the following: (1) regrinding the cutting tool for less front clearance, (2) reducing the distance between the tool and the work, (3) retightening the work in the vise or on the table, and (4) adjusting the gibs of the ram for a minimum of clearance.

NOTE: Do not use a hammer on the handle of a vise in an effort to tighten it. The vise handle is long enough so that the leverage gained when pressure is exerted on the end of it is sufficient to clamp the jaws tightly on the work.

16. How should the toolhead and clapper block be set for shaping a horizontal surface?

Ans. The toolhead and cutting tool should be vertical and the clapper box turned away from the direction in which the tool is feeding, as in Fig. 12–12. This position will prevent the tool from digging into the work, and it will swing away from the finished surface on the return stroke.

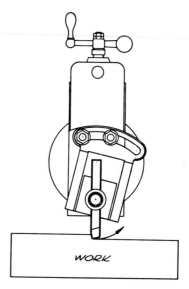

Fig. 12–12. Setting of toolhead and clapper block for horizontal shaping. (Cincinnati Shaper Co.)

17. How should the toolhead and clapper block be set for shaping an angular surface?

Ans. The toolhead and the cutting tool should be adjusted to the same angle, and in the same direction, as the surface to be cut, as in Fig. 12–13. The clapper block should be turned away from the surface to be cut.

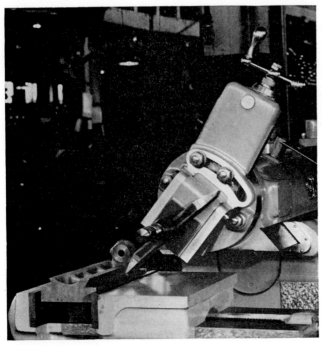

Fig. 12–13. Setting of toolhead and clapper block for angular shaping. (Cincinnati Shaper Co.)

18. How should stock be held in a vise?

Ans. The material may be held in a vise without additional tools when it is large enough so that the stock to be removed is above the vise jaws. Thin stock may be raised to a convenient height in the vise by placing a pair of parallels under the work. A round bar of soft metal, as in Fig. 12–14, or a steel wedge, as in Fig. 12–15, are helpful in preventing wide pieces of material from being forced out of the vise.

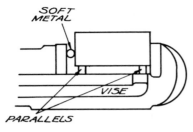

Fig. 12–14. A bar of soft metal helps to hold a wide piece of work for parallel shaping. (Cincinnati Shaper Co.)

19. How is work held on the table?

Ans. Most jobs can be securely held by means of clamps which are bolted to the table with T bolts, as in Fig. 12–16. A block of suitable height is placed under one end of the clamp to keep it level. Figure 12–17 shows a casting fastened to the shaper table with several clamps.

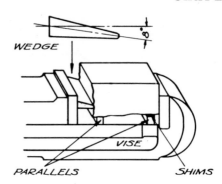

Fig. 12–15. A steel wedge helps to hold a piece of work for shaping at right angles. (Cincinnati Shaper Co.)

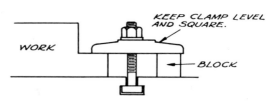

Fig. 12–16. Work held on table with clamp and T bolt. (Cincinnati Shaper Co.)

Fig. 12–17. Some jobs require several clamps in order to hold them securely. (Cincinnati Shaper Co.)

20. How may a thin piece of work be fastened to the table?

Ans. A thin piece of work may be held with toe dogs, as in Fig. 12–18. Several pairs of dogs would be used to hold the work, according to the length of the material.

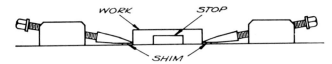

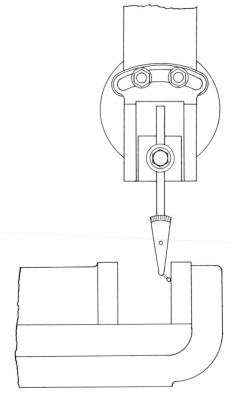

Fig. 12–18. Holding thin work with toe dogs. (Cincinnati Shaper Co.)

21. How may the solid jaw of the vise be checked for being square with the stroke of the ram?

Ans. Fasten the vise securely to the table with the solid jaw towards the ram. Place an indicator in the toolholder so that the point of the indicator touches the finished surface, as in Fig. 12–19. Note the movement of the indicator as the vise is moved back and forth with the aid of the cross-feed.

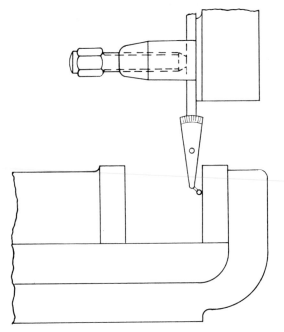

Fig. 12–19. Checking jaw of vise for being square with the stroke of the ram.

22. How may the solid jaw of the vise be checked for being parallel with the stroke of the ram?

Ans. Fasten the vise securely to the table with the edge of the solid jaw parallel to the ram. Place an indicator in the toolholder with the point of the indicator touching the finished surface of the jaw, as in Fig. 12–20. Note the movement of the indicator as the ram is moved slowly back and forth.

23. What should be done if the work is not parallel within reasonable limits, after a cut has been taken from each side of the work?

Fig. 12–20. Checking jaw of vise for being parallel with the stroke of the ram.

Ans. Inspect the vise thoroughly for dirt and chips and make sure that it is clean. If this does not correct the condition, check the vise jaw with an indicator.

24. How may a piece of work be checked for being level with the surface of the table and parallel with the side of the table?

Ans. For most jobs, the surfaces may be checked with a surface gage, as in Fig. 12–21, by sliding the surface gage along the table and noticing any

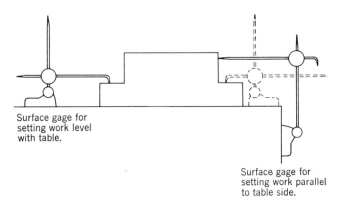

Surface gage for setting work level with table.

Surface gage for setting work parallel to table side.

Fig. 12–21. Setting a job level and parallel with the table, using a surface gage. (Cincinnati Shaper Co.)

variations. When a more accurate check is required, an indicator may be fastened to the tool-holder, as in Fig. 12–22, and moved across the surfaces with the aid of the cross-feed or the movement of the ram.

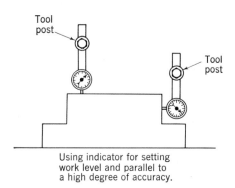

Tool post

Tool post

Using indicator for setting
work level and parallel to
a high degree of accuracy.

Fig. 12–22. To set a job level and parallel with the table to a high degree of accuracy, an indicator should be used. (Cincinnati Shaper Co.)

25. How should the cutting tool be started when taking the first cut?

Ans. When the length of the stroke of the ram has been adjusted, the machine is started and the tool is fed downward toward the work, while the table is moved crosswise by hand until the required depth of cut is started on the edge of the work. The automatic feed is then engaged.

26. What is the purpose of layout lines on a job?

Ans. Layout lines are generally used as a guide to show the amount of material to be machined. However, the job must be machined to the dimensions given on the blueprint. If the job is a casting on which the line has been scribed from the outline of a template, then, in machining it, the tool point must split the layout line. On a job of this type, consult your instructor or foreman.

27. State the operations in shaping a rectangular job on the shaper?

Ans. Set the vise on the table with the jaws parallel with the stroke of the ram. Place the material in the vise and shape it to the required thickness. Next, turn the material so that this finished surface is against the solid jaw of the vise and shape to the required width. Turn the vise 90 deg so that the jaws are perpendicular to the stroke of the ram. Place the job in one end of the vise, so that the surface to be machined will be close to the top surface of the vise jaws. The other end of the

Fig. 12–23. When a piece of work is held in one end of a vise, the other end should be blocked to keep the vise jaws parallel. (Cincinnati Shaper Co.)

vise should be blocked with a piece of material of the same thickness, to keep the jaws parallel (see Fig. 12–23). The solid jaw of the vise will keep the work square in the plane parallel to the jaws. A solid square must be used to set the work square in the plane perpendicular to the jaws before the jaws of the vise are tightened. The end may then be machined to the required length.

28. How should a thin job be machined on a shaper to prevent the material from warping?

Ans. First a light cut should be taken off each side to relieve the internal strain of the metal. Then more light cuts should be taken off each side, alternately, until the correct thickness is obtained.

29. Why should the speed of the shaper be increased when taking a finishing cut?

Ans. The speed should be increased because this gives a smoother finish to the surface of the material and shortens the length of time required for machining.

30. When cutting an angle on a large job, using a shaper which has a universal table, should the table be tilted, or should the toolhead be swung to the required angle?

Ans. The universal table should be tilted, because this makes it possible to use the automatic table feed. If the toolhead were set on the required angle and there were no automatic downfeed, it would be necessary to use the hand downfeed.

31. How should a job similar to the one shown in the sketch of Fig. 12–24 be machined?

Ans. First, machine the six sides, following the instructions given in question 27. Next, lay out the angle and the step according to the required dimensions. Place the work in the vise on parallels, swivel the vise to 15 deg and rough out. Complete the machining by setting the toolhead at 7 deg and feeding the tool down to the layout on this angle until the operation is completed.

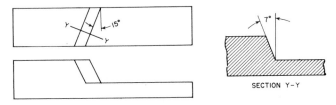

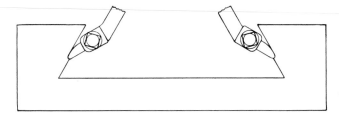

Fig. 12–24. Stock guide with compound angle to be shaped.

32. Explain how a dovetail bearing may be cut on a shaper.

Ans. The toolhead of the shaper should be set at the same angle as that of the dovetail to be cut. When dovetail bearings, such as those shown in Fig. 12–25, are to be cut, the work should not be disturbed in shaping the angular and flat surfaces

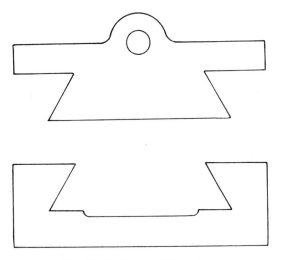

Fig. 12–25. Dovetail bearings.

of the dovetail. The horizontal surfaces should be machined before completing the angular surfaces. A right-hand tool and a left-hand tool are used to machine the angular sides, one at a time, as shown in Fig. 12–26. Both a roughing and a finishing tool should be used if considerable stock is to be removed. In using two tools and moving the toolhead from one side of the center line to the other, great care must be exercised, because, if there is any variation in the angular setting of the head, a variation in the angular sides of the dovetail will result.

Fig. 12–26. Shaping a dovetail with a right-hand and a left-hand toolholder.

Another way of cutting a dovetail, when the sides of the work are parallel and the solid jaw of the vise is parallel with the stroke of the ram, requires only one tool. First, rough out the sides of the dovetail to within 1/64 or 1/32 of the finished size. Next, take a light cut on one side; then, reverse the work in the vise but do not disturb the setting of the table, and take a light cut off the other side. Check for size and repeat the process until the finished size is obtained. Using this method, the dovetail will be held central with the work and the angles will be the same.

In shaping dovetail bearings, it is very important to incline the clapper box in the proper direction so that the tool will swing away from the work on the return stroke of the ram, as in Fig. 12–13. The beginner should pay strict attention to this point, because the setting may not be correct even though it may appear to be. Remember that the top of the clapper box must be set in a direction away from the surface being machined.

33. How should a dovetail be checked for size?

Ans. In order to check the size of a dovetail to determine the amount necessary to machine off, or to check the finished product accurately, two plug gages are placed in the angles of the dovetail and a measurement is taken either over or between the plug gages (see Fig. 12–27 and Fig. 12–28).

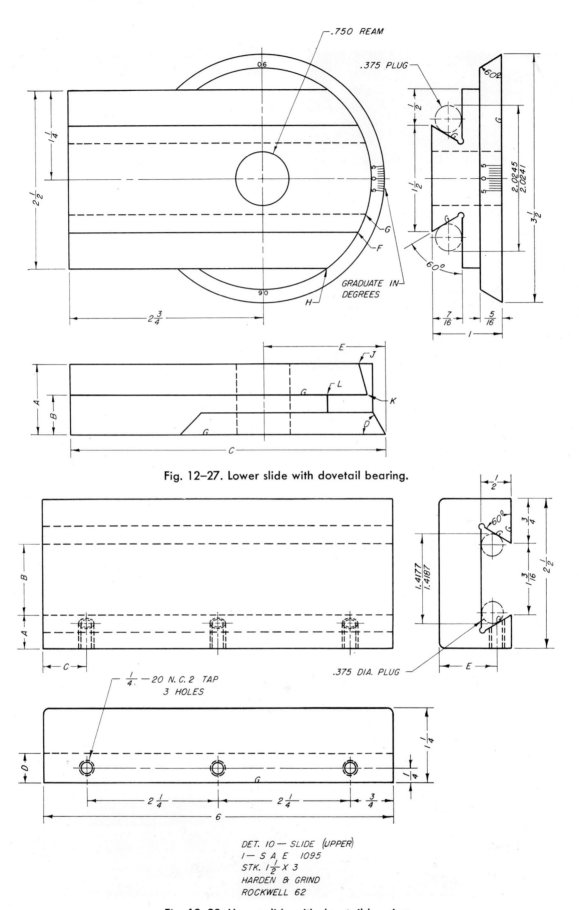

.750 REAM

.375 PLUG

06

90

.750 REAM

GRADUATE IN DEGREES

H

G

F

60°

2 1/4

2 1/2

2 3/4

7/16

5/16

I

2.0245
2.0241

3 1/2

E

A

B

C

G

G

J

L

K

D

Fig. 12–27. Lower slide with dovetail bearing.

1/2

60°

G

3/4

2 1/2

1.4177
1.4187

1 3/16

.375 DIA. PLUG

E

B

A

C

1/4 —20 N.C.2 TAP
3 HOLES

D

G

1 1/4

1/4

2 1/4

2 1/4

3/4

6

DET. 10 — SLIDE (UPPER)
1— S A E 1095
STK. 1 1/2 X 3
HARDEN & GRIND
ROCKWELL 62

Fig. 12–28. Upper slide with dovetail bearing.

Fig. 12–29. Shaping an irregular surface by adjusting the tool to the layout line. (Cincinnati Shaper Co.)

34. Explain the method used to shape a V or keyway centrally in a block.

Ans. One method is to lay out the job and shape to scribed layout lines. A more accurate method of shaping a V is to set the vise jaws parallel to the stroke, set the toolhead at the required angle, and rough out to the layout lines. Next, take a cut from one side of the V, then reverse the job in the vise. With the table set in the same position, take a cut off the opposite side. Continue this until both sides of the V are cleaned up and the proper depth has been obtained. The V will then be in the center of the block. The same procedure may be used in shaping a keyway.

35. What is the method of shaping an irregularly curved surface?

Ans. The required shape is scribed on the surface of the material. After the work has been secured in position on the machine, the operator, by skillful manipulation of the vertical and horizontal feeds, as in Fig. 12–29, guides the cutting tool so that it will follow the layout lines. This is known as *contour shaping.*

36. How should work of unusual size be handled on the shaper?

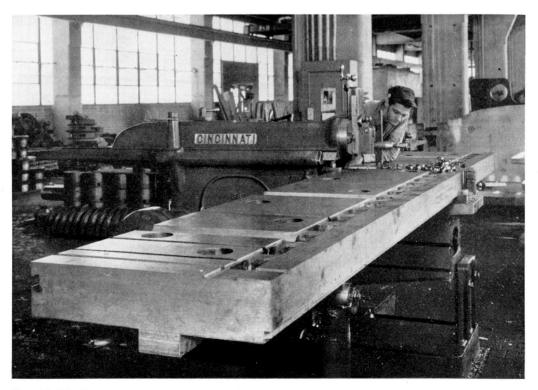

Fig. 12–30. Supports must be used with large pieces of work to avoid damage to the worktable. (Cincinnati Shaper Co.)

Ans. If the operation required is within the capacity of the stroke of the ram, the size of the work does not necessarily matter. Care must be used to see that the table is relieved of as much weight as possible by using suitable supports (Fig. 12–30).

37. *How may a keyway be cut on a shaper when the keyway does not extend the entire length of the shaft?*

Ans. Drill a hole slightly larger and deeper than the width and depth of the keyway at the place where the keyway ends. Set the position of the shaper stroke so that the tool will stop in the center of the drilled hole at the end of the forward stroke. Then cut the keyway in the usual manner.

38. *Can the shaper be used for internal work?*

Ans. Yes. The shaper can be used to cut keyways (Fig. 12–31), as well as a variety of differently shaped holes. First the holes must be bored and they must be of a sufficient size to permit the entry of the internal toolholder, which takes the place of the tool post. An example of this kind of work is shown in Fig. 12–32.

39. *What is a vertical shaper?*

Ans. A vertical shaper (Fig. 12–33) is similar to

Fig. 12–32. Squaring the side of a hole on a shaper. (Cincinnati Shaper Co.)

a regular shaper, the difference being that the ram is in a vertical position instead of being horizontal. Also, the table is mounted on a heavy base and provided with mechanisms that make it possible to move it forward and back and from side to side, and to rotate it. The ram may also be adjusted to an angular position.

Fig. 12–31. Cutting a keyway on a shaper. (Cincinnati Shaper Co.)

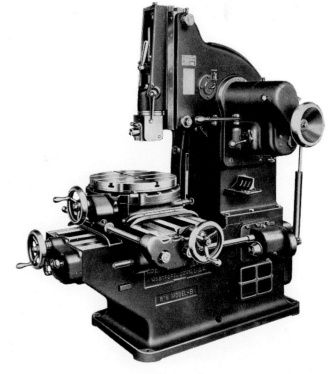
Fig. 12–33. Vertical shaper. (Pratt & Whitney)

Chapter 13 PLANER

1. What is a planer?

Ans. A planer (Fig. 13–1) is a rather large machine that is designed for producing flat surfaces on a piece of work.

2. In what way does a planer differ from a shaper?

Ans. A planer is designed with a stationary housing for holding toolheads and a table with a reciprocating movement for holding the work; thus, the work is moved against the cutting tool. A shaper differs from a planer in that the work is held stationary and the cutting tool is moved across the work.

Fig. 13–1. Planer. (Cincinnati Planer Co.)

A. Bed	H. Rail screw, left-hand head
B. Table	J. Elevating screw, right-hand
C. Housing	K. Slide
D. Rail	L. Tool block
E. Saddle	M. Downfeed screw
F. Toolhead	N. Table dogs
G. Rail screw, right-hand head	

3. What type of work is done on a planer?

Ans. The planer is a large machine designed to do jobs that would be too large or too awkward for a shaper.

4. What are the principal parts of a planer?

Ans. The principal parts of a planer are (1) the bed, (2) the table, (3) the housing, (4) the crossrail, (5) the saddle, and (6) the toolhead.

5. What is the function of the planer bed?

Ans. The planer bed is a large boxlike casting which acts as the foundation of the machine. The other parts are attached to, or supported by, the bed.

6. What is the table of a planer?

Ans. The table is a large, rectangular casting that is mounted on the top of the bed, on sliding V ways. Its purpose is to hold the work. The upper surface has T slots in it to facilitate the clamping of the work or vises and special fixtures with T bolts.

7. What is the housing of a planer?

Ans. The housing is the large vertical casting that straddles the table and bed of the planer and supports the mechanism for the operation of the toolheads.

8. What is the crossrail of a planer?

Ans. The crossrail is a unit that is mounted in a horizontal position on the vertical ways of the housing. Its purpose is to carry the vertical toolheads, which, by means of feed screws—one for each head—may be moved from left to right. The crossrail is moved up or down by means of elevating screws that are located within the ways of the housing.

9. What is the saddle of a planer?

Ans. The saddle is a unit that is fitted to the ways of the crossrail. On its front surface are ways to which the toolhead is fitted, together with a vertical feed screw that provides for a vertical movement of the toolhead. There are two saddles, one for the left toolhead, the other for the right toolhead. Each one may be operated independently of the other.

10. What is the toolhead of a planer?

Ans. The toolhead is a part attached to the saddle which contains the tool post which, in turn, holds the cutting tools. The tool post is hinged to

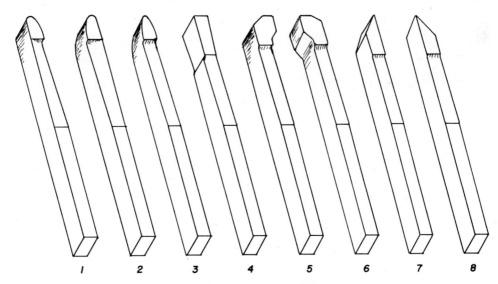

Fig. 13–2. Planer tools, solid type.

1. Right-hand roughing tool
2. Left-hand roughing tool
3. Roundnose roughing tool
4. Squarenose slotting tool
5. Right-hand side-cutting tool
6. Left-hand side-cutting tool
7. Right-hand dovetail tool
8. Left-hand dovetail tool

the head so that on the return movement of the table the cutting tool will be raised and ride on the top of the work. This saves the cutting edge of the tool from being damaged and permits the automatic-traverse feed to operate without interference. There are three toolheads, two in a vertical position on the crossrail, the other in a horizontal position on the housing below the crossrail.

11. What types of cutting tools are used on a planer?

Ans. Planer cutting tools may be of the solid type, as shown in Fig. 13–2, the cutting end being shaped for various cutting situations. Small tool bits, held in holders, are also used, as in Fig. 13–3. This type is preferred by some because it is more economical than a set of solid tools and often is more convenient. Another type is the gang planer tool (Fig. 13–4). The head is solidly secured to

Fig. 13–3. Toolholder. (Armstrong Bros. Tool Co.)

Fig. 13–4. Gang planer tool. (Armstrong Bros. Tool Co.)

the shank, upon which it swivels to a limited degree, by means of a deep and closely fitted tongue and socket, and, when set, its position is fixed by two steel collar screws, while two stop screws render slipping of the head impossible. The head is graduated, thus enabling the tool to be quickly and accurately set to any desired feed. This makes it possible to have the tool cutting always at the greatest speed practicable, on metals of varying degrees of hardness. As each chip is comparatively light, a planer equipped with this tool will carry with ease a feed and depth of cut much greater

than is possible when using an ordinary tool, and there is much less tendency to break out at the end of the cut.

12. How is work held on a planer?

Ans. The work may be held in a vise that has been fastened to the table, but usually jobs that are small enough to be so held are machined on a shaper. The most common way to hold work is to clamp it directly to the table of the planer. Many styles of clamps are available to suit particular situations. Several such clamps are shown in Fig. 13–5. One end of a clamp is set on the work, and the other end is supported by a step block (Fig. 13–6) or an adjustable step block (Fig. 13–7).

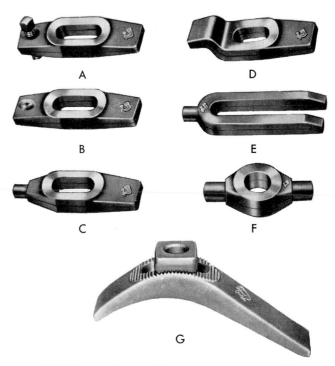

A   D

B   E

C   F

G

Fig. 13–5. Strap clamps. (A) Screw heel clamp, (B) plain clamp, (C) finger clamp, (D) gooseneck clamp, (E) U clamp, (F) double-finger clamp, and (G) universal adjustable clamp. (Armstrong Bros. Tool Co.)

Fig. 13–6. Step block.

Blocks of this kind are preferred to odd pieces of wood or steel. Another type of clamp is the T-slot clamp (Fig. 13–8). The base of this clamp is bolted securely to the table close to the work and then the vertical bar is screwed firmly on the surface of the work.

Fig. 13–10. Standard planer jack. (Armstrong Bros. Tool Co.)

Fig. 13–7   Fig. 13–8

Fig. 13–7. Adjustable block. (Armstrong Bros. Tool Co.)

Fig. 13–8. T-slot clamp. (Armstrong Bros. Tool Co.)

Fig. 13–11. Vertical jack. (Armstrong Bros. Tool Co.)

Fig. 13–12. Bracing jack. (Armstrong Bros. Tool Co.)

13. What are some of the devices used to keep work level on the table?

Ans. In order to have work level on the table, it is sometimes necessary to use a setup wedge under one or more corners of the work. In other circumstances, a piece of work may need support at some points, as in Fig. 13–9. It will be noted that the support is provided by vertical and bracing jacks (Figs. 13–10, 13–11, and 13–12). These jacks reduce the time required for preliminary arrangements, compared with looking for and adapting a haphazard group of blocks. The design of the bracing jack prevents creeping and permits setting the

jack under a fillet or sloping surface without danger of sideslipping.

14. What is a planer gage?

Ans. A planer gage (Fig. 13–13) is a device that is designed for the purpose of setting the cutting

Fig. 13–9. A piece of work supported and leveled by jacks and clamps. (Armstrong Bros. Tool Co.)

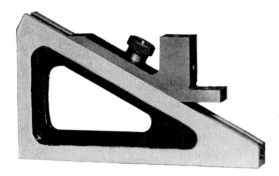

Fig. 13–13. Planer gage. (Brown & Sharpe Mfg. Co.)

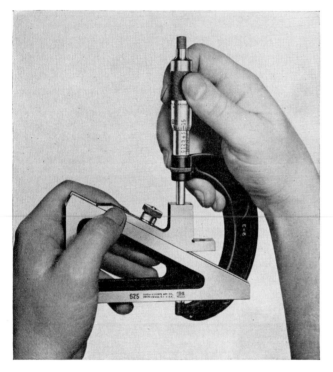

Fig. 13–14. Setting planer gage to size with a micrometer. (Brown & Sharpe Mfg. Co.)

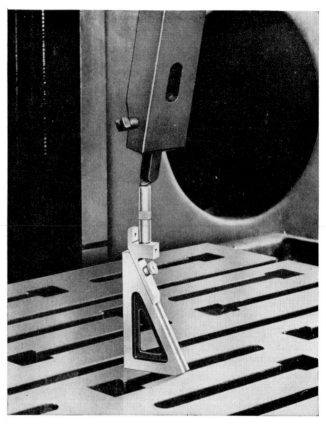

Fig. 13–15. Planer gage is used to adjust the cutting tool to a required dimension. (Brown & Sharpe Mfg. Co.)

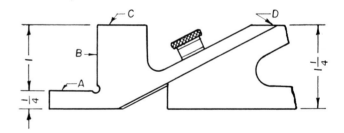

Fig. 13–16. Surfaces C and D of the slide are in the same horizontal plane.

tool on a planer to a required distance from the table or a finished surface of the work. By setting the gage to a micrometer, as in Fig. 13–14, or to a surface gage or caliper and bringing the planer tool in contact with it, the first cut may be relied upon to give the desired dimension (see Fig. 13–15). The slide of the gage is so designed that with one extension it is possible to get a tool setting from 1/4 to 8 1/2 in. Desirable feature of this slide is that the surfaces C and D (see Fig. 13–16) are in the same plane and 1.000 in. from the plane of surface A, a combination that simplifies many set-

tings, particularly for small measurements; also, the extension which screws into any of the three surfaces A, B, or C of the slide, being 2.500 in. long, further simplifies the making of accurate settings, particularly in the higher ranges.

15. Describe a method of ascertaining if the crossrail is parallel to the table top.

Ans. Clamp an indicator on the tool box, with the point of it touching the table top, and note if there is any variation in the indicator reading as the toolhead is moved across the length of the cross-rail.

16. *Give some hints on clamping work to the planer table.*

Ans. In clamping work on the planer table, the operator must take great care to see that the work is fastened securely by clamps, bolts, toe dogs, and so forth.

Clamps should not be placed on a finished part of the work unless it is protected by covering it with a piece of copper, brass, heavy paper, fiber, or similar material.

Flat, thin work is held down best by the use of toe dogs.

See that the work does not spring when tightening clamps or toe dogs.

A washer must be used with every T bolt and nut. Select bolts of the proper length.

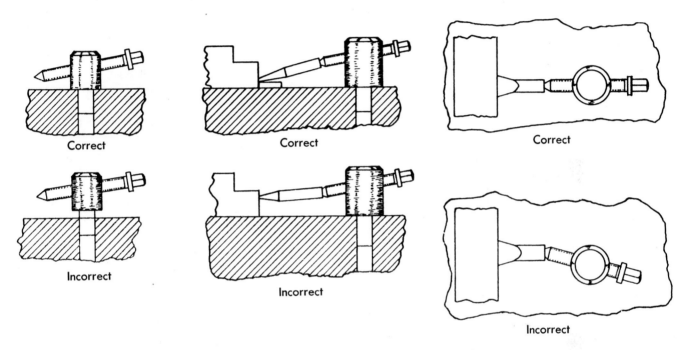

Fig. 13–17. Correct and incorrect use of toe dogs and poppets.

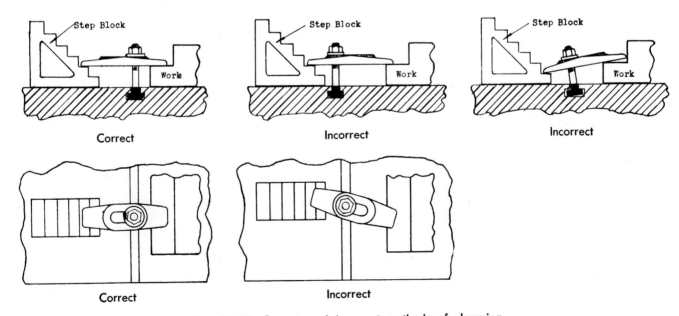

Fig. 13–18. Correct and incorrect methods of clamping.

An open-end wrench of the correct size should be used on all square and hexagon nuts. An adjustable wrench is not desirable.

When placing the work in position, see that it does not mar the finished surface of the planer table.

Allow enough clearance for the work to pass under the crossrail and between the housings.

Figures 13–17 to 13–19 show some correct and incorrect methods of clamping work to the planer table.

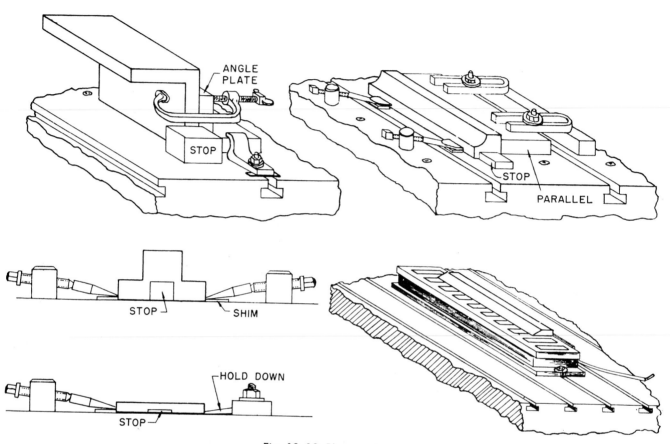

Fig. 13–19. Planer setups.

Chapter 14 LATHES

The lathe is one of the most important machines in any work shop. It has been in use for many centuries and has been greatly improved in design and versatility during that time. The initial objective when using a lathe was to be able to remove material from the outside of logs of wood while they were revolving, thus producing a cylindrical shape that was uniform in its diameter. The removing of

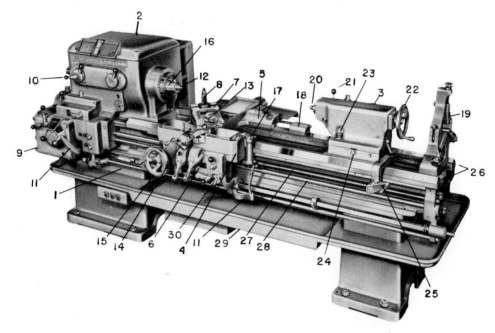

Fig. 14–1. Engine lathe. (Lodge & Shipley Company)

1. Bed	16. Spindle
2. Headstock	17. Thread-chasing dial
3. Tailstock	18. Taper attachment
4. Carriage	19. Steady rest
5. Saddle	20. Dead center
6. Apron	21. Tailstock-spindle binding lever
7. Compound rest	22. Tailstock handwheel
8. Tool post	23. Tailstock clamping screws
9. Feeding mechanism	24. Screw for setting-over tailstock (for taper turning)
10. Speed-change levers	25. Lever for moving tailstock
11. Spindle start, stop, and brake levers	26. Bed ways
12. Live center	27. Lead screw
13. Compound rest feed-screw handle	28. Feed rod
14. Handle for operating cross-feed by hand	29. Chip and oil pan
15. Handwheel for longitudinal carriage travel	30. Lead-screw reverse lever

129

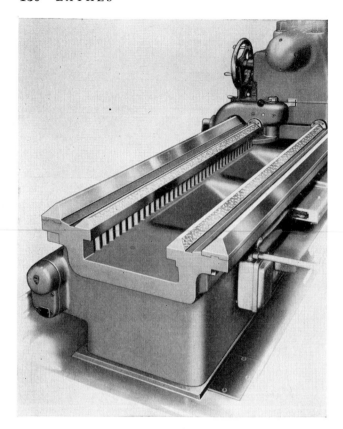

Fig. 14–2. Bed of engine lathe. (American Tool Works Company)

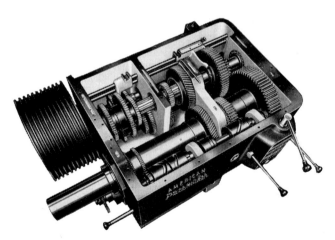

Fig. 14–3. Headstock of lathe showing the gearing mechanism for the spindle. (American Tool Works Company)

material from a piece of revolving work is still the main purpose of a lathe but it can be and is used to enable a workman to do a great many other jobs as well. If a mechanic was limited to only one machine with which to do all of his work, he would have no hesitation in choosing a lathe in preference to any other machine.

1. What are the principal parts of a modern engine lathe?

Ans. The principal parts of an engine lathe (Fig. 14–1) are (1) the bed, (2) the headstock, (3) the tailstock, (4) the carriage, (5) the feed mechanism, and (6) the thread-cutting mechanism.

2. Describe the bed.

Ans. The bed (Fig. 14–2) consists of two heavy metal sides running lengthwise, with ways or Vs formed upon them. The bed is rigidly supported by cross girths.

3. Describe the headstock.

Ans. The complete headstock (Fig. 14–3) consists of the headstock casting, which is located on the ways of the bed at the left of the operator, the spindle, in which the live center is rigidly held by a taper, and the necessary gears and mechanism for obtaining the various spindle speeds. Figure 14–4 shows a speed-index plate which is attached to the headstock for the guidance of the operator.

4. Describe the tailstock.

Ans. The tailstock (Fig. 14–5) is a movable casting located opposite the headstock on the ways of the bed. It contains the dead center, the adjusting screw, and the handwheel.

5. What is the carriage?

Ans. The carriage, consisting of the saddle and apron, is the movable part which slides over the ways between the headstock and tailstock. The saddle has the form of the letter H, being bridged across the lathe bed to carry the cross slide and tool rest, fitted to the outside ways, and gibbed to the bed. Another function of the carriage is to carry the compound rest.

6. What is the apron?

Ans. The apron (Fig. 14–6) contains the gears and clutches for transmitting motion from the feed rod to the carriage, and the split nut which engages with the lead screw in cutting threads.

7. What is the purpose of the compound rest?

Ans. The compound rest (Fig. 14–7) supports the tool post and cutting tool in its various positions. It may be swiveled on the cross slide to any angle in the horizontal plane. Its base is graduated

Fig. 14–4. Speed-index plate. (American Tool Works Company)

Fig. 14–5. Tailstock of lathe. (American Tool Works Company)

to 180, or 90 deg each way from the center, and the feed-screw collar is graduated in thousandths of an inch. A compound rest is essential in turning and boring short tapers and in turning angles and forms on forming tools.

In cutting American National and sharp V threads the compound rest is swiveled to 30 deg from the center, which is one-half the included angle of these threads. The reason for this is, that the cutting tool acts similarly to a facing tool when it is forced into the work at an angle of 30 deg in-

stead of 90 deg. This causes the tool to cut on one side only, giving a better finish to the thread because the chips do not have a tendency to clog up the point.

CAUTION: Take great pains not to force the corner of the compound rest into the lathe chuck. This is done too frequently. Always keep the dovetail slide covered with the compound rest to exclude all dirt and protect the slide from being nicked or marred by tools falling on it.

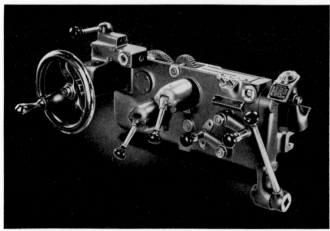
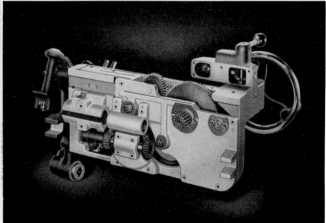

Fig. 14–6. Front and rear views of lathe apron. (American Tool Works Company)

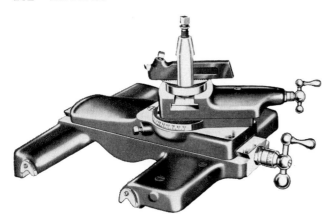

Fig. 14-7. Compound rest of lathe. (South Bend Lathe Works)

When facing the thickness of a piece of work, such as a spacer, to a size which is held to close limits, the compound rest may be swiveled at an angle of 30 deg from the face of the work and the tool fed in with the compound feed screw. The distance this screw advances is shown on a dial graduated in thousandths. Figure 14-8 shows the compound rest set at a 30 deg angle. The tool is fed in along the hypotenuse of triangle ABC. In a 30 deg right triangle, the side opposite the 30 deg angle is always one-half the hypotenuse. In Fig. 14-8, BC equals one-half of AB. Then if point B is moved in 0.002 in. along the line AB, BC will move in 0.001 in. against the face. It can be seen that the thickness of the work is reduced one-half thousandth for every thousandth the tool is advanced with the compound feed screw.

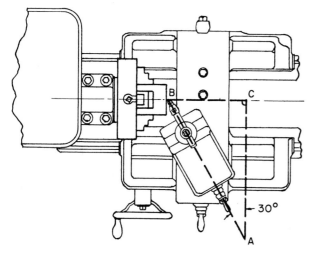

Fig. 14-8. With the compound rest set at an angle of 30 deg, the feed of the tool along the line BC is only half of the movement of the slide on line AB.

8. *What is the feeding mechanism?*

Ans. The feeding mechanism of a lathe is a train of gears (series of gears in mesh) (Fig. 14-9) which transmits motion from the headstock or main spindle to the feed rod, and also to the lead screw, when it is being used. The motion is then transmitted from the feed rod to various gears in the apron. The feed gears are generally controlled by friction, through small knobs located on the front of the apron.

Fig. 14-9. Interior view of feeding mechanism. (American Tool Works Company)

9. *What is the thread-cutting mechanism?*

Ans. The thread-cutting mechanism includes any gear or mechanism which transmits motion from

Fig. 14-10. Exterior view of quick-change gear mechanism. (American Tool Works Company)

GEARS	½	⁹⁄₁₆	⅝	¹¹⁄₁₆	²³⁄₃₂	¾	¹³⁄₁₆	²⁷⁄₃₂	⅞	¹⁵⁄₁₆		LEVERS
STUD 80	2.0000	1.7777	1.6000	1.4545	1.3913	1.3333	1.2308	1.1851	1.1429	1.0666	LEAD	**CE**
	.2400	.2133	.1920	.1745	.1669	.1600	.1477	.1422	.1371	.1280	FEED	
	1	1⅛	1¼	1⅜	1⁷⁄₁₆	1½	1⅝	1¹¹⁄₁₆	1¾	1⅞	TH'DS	**AE**
	1.0000	.8888	.8000	.7272	.6956	.6666	.6154	.5925	.5714	.5333	LEAD	
	.1200	.1066	.0960	.0872	.0834	.0800	.0738	.0711	.0685	.0640	FEED	
	2	2¼	2½	2¾	2⅞	3	3¼	3⅜	3½	3¾	TH'DS	**BE**
	.5000	.4444	.4000	.3636	.3478	.3333	.3077	.2962	.2857	.2666	LEAD	
	.0600	.0533	.0480	.0436	.0417	.0400	.0369	.0355	.0342	.0320	FEED	
	4	4½	5	5½	5¾	6	6½	6¾	7	7½	TH'DS	**CD**
	.2500	.2222	.2000	.1818	.1739	.1666	.1538	.1481	.1428	.1333	LEAD	
BOX 80	.0300	.0266	.0240	.0218	.0208	.0200	.0184	.0177	.0171	.0160	FEED	
	8	9	10	11	11½	12	13	13½	14	15	TH'DS	**AD**
	.1250	.1111	.1000	.0909	.0869	.0833	.0769	.0740	.0714	.0666	LEAD	
	.0150	.0133	.0120	.0109	.0104	.0100	.0092	.0088	.0085	.0080	FEED	
	16	18	20	22	23	24	26	27	28	30	TH'DS	**BD**
	.0625	.0555	.0500	.0454	.0434	.0416	.0384	.0370	.0357	.0333	LEAD	
	.0075	.0066	.0060	.0054	.0052	.0050	.0046	.0044	.0042	.0040	FEED	
TUMBLER POSITION	1	2	3	4	5	6	7	8	9	10	OUT	

THREADS PER INCH — LEAD IN INCHES — FEEDS IN THOUSANDTHS PER REVOLUTION OF SPINDLE

Fig. 14–11. Chart showing position of levers for various feeds. (American Tool Works Company)

the main spindle to the lead screw. The carriage movement is adjusted by the split nut on the lead screw, using the lever on the outside of the apron to move the split nut. The lead screw is used only for thread cutting, except on a lathe that does not have a feed rod. The apron on such a lathe is moved along by a spline in the lead screw instead of using the thread.

Figure 14–10 shows an exterior view of the quick-change gear mechanism with the levers used to adjust the gears for the required number of threads per inch. The correct position of each lever is determined by a chart, as in Fig. 14–11, which is attached to the gearbox.

10. What is a tool post?

Ans. A tool post (Fig. 14–12) is used to hold various cutting-tool holders. The holders rest on a wedge which is shaped on the bottom to fit into a concave-shaped ring, providing a means of adjusting the toolholder to a required position. Another kind of tool post is shown in Fig. 14–13. This type has provision for holding four separate toolholders, which may be swiveled to a variety of positions.

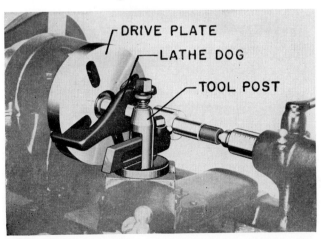

Fig. 14–12. Drive plate and tool post. (South Bend Lathe Works)

Fig. 14–13. Four-way tool post. (Cincinnati Lathe & Tool Co.)

11. What are toolholders?

Ans. Toolholders are devices for holding various kinds of cutting tools. They are made in many sizes and styles. Figure 14–14 shows several types of toolholders and the kind of operation for which each is designed.

Fig. 14–14. Various types of toolholders. (Armstrong Bros. Tool Co.)

12. What are some of the most important cutting tools used on a lathe?

Ans. The most important cutting tools are common tool bits. These are ground in a variety of shapes, according to the type of operation to be performed. Some of these are shown in Fig. 14–15. Additional information on the preparation of lathe cutting tools was given in Chap. 11, "Cutting Tools," pages 106 to 109.

13. Explain how the toolholder should be placed in the tool post for turning work.

Ans. As a general rule, place the toolholder in the tool post at approximately 90 deg with the center line, or a little in the direction of the dead center when feeding toward the headstock. The point of

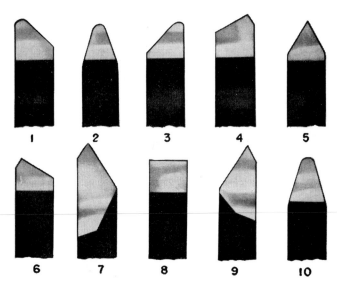

Fig. 14–15. Tool bits ground for lathe work. (Armstrong Bros. Tool Co.)

1. Left-hand turning tool	6. Right-hand corner tool
2. Roundnose turning tool	7. Left-hand side tool
3. Right-hand turning tool	8. Square-nose tool
4. Left-hand corner tool	9. Right-hand side tool
5. Threading tool	10. Brass tool

the cutting tool should be on the center line between the dead center and the live center, and should not extend far from the toolholder. Neither should the toolholder extend far from the tool post, if chattering is to be avoided. A very good illustration is shown in Fig. 14–16.

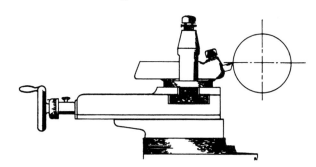

Fig. 14–16. Sketch showing the relationship of tool post, toolholder, and cutting tool to the work.

CAUTION: When taking a heavy cut, do not have the tool pointing in the direction of the live center. If the tool is pointed in that direction and runs into a hard spot, the material will have a tendency to push the tool away, forcing the tool to dig into the material and perhaps scrapping the job. This caution is unnecessary in taking a light cut.

Bear in mind that when you force the tool into the work 0.001 in. on the periphery, you are cutting 0.002 in. off the diameter.

14. State the usual cutting speeds for the most commonly used metals.

Ans. The peripheral speeds in feet per minute (fpm), recommended for cutting metals on the lathe when using high-speed-steel tool bits, are shown in Table 14–1.

Table 14–1. CUTTING SPEEDS FOR COMMON METALS

Material	Fpm
SAE 6470 high-speed steel	40–50
Cast iron	55–65
SAE 1095 tool steel	60–65
SAE 5132 steel	80–85
SAE 1014 cold-rolled steel, machine steel	110–120
Brass	115–125
Bronze, copper, aluminum	200–250

15. Why is it a good policy to use a coarse feed when machining stock that is to be ground?

Ans. Much time will be saved by taking a coarse feed.

16. What are some of the methods and equipment for holding work on a lathe?

Ans. The work may be held (1) in a chuck, (2) between centers, (3) in a collet, and (4) on a faceplate.

Fig. 14–17. Four-jaw independent lathe chuck. (Cincinnati Lathe & Tool Co.)

17. Name the two most commonly used lathe chucks and give the use of each one.

Ans. The four-jaw independent lathe chuck (Fig. 14–17) is used for holding most of the work for which a chuck is required. The hardened-steel jaws are reversible and will hold work of different sizes and shapes. Each jaw may be moved independently of the others.

The three-jaw universal chuck (Fig. 14–18) holds cylindrical work. All three jaws move universally, that is, together, to bring the work on center. This chuck is easier to operate than the four-jaw chuck but it can be used only on round or hexagon stock.

18. What is a magnetic chuck?

Ans. A magnetic chuck (Fig. 14–19) holds work made of steel, by means of permanent magnets

Fig. 14–18. Three-jaw universal lathe chuck. (Cincinnati Lathe & Tool Co.)

Fig. 14–19. Magnetic lathe chuck. (Brown & Sharpe Mfg. Co.)

contained within the chuck. The face of the chuck is magnetized by inserting a key in the edge of the chuck and turning it 180 deg. The degree of magnetism may be controlled by turning the key only part of the required amount. In this manner, a piece of material may be held lightly on the face of the chuck while it is being adjusted to the required position, after which the full power of the magnets may be turned on. This type of chuck is suitable for work that requires only light cuts and is especially good for holding parts that are too thin to be held in an ordinary chuck, as shown in Fig. 14–20.

Fig. 14–20. The magnetic chuck is useful for holding parts that are thin. (Brown & Sharpe Mfg. Co.)

19. What equipment is used to hold work between centers on a lathe?

Ans. The equipment used to hold work between centers consists of (1) a live center, (2) a dead center, (3) a drive plate, and (4) a driving dog.

20. What is the difference between a dead center and a live center?

Ans. The dead center is supported in the tailstock and does not revolve. The live center is contained in the spindle of the headstock and revolves with the work.

Because the work revolves on the dead center, this center should be well lubricated. The friction

between the work and the dead center will cause both parts to become hot and expand a little. To avoid excessive friction and consequent burning of the metal, the dead center should be readjusted to the work after the work has been revolving a short time.

21. What is a drive plate?

Ans. A drive plate (Fig. 14–12) is a round steel plate that is attached to the headstock of a lathe. Into the slots in the face of the plate is inserted the bent end of a driving dog. The dog is firmly attached to the work.

Two types of lathe dogs are illustrated. The style of dog in Fig. 14–21 is for cylindrical work. The other, a clamp type, is for holding flat pieces of work. It is shown in Fig. 14–22.

Fig. 14–21. Bent-tail lathe dog. (Armstrong Bros. Tool Co.)

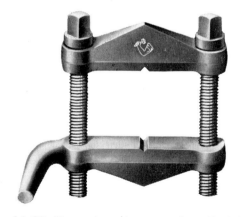

Fig. 14–22. Clamp dog. (Armstrong Bros. Tool Co.)

22. How is the work mounted on centers?

Ans. When mounting work between centers, be careful to see that the centers are in good condition. The dead center in the tailstock will be the first to show wear. Figure 14–23 shows a shaft correctly mounted between centers *A* and *B*. The lathe dog is fastened to the work and the tail should clear the bottom of the slot (as shown at *C*). The work is held firmly but not too tightly on the live and dead centers. Adjusting the centers to the work in the proper manner can be learned in a short time. Too great a pressure of the dead center against the work will cause a squeaking noise, and the center and work will become overheated.

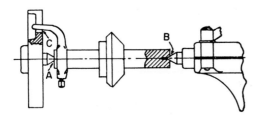

Fig. 14–23. Shaft correctly mounted between centers.

An incorrect mounting of work on centers is shown in Fig. 14–24. In this case, the lathe dog is of such a size that the tail will not clear the bottom of the slot in the driving plate (as shown at *C*). This situation causes the work to be pulled away from the centers, as indicated at points *A* and *B*, and so to revolve eccentrically. This condition may be overcome by using a larger dog or by placing the tail of the dog in a deeper slot of the driving plate.

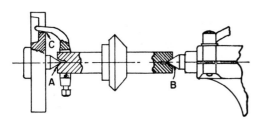

Fig. 14–24. Lathe dog is bearing on bottom of slot in drive plate, pulling the work off the center.

23. *What extra care should be taken in inserting a piece of work between the centers?*

Ans. Do not carelessly force the dead center against the end of the work close to the edge of the countersunk hole, as this may cause the hole to be burred or nicked. If this happens, the work will not run true.

24. *What attachment should be used for holding cylindrical shafts of small diameter?*

Ans. The draw-in collet chuck attachment, shown in Fig. 14–25, is used on the lathe for the

Fig. 14–25. Collets, draw spindle, and adapter for use with toolroom lathes. (Hardinge Brothers, Inc.)

production of small metal parts, and in the tool room for fine, accurate work. A long bar is passed through the drawbar and held in the collet chuck while the end of the bar of material is being machined. Short work may also be held in this type of chuck.

Figure 14–26 shows another type of holder, the Jacobs spindle-nose chuck and rubber-flex collets. Each collet handles a wide range of work diameters. The eleven collets shown will hold diameters

Fig. 14–26. Jacobs spindle-nose lathe chuck and rubber-flex collets. (Monarch Machine Tool Co.)

from 1/16 through 1 3/8 in. The Sjogren spindle-nose-type collet chuck operates in the same manner as the Jacobs chuck, but collets of spring steel are used instead of rubber (see Fig. 14–27). The collets are tightened on the work by turning the handwheel in a clockwise direction.

Fig. 14–27. Sjogren spindle-nose collet chuck. (Cincinnati Lathe & Tool Co.)

Fig. 14–28. Faceplate. (Cincinnati Lathe & Tool Co.)

25. What is a faceplate?

Ans. A faceplate (Fig. 14–28) is a round metal plate that is attached to the headstock of a lathe. By means of clamps, articles to be machined that cannot be conveniently held in a chuck may be secured to the plate.

26. When using a driving plate and a steady rest, what is a good method for holding a shaft on center so that the end of the shaft may be bored?

Ans. A good way to do this job is to tie the shaft to the driving plate, as shown in Fig. 14–29. The plate is unscrewed about three or four revolutions from the shoulder of the spindle. Then the work is placed on the live center and tied securely to the driving plate with a rawhide strap. Finally, the driving plate is screwed back on to the shoulder of the spindle. This tightens the strap on the work and holds it firmly.

27. What are some of the attachments that may be used on a lathe?

Ans. Some lathe attachments are (1) taper attachment, (2) relieving or backing-off attachment,

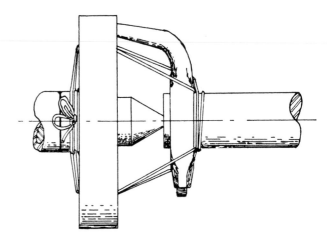

Fig. 14–29. Holding shaft on center with rawhide strap.

(3) milling attachment, (4) steady rest, (5) follower rest, (6) grinding attachment, and (7) micrometer carriage stop.

28. Describe the taper attachment.

Ans. The taper attachment (Fig. 14–30) is a device that is attached to the back of the carriage. It is used to turn and bore tapers. An important part of the attachment is the guide bar which is graduated in degrees at one end and in taper per foot at the other end.

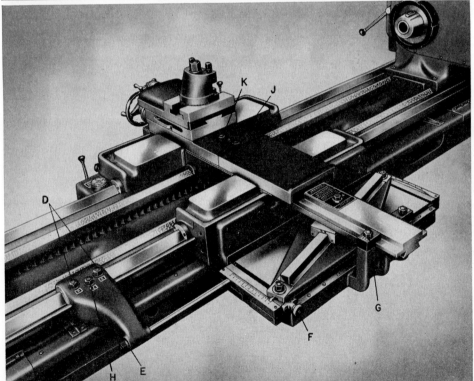

Fig. 14–30. Taper attachment on back of a lathe and enlarged view of main parts. (American Tool Works Co.)

INSTRUCTIONS FOR OPERATING
TAPER ATTACHMENT

To set this attachment for any desired taper, loosen the nut *A* holding the guide plate to the sliding shoe, and nuts *B* and *C* at the ends of the swiveling bar. Set the swiveling bar to the desired taper indicated on the scale, using the micrometer adjusting screw, *F*, and tighten the nuts mentioned above. Except when setting the taper, these nuts

Fig. 14–31. Relieving attachment. (American Tool Works Co.)

Fig. 14–32. Relieving attachment is operated by a drive shaft connected to a change-gear mechanism attached to the end of the headstock. (Monarch Machine Tool Co.)

should always be tight, even when the taper attachment is not being used. Clamp screw G and lock nut H must be loose when using taper attachment and tightened only when attachment is not in use. To engage or disengage the taper attachment, tighten or loosen the nuts marked D which clamp the locking arm to the bed. When the taper attachment is being used, nut E, holding the bar to the locking arm, should be tight. Be sure to have the point of the tool on the center line.

If the taper attachment is used consistently on one job, it would be advisable to shift the sliding bar occasionally, to distribute equally any wear on the swiveling bar.

The compound rest and the taper-attachment slide should move freely, but there should be no looseness or play. If chatter or nonuniform taper occurs, this is the result of looseness in these slides and can be corrected by adjusting the gib on the compound-rest base and the gibs on the taper attachment.

Should any looseness or backlash develop in the cross-feed-screw nuts, it can be removed by loosening screw J and tightening screw K, then retightening screw J.

29. *What is a relieving attachment?*

Ans. A relieving or backing-off attachment of the kind shown in Fig. 14–31 is used for external, internal, and end relieving of cutters, taps, and so forth. The oscillating movement of the tool slide is obtained by a cam which is operated by a drive shaft with universal joints connected to the headstock. It requires little time to attach it to a lathe, and it may be readily disconnected when the required work is done. Another style of relieving attachment is shown in Fig. 14–32.

Fig. 14–33. Milling attachment for lathe fastened to T slot of compound. (Cincinnati Lathe & Tool Co.)

30. *What is a milling attachment?*

Ans. One type of milling attachment for a lathe is shown in Fig. 14–33. It is fastened to the lathe compound in place of a toolholder. It has a graduated swivel. The vertical hand-feed screw is graduated in thousandths of an inch. Another type of milling attachment is mounted directly on the bottom slide in place of the compound. It is suitable for face milling, dovetail milling, squaring of shafts, cutting slots, and, as shown in Fig. 14–34, for cutting keyways. It has graduations on the base and on the vise swivel.

Fig. 14–34. Cutting a keyway on milling attachment mounted on cross slide. (Cincinnati Lathe & Tool Co.)

31. *What is a steady rest?*

Ans. A steady rest (Fig. 14–35) is a device for supporting long shafts of small diameter while turning them, and also when boring or threading long spindles. The support given to the work by a steady rest prevents the work from yielding to the pressure of the cutting tool. A steady rest with rollers in the jaws is recommended for operations requiring high work speeds (see Fig. 14–36).

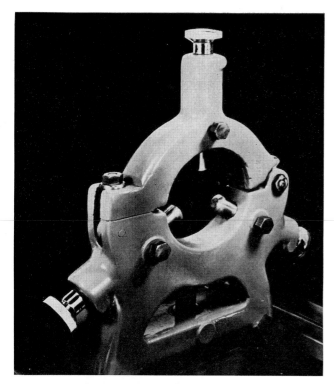

Fig. 14–35. Steady rest. (Monarch Machine Tool Co.)

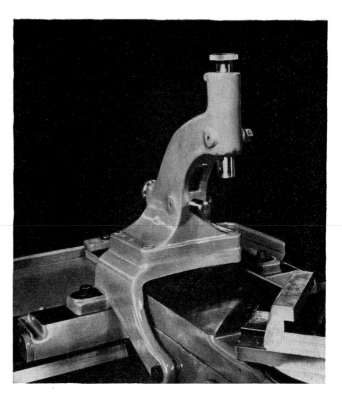

Fig. 14–37. Follower rest. (Monarch Machine Tool Co.)

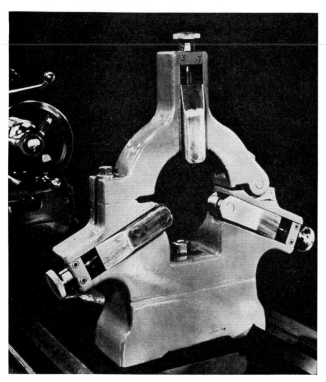

Fig. 14–36. Roller-jaw steady rest. (Monarch Machine Tool Co.)

32. What is a follower rest?

Ans. A follower rest (Fig. 14–37) is similar in purpose to a steady rest but differs in that it is at-tached to the saddle of the lathe. The adjustable jaws of the follower rest bear directly on the fin-ished diameter of the work, following the cutting edge of the cutting tool on the opposite side of the work. As the tool feeds along the work, the fol-lower rest, being attached to the saddle, travels with it.

33. What is a grinding attachment?

Ans. A grinding attachment (Fig. 14–38) is a self-contained unit that is attached to the com-pound rest of the lathe. It is used for internal grind-ing. A grinding attachment especially designed for grinding screw threads is shown in Fig. 14–39.

34. What is a micrometer carriage stop?

Ans. A micrometer carriage stop (Fig. 14–40) is a device, attached to the bedway of the lathe, for stopping the carriage at a definite point. It is help-ful for accurate facing, shoulder turning, and bor-ing operations. The micrometer collar permits ad-justments of one-thousandth of an inch.

35. What is the difference between an arbor and a mandrel?

Ans. An arbor is a shaft that is designed to hold and drive cutting tools such as milling cutters. As

Fig. 14–38. Internal-grinding attachment. (Cincinnati Lathe & Tool Co.)

Fig. 14–39. Thread-grinding attachment. (Kurt Orban Company, Inc.)

Fig. 14–40. Micrometer carriage stop. (Cincinnati Lathe & Tool Co.)

in Fig. 14–41, one end of the arbor is tapered to fit the spindle of a machine.

A mandrel is a shaft or bar for holding work to be machined. There is a countersunk hole in each end so that it may be held between centers. Plain mandrels (Fig. 14–42) are usually tapered 0.001 to 0.005 in. so that a piece of work may be securely wedged on it. Expanding mandrels are also available in many sizes (see Fig. 14–43). They are pre-

ferred by some mechanics because one mandrel may fit several jobs of different size. The amount of expansion is from about 1/16 in. for small sizes up to 1/2 in. for large sizes.

36. What are some of the machining operations that may be performed on a lathe?

Ans. Straight turning, taper turning, facing, straight boring, taper boring, knurling, external

Fig. 14–41. Milling-machine arbor. (Brown & Sharpe Mfg. Co.)

Fig. 14–42. Plain mandrel. (Whitman & Barnes)

Fig. 14–43. Expanding mandrel. (Morse Twist Drill & Machine Co.)

threading, internal threading, drilling, reaming, and undercutting.

37. What is the machining operation called turning?

Ans. Turning is the operation of removing stock from the outside of a piece of material while it is being revolved in a lathe. The stock is removed by a suitable cutting tool, as in Fig. 14–44. Turning produces a piece of work that is cylindrical in shape.

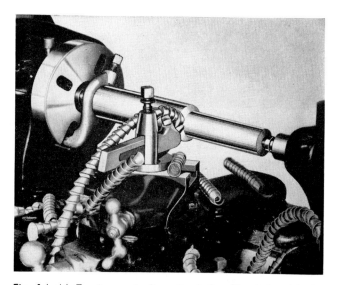

Fig. 14–44. Turning a shaft on the lathe. (South Bend Lathe Works)

38. What are some of the methods for turning tapers?

Ans. For short-taper turning, the compound rest may be swiveled to the required angle and the cutting tool fed against the work by hand.

Long tapers may be turned by holding the work between centers and moving the tailstock to one side of center. Several cuts are usually required, making adjustments of the tailstock between each cut, before a satisfactory adjustment is made. Long tapers are more easily and accurately turned, by using the taper attachment.

39. What is the operation of facing?

Ans. Facing is the operation of removing stock from the end of a bar of material as it is being revolved in a lathe. Figure 14–45 shows a piece of work that is held between centers being faced. Light cuts only are taken, to square the ends of the work. Work should be held in a chuck and supported by a steady rest if a large amount of material is to be faced.

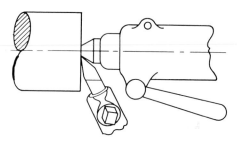

Fig. 14–45. Facing the end of a bar on the lathe.

40. What is the operation of boring?

Ans. Boring is the removal of stock from a hole in a piece of work. The cutting tool shaves off a thin layer of material as it is fed against the revolving work. Holes are bored to make them accurate in size and concentric with the outside surface. Tapered holes may be bored by adjusting the compound rest or the taper attachment in the same manner as for taper turning. An example of boring is shown in Fig. 14–46.

41. What is the operation of knurling?

Ans. Knurling is a process of roughening the surface of a piece of work by making a series of indentations or depressions on it. A knurling tool (Fig. 14–47) held in the tool post is used for this operation. The indentations are usually in a crisscross pattern and may be either coarse, medium,

Fig. 14–46. Boring a hole on the lathe. (South Bend Lathe Works)

Fig. 14–47. Knurling tool. (J. H. Williams & Co.)

Fig. 14–48. Coarse, medium, and fine diamond-pattern knurling. (J. H. Williams & Co.)

Fig. 14–49. Coarse, medium, and fine straight-line knurling. (J. H. Williams Co.)

or fine, as in Fig. 14–48. Another type of knurling, shown in Fig. 14–49, is called *straight* knurling and may also be made fine, medium, or coarse.

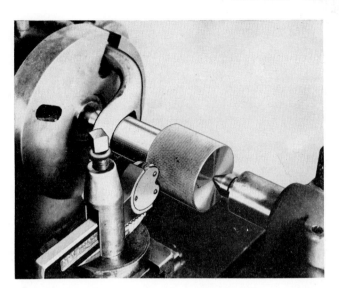

Fig. 14–50. Knurling a piece of work on the lathe. (South Bend Lathe Works)

A slow speed should be used to knurl a piece of work. Force the knurling tool slowly into the work to a depth of approximately 1/64 in. Set the feed so that the tool will feed across the surface of the work. Reverse the feed of the carriage at the end of the cut, and repeat the operation until the knurling has been completed. The knurls should be lubricated while cutting. An illustration of a knurling job is shown in Fig. 14–50.

42. What is the operation of threading?

Ans. External threading is the cutting of threads on the outside of a bar of material. Internal threading is the cutting of threads on the inside of a hole. Lathes are designed to do this type of work, special devices being built into them for that purpose, such as the quick-change gear mechanism, the lead screw, and thread dial. A detailed account of external and internal threading was given in Chap. 9, "Threads," pages 72 to 91. An example of threading on a lathe is shown in Fig. 14–51.

43. Explain the difference in cutting a right-hand and a left-hand thread.

Ans. To cut a right-hand thread, the compound rest is set at the proper angle over toward the right on the saddle. The feed of the carriage is toward the headstock. In cutting a left-hand thread, the compound rest is moved toward the left on the saddle and the feed of the carriage is toward the tailstock.

Fig. 14–51. Cutting an external thread on the lathe. (South Bend Lathe Works)

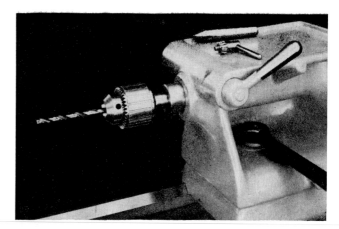

Fig. 14–52. Drill chuck held in tailstock of a lathe. (Cincinnati Lathe & Tool Co.)

44. *Describe three methods of cutting a double thread.*

Ans. The following examples will show how to cut a double thread having 1/4 in. lead and 1/8 in. pitch:

Swivel the center line of the compound rest to a line parallel with the dead and live centers. In cutting the first groove, use a roughing tool, which is narrower than the finishing tool. By dividing 1 in. by the lead, which is 1/4 in., four single threads per inch will be obtained. Set the lathe to cut four threads per inch. Force the tool into the work the required depth by using the cross-slide feed. By using the feed screw on the compound rest, on which a graduated collar is attached, move the roughing tool over the length of the pitch and proceed to rough out as before.

Another way to do this job is to use a faceplate having two equally spaced slots in which to insert the tail of the lathe dog. Be careful not to move the dog after the job has been started.

Still another way to do this job is to mark two teeth equally spaced on the gear that is attached on to the end of the spindle, and after roughing out the first groove, disengage the marked gear on the spindle, and turn both spindle and gear one-half a revolution and then re-mesh the gears. The second groove may then be roughed out.

45. *What is the procedure for drilling and reaming on a lathe?*

Ans. Holes are drilled in a contrary manner on a lathe as compared to drilling on a drill press. On a lathe, the work revolves and the drill is held

stationary. Small sizes of drills are held in a drill chuck of the same design as those used on a drill press. The chuck is attached to the tailstock, as in Fig. 14–52. Larger drills are held in a drill holder (Fig. 14–53) which is supported by the tool post on the left side of the handle and by the dead center of the tailstock on the right side.

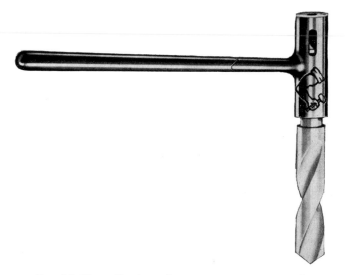

Fig. 14–53. Drill holder. (Armstrong Bros. Tool Co.)

Holes are reamed by inserting a tapered-shank reamer (Fig. 14–54) into the tailstock and feeding it slowly into the drilled hole.

Fig. 14–54. Tapered-shank machine reamer. (Pratt & Whitney)

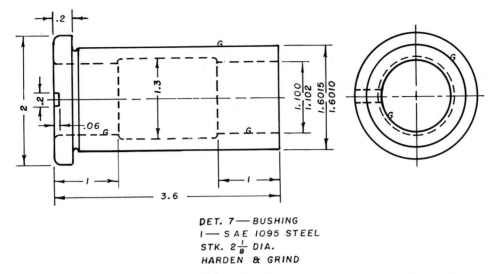

DET. 7 — BUSHING
1 — S A E 1095 STEEL
STK. 2 1/8 DIA.
HARDEN & GRIND

Fig. 14–55. Bushing is undercut at the shoulder for the grinding operation. The surfaces to be ground are marked with the letter G.

46. *What is meant by undercutting?*

Ans. Undercutting is the cutting of a groove next to a shoulder on a piece of work, as in Fig. 14–55. This is done when the smaller diameter has to be ground, inasmuch as the corner of a grinding wheel is not capable of producing a sharp corner.

47. *How much grinding stock should be left on a shaft 1 in. in diameter and 48 in. long, if it is to be ground soft?*

Ans. Leave 0.015 in.

48. *How much grinding stock should be allowed on a shaft 1 in. in diameter and 48 in. long, if it is to be hardened and ground?*

Ans. Allow 0.035 in.

49. *How much grinding stock should be left on the OD and ID of a bushing with a 2-in. bore and 2 1/2 in. OD, if it is to be ground soft?*

Ans. Leave 0.015 in. on each diameter.

50. *How much grinding stock should be allowed on the bushing in the previous question, if it is to be made of high-speed steel, hardened and ground?*

Ans. Allow 0.025 in. on each diameter.

51. *When a drawing calls for grinding on a diameter and against a shoulder, what kind of an undercut should be made?*

Ans. The undercut should be made with a narrow, roundnose tool, fed in at an angle of 45 deg.

52. *What kind of tool is used to undercut corners on a job that is to be hardened and ground?*

Ans. Use a roundnose tool, as a square-nose tool will leave a sharp corner that will tend to cause the steel to crack or break when it is hardened.

53. *What is a center gage and for what is it used?*

Ans. A center gage is a small, flat piece of steel which is graduated in fractions of an inch. Included angles of 60 deg are cut in it, as shown in Fig. 14–56. It is used in setting American National and sharp V threading tools, as shown in Fig. 14–57 and Fig. 14–58.

Fig. 14–56. Center gage. (Brown & Sharpe Mfg. Co.)

54. *What precaution should be taken in fitting a plug gage into work that has just been bored?*

Ans. Before fitting a plug gage into work, be sure that the temperature of the work is almost the same as that of the gage, or the plug gage may freeze in the work.

55. *How may cast iron be machined rapidly and efficiently?*

Ans. Use soda water with a slow speed and heavy feed.

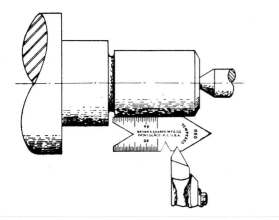

Fig. 14–57. Setting the cutting tool for external threading.

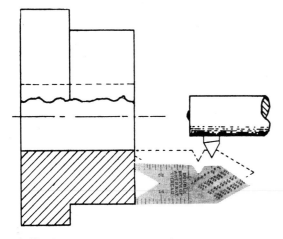

Fig. 14–58. Setting the cutting tool for internal threading.

56. How should a tool be ground for finishing cast iron?

Ans. Grind the tool with a flat top, rounded nose, and with a small side clearance.

57. Should a deep or shallow cut be made in cutting cast iron?

Ans. Cast iron has a very hard scale on the outside, caused by the iron becoming chilled in casting. In cutting this iron, the tool must be immediately forced under this scale or the cutting edge of the tool will be ruined. Never take a shallow cut on cast iron, unless the size of the stock is almost down to the size of the finished job.

58. Give some reasons why the end of a piece of work may not be 90 deg with the center line when faced with a side tool.

Ans. (1) The lathe centers may be out of line. (2) The tool may be springing away from the work. (3) The cutting edge of the tool may have worn off. (4) The gibs of the compound rest may be loose.

59. What is the first thing to do when given a piece of work, and a drawing which gives several length dimensions and the over-all length?

Ans. Add the several lengths and see if they coincide with the over-all length given. Also, determine whether the work has sufficient stock to finish to the outside diameter shown on the drawing.

60. When is the combined drill and countersink used?

Ans. To machine a piece of stock on centers, each end of the stock must be countersunk. This is accomplished with a combined drill and countersink (see Fig. 14–59). The included angle of the combined drill and countersink is 60 deg. This angle is the same as that of the dead and live centers.

Fig. 14–59. Combined drill and countersink. (Whitman & Barnes)

61. Why should a countersunk hole be used for a center hole instead of a large prick-punch mark?

Ans. If a large prick-punch mark is used instead of a hole made with a combined drill and countersink, the work will ride on the point of the steel center and not on the sides of it as it should. The work will soon heat and run untrue, due to improper location and lack of lubrication. The hole produced by the combined drill and countersink should contain center compound to lubricate the point of the dead center.

62. What are some of the rules which should be observed in the lathe department?

Ans. (1) Have the first piece of every job inspected. (2) Do not touch any chips with your hand. Use a wooden paddle. (3) Do not use an adjustable wrench on any nut or screw. Use an open-end wrench, a compound wrench, and the standard tool-post wrench. (4) Do not leave the chuck wrench in the chuck at any time. Oil the spindle nose before putting on chuck or plate. (5) Be neat. Do not allow oil or chips to collect around your lathe. (6) Keep tools off ways and top of carriage. (7) Cover all boring and internal-threading tools with a towel while using gages or calipers to check bore. (8) Goggles must be worn on the following types of work: turning of square, hexagon, or irregular stock of any kind; turning of all broach jobs; on bronze or brass at all times; and on all tough stock, where the chips have a tendency to fly.

63. *How is the size of the engine lathe determined?*

Ans. Engine lathes vary in size, ranging from the small bench lathe of only a few inches, to one many feet in length. The size of the engine lathe is based upon two measurements: the approximate largest diameter that can be revolved over the ways and the total length of the bed. The actual size of the maximum swing is usually somewhat greater than the nominal size listed. For example, an 18-in. lathe may actually swing 18 1/2 in. over the ways of the bed.

Chapter 15 TURRET LATHES

The turret lathe is an adaptation of the engine lathe. One early development of it was the screw machine, primarily designed for the rapid production of screws, from which it derived its name. This machine gained wide prominence, later, by the addition to it of certain tools and attachments which could be used for the completion of small, cylindrical, duplicate parts. The name *screw machine* is sometimes loosely used as a synonym for turret lathe. A horizontal universal turret lathe is shown in Fig. 15–1.

1. What are the principal parts of a turret lathe?
Ans. The principal parts of a turret lathe are (1) the bed, (2) the headstock, (3) the carriage, and (4) the turret.

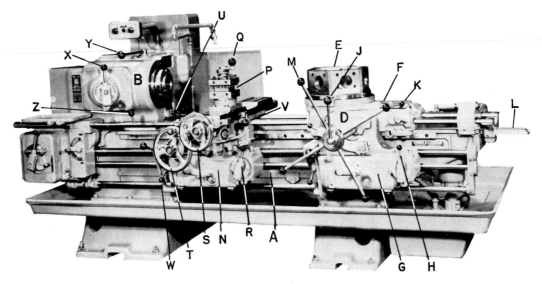

Fig. 15–1. Nomenclature of turret lathe. (Jones & Lamson Machine Co.)

A. Bed
B. Headstock
C. Carriage
D. Turret unit
E. Hexagon turret
F. Saddle
G. Saddle apron
H. Pre-selector for longitudinal saddle feeds
J. Power-traverse lever
K. Slide-binder lever
L. Saddle stops
M. Turnstile

N. Carriage apron
P. Square turret
Q. Square-turret indexing and binder handle
R. Pre-selector for longitudinal carriage feeds
S. Cross-feed handwheel
T. Longitudinal-feed handwheel
U. Carriage clamp
V. Cross-feed engagement lever
W. Longitudinal-feed engagement lever
X. Pre-selector for spindle speeds
Y. Spindle-control lever
Z. Longitudinal stop rod

2. Describe the bed.

Ans. The bed is a long boxlike casting fitted with rectangular ways upon which are mounted the carriage and turret. It also supports the headstock.

3. What is the headstock?

Ans. The headstock is a large casting located on the left end of the bed. It houses the transmission mechanism (see Fig. 15–1) which operates the spindle at various speeds. These speeds are controlled by the built-in speed selector.

4. What is the carriage?

Ans. The carriage (Fig. 15–1) is a unit that is fitted over the ways of the bed. Mounted upon it is the tool post. The front of the carriage includes the apron which contains the feed mechanism. The carriage has reversible, power longitudinal feeds ranging from 0.005 to 0.176 in. and also reversible, power cross-feeds ranging from 0.002 to 0.088 in. per revolution of the spindle. Most models have longitudinal- and cross-feed positive stops which act to disengage the feed according to the specifications of the work.

5. What is the turret?

Ans. The turret (Fig. 15–2) is a hexagon-shaped toolholder mounted on a saddle that slides on the bed ways. It has power longitudinal and cross-feeds similar to the carriage. Figure 15–3 shows a turret with a variety of standard chucking tools. These are specially designed to be attached to the six sides of the turret, and many different kinds of drills, reamers, boring bars, and cutting tools are held by them. The term *chucking tools* refers to the type of tools used for machining work that is best held in a chuck.

Figure 15–4 shows a turret with a standard set of bar tools. It may be seen that these tools are also held by holders that have been purposely made to fit the turret. Tools of this kind are used for machining round bars of steel or other material.

The turret rotates on a hardened, ground-and-lapped center pin. It may be locked in each of the six positions. The tools used in the turret are: drills, reamers, counterbores, taps, dies, boring bars and a large variety of forming tools and cutters.

The tools held in the turret may be used to perform certain operations on a piece of work, while,

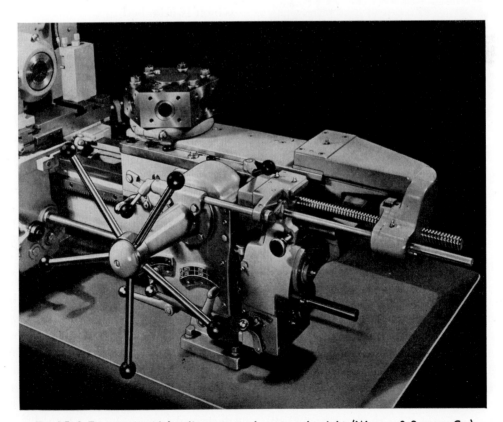

Fig. 15–2. Turret unit with leading-on attachment on the right. (Warner & Swasey Co.)

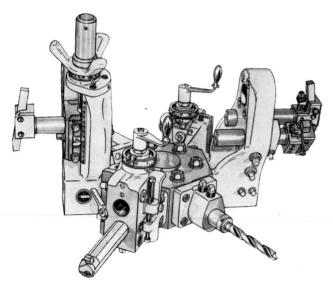

Fig. 15–3. Turret with a variety of tools for chucking work. (Warner & Swasey Co.)

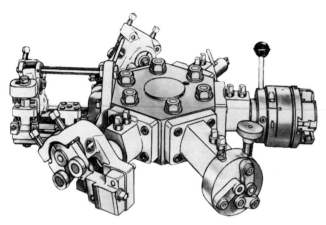

Fig. 15–4. Turret with a variety of tools for bar work. (Warner & Swasey Co.)

at the same time, other tools held in the square tool post mounted on the carriage do other operations. A selection of universal tooling equipment for bar work, with an identification of each one, is shown in Fig. 15–5. A selection of universal chucking tools, with their identifications, is shown in Fig. 15–6.

A permanent setup of universal tooling equipment can be arranged so that the large, heavy tools of the flanged type are permanently mounted in their logical order on the machine. If necessary for certain jobs, the tool stations can be back-indexed, or skip-indexed, to suit the requirements of the job, but the flanged tools themselves are not changed from one turret face to the other. Ordi-

narily, the extra machine-handling time required to remove these tools from the machine or to change their position on the turret is more than the time required to skip-index a station. The lighter tools which can be quickly mounted in the turret or holder are of the shank type. Figure 15–7 shows a permanent setup for bar work; Fig. 15–8 shows a permanent setup for chucking work.

A complete bar-tooling layout for machining the steel shaft of Fig. 15–9 is shown in Fig. 15–10. All of the tool stations are used. The cutters are made of high-speed steel and are standard stock shapes. The order of operation is shown in Fig. 15–11.

When the accuracy requirements of the job are studied, it is found that the diameters do not have to be turned to very close limits since they are to be ground after hardening. However, it is necessary to keep the diameters closely concentric in order to allow for clean-up in the grinding operations. The thread diameter, which is not ground, must run true with the other diameters.

6. What is a thread-chasing attachment?

Ans. A thread-chasing attachment (Fig. 15–12), which is attached to the carriage, is used for cutting threads. It is actuated by means of a leader and follower. The leader is clamped on the carriage feed rod and the follower nut is bolted to the chasing lever. Each leader cuts only one size of thread.

7. What is a taper attachment?

Ans. A taper attachment (Fig. 15–13) is a device for turning and boring tapers, that may be attached to the carriage. The usual capacity of the taper attachment is 3 in. taper per foot, 8 in. long. The graduated scale may be adjusted for degrees or for taper per foot.

8. What is a pre-selector?

Ans. A pre-selector is a device that permits the machine operator to pre-select the spindle speed for the next operation while the present operation is in progress. The new speed is then automatically actuated while the operator is turning the tools into position for the next operation. Each manufacturer of turret lathes has his own particular design of a pre-selector. Two different designs of

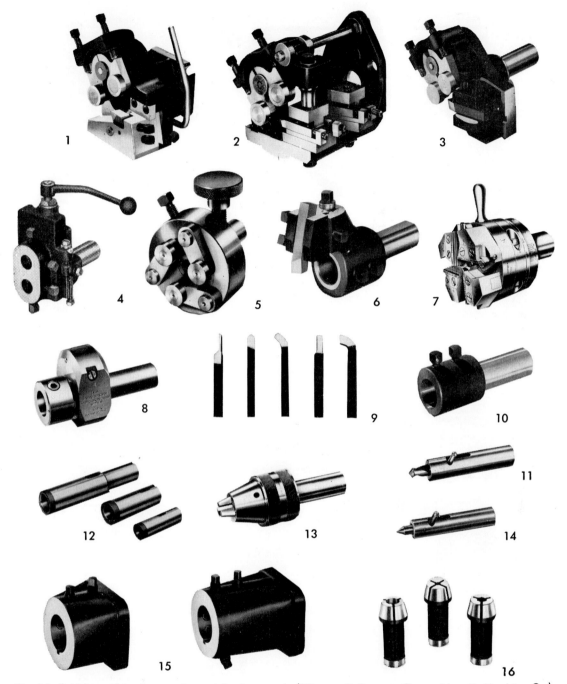

Fig. 15–5. Universal tooling equipment for bar work. (Warner & Swasey Co. and Landis Machine Co.)

1. Single cutter turner
2. Multiple cutter turner
3. Combination end facer and turner
4. Quick-acting slide tool
5. Center drilling tool
6. Adjustable knee tool
7. Die head
8. Clutch tap and die holder

9. Forged cutters for square turret
10. Floating toolholder
11. Combination stock stop and starting drill
12. Taper drill sockets
13. Drill chuck
14. Combination stock stop and center
15. Flanged toolholders (short and long)
16. Collets

pre-selectors are shown in Figs. 15–14 and 15–15.

A detailed outline of the Warner and Swasey pre-selector follows:

A. Set the pre-selector when setting up tools. First, rotate the drum until the desired surface speed in feet per minute showing on the dial cor-

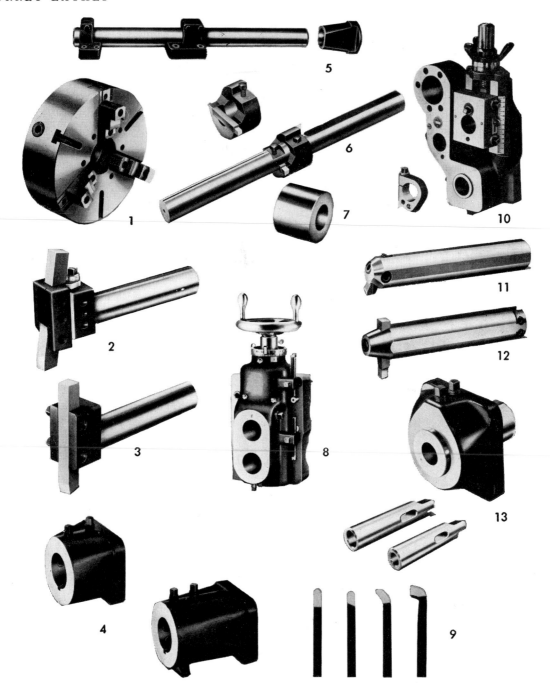

Fig. 15–6. Universal chucking tools. (Warner & Swasey Co.)

1. Three-jaw geared scroll chuck
2. Reversible adjustable angle cutter holder
3. Reversible straight and angle cutter holder
4. Flanged toolholders (short and long)
5. Stationary overhead pilot bar and pilot sleeves
6. Piloted boring bar
7. Spindle pilot bushing
8. Slide tool
9. Forged cutters for square turret
10. Adjustable single turning head
11. Angular cutter stub boring bar
12. Straight cutter stub boring bar (double-ended)
13. Straight shank taper socket and holder with taper shell sockets

responds to the work diameter to be cut. Then, number that cut, using master numeral 1 at the top of the drum.

B. Set the indicator for the second cut, by selecting the desired surface speed in feet per minute for the second work diameter. Number this cut

UNIVERSAL BAR EQUIPMENT
Permanent Set-up

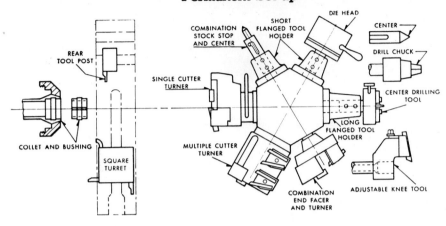

Fig. 15–7. A permanent setup of universal bar equipment. (Warner & Swasey Co.)

UNIVERSAL CHUCKING EQUIPMENT
Permanent Set-up

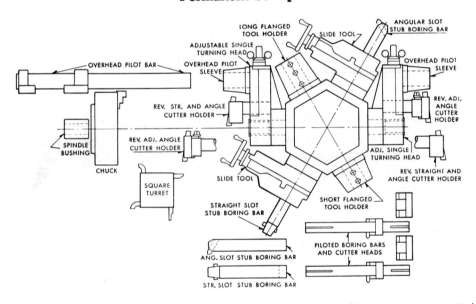

Fig. 15–8. A permanent setup of universal chucking equipment. (Warner & Swasey Co.)

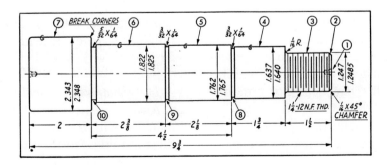

Fig. 15–9. A typical bar job; a shaft. (Warner & Swasey Co.)

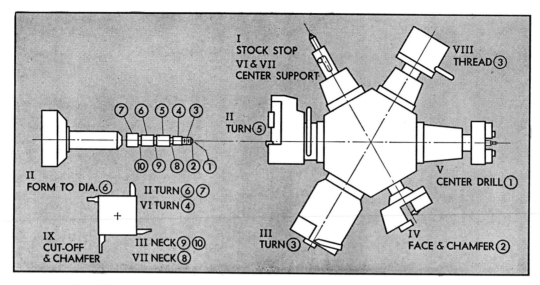

Fig. 15–10. Tooling setup for the shaft in Fig. 15–9. (Warner & Swasey Co.)

with master numeral 2. Continue similarly for additional operations.

C. Cuts are now shown in order by the master numerals, 1, 2, 3, and so forth. Now, use these numerals in their turn from one cut to the next. In this way, the correct surface speed in feet per minute will be set for each cut, regardless of the number of speed changes.

D. In actual use, it is possible to pre-select the next speed by turning to the next numeral while the machine is cutting. Then, when the cut is finished, it is necessary merely to move the lever, bringing the next speed into play, without stopping the spindle: forward—reverse—stop—start, with the one lever.

Pre-selector is set for surface speeds as shown in Fig. 15–16.

The operator can select the correct spindle rpm to produce the proper surface feet per minute for any diameter to be cut by turning the handwheel.

9. What is the stationary overhead pilot bar?

Ans. The stationary overhead pilot bar, which fastens to the head of the machine, can be heavier than the pilot bars which are attached to the turning heads, because this bar does not add any weight to the hexagon turret and its tools. This type of pilot bar can be adjusted endwise in the machine for various lengths of work and clamped in place. The purpose of the overhead pilot bar is to fasten the turret of the machine to the head-stock, thus providing greater rigidity so that deeper cuts can be taken with heavier feeds.

10. What is a full universal-threading turret lathe?

Ans. A full universal-threading turret lathe combines toolroom threading performance, and the advantages of high-speed production in a thread-cutting lead-screw machine. The single-thread fine-pitch lead screw is used for thread cutting only. The remote-control lever, located at the operating position, gives forward and reverse motion to the carriage. It is not necessary to disengage the double half nuts or reverse the spindle for the threading operation. This remote-control lever is also used in cutting left-hand threads. An automatic knock-off for right-hand threads permits threading to accurate shoulder lengths. The change from threading to regular feeding is accomplished by shifting a single lever on the head-end lead-screw gearbox. A safety interlock prevents the screw-cutting and feeding mechanisms from engaging at the same time. The threading range is 2 to 56 threads per inch in lengths to 20 in.

11. What is a vertical-turret lathe?

Ans. A vertical-turret lathe (Fig. 15–17) is a machine with a vertical turrethead and a horizontal worktable. Most of the operations performed on a regular turret lathe may be done on this type of machine. It is preferred for large, heavy work.

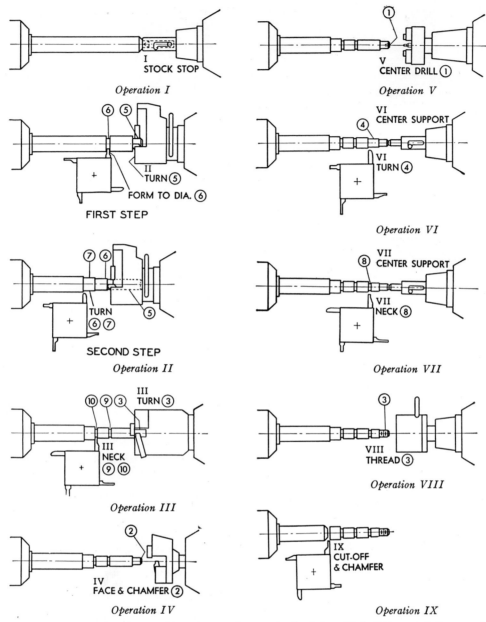

Fig. 15–11. Sequence of operations for machining shaft of Fig. 15–9. (Warner & Swasey Co.)

12. *What are the principal parts of a vertical-turret lathe?*

Ans. The principal parts are (1) base and column, (2) table, (3) rail, (4) saddle and turret-head, and (5) sidehead.

13. *What is the purpose of the base and column?*

Ans. The base and column is one massive casting including bearing ways for the rail- and sidehead, and support for the worktable.

14. *What is the table?*

Ans. The table is a cylindrical casting which is

attached to the main spindle of the machine. It rotates at speeds ranging from 3 to 180 rpm. Its upper surface may vary according to the requirements of the user. The one shown on the machine in Fig. 15–17 is fitted with four independent chuck jaws and has T slots. Other tables are available with a three-jaw universal chuck and T slots, as in Fig. 15–18; with four faceplate jaws and T slots as in Fig. 15–19; and with T slots only.

15. *What is the rail?*

Ans. The rail is a box-type casting which is attached in a horizontal position to the vertical bear-

Fig. 15-12. Thread-chasing attachment. (Jones & Lamson Machine Co.)

Fig. 15-14. Pre-selector for spindle speeds; Jones & Lamson design. (Jones & Lamson Machine Co.)

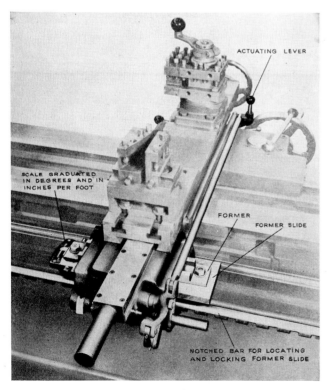

ACTUATING LEVER

SCALE GRADUATED
IN DEGREES AND IN
INCHES PER FOOT

FORMER

FORMER SLIDE

NOTCHED BAR FOR LOCATING
AND LOCKING FORMER SLIDE

Fig. 15-13. Taper attachment. (Jones & Lamson Machine Co.)

FORWARD

No 5
WARNER & SWASEY

NEUTRAL
RANGE

BRAKE

REVERSE

Fig. 15-15. Pre-selector for spindle speeds; Warner & Swasey design. (Warner & Swasey Co.)

ing ways of the column. It may be raised or lowered under power, by feed screws located within the ways of the column. The rail supports the saddle for the turrethead and contains the feed screws by means of which the saddle may be moved from side to side, either by rapid traverse or by automatic feed.

16. What are the saddle and turrethead used for?

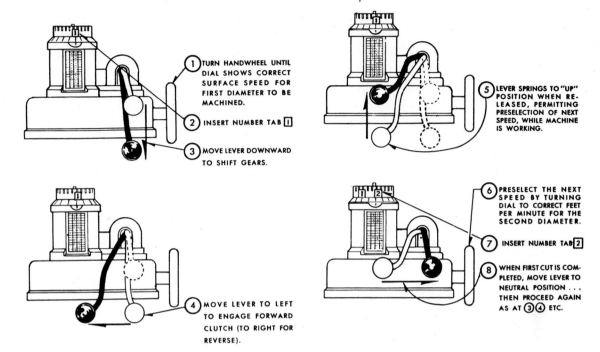

1. TURN HANDWHEEL UNTIL DIAL SHOWS CORRECT SURFACE SPEED FOR FIRST DIAMETER TO BE MACHINED.

2. INSERT NUMBER TAB 1

3. MOVE LEVER DOWNWARD TO SHIFT GEARS.

4. MOVE LEVER TO LEFT TO ENGAGE FORWARD CLUTCH (TO RIGHT FOR REVERSE).

5. LEVER SPRINGS TO "UP" POSITION WHEN RELEASED, PERMITTING PRESELECTION OF NEXT SPEED, WHILE MACHINE IS WORKING.

6. PRESELECT THE NEXT SPEED BY TURNING DIAL TO CORRECT FEET PER MINUTE FOR THE SECOND DIAMETER.

7. INSERT NUMBER TAB 2

8. WHEN FIRST CUT IS COMPLETED, MOVE LEVER TO NEUTRAL POSITION . . . THEN PROCEED AGAIN AS AT 3 4 ETC.

Fig. 15–16. Setting the pre-selector for surface speeds. (Warner & Swasey Co.)

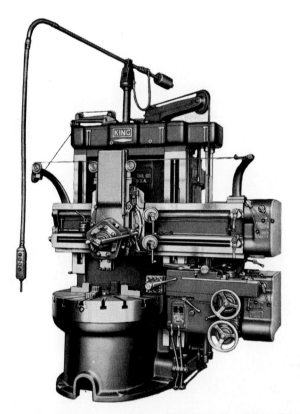

Fig. 15–17. Vertical-turret lathe. (American Steel Foundries)

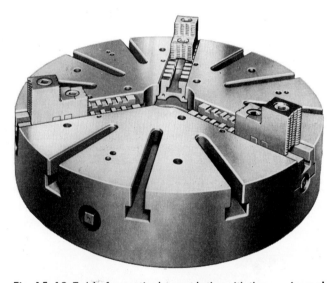

Fig. 15–18. Table for vertical-turret lathe with three universal jaws and T slots. (American Steel Foundries)

Ans. The saddle and turrethead are attached to the rail. The saddle may be swiveled from side to side, the turrethead may be raised or lowered on the saddle. The five-sided head itself may be revolved to any of five positions. Various cutting tools may be attached to the head.

17. What is the sidehead?

Ans. The sidehead is located below the rail. It is a nonswiveling unit having complete feed and rapid-traverse mechanism. It is fitted with a square toolholder for cutting tools.

18. What attachments are available for a vertical-turret lathe?

Ans. Many attachments are used on vertical-turret lathes. Some of them are (1) a screw-cutting attachment for cutting threads from 2 to 18 per inch. (2) A tool-lubricating attachment for

Fig. 15–19. Table for vertical-turret lathe with four faceplate jaws and T slots. (American Steel Foundries)

reducing the friction of the work and chips against the cutting tool, and also for absorbing and diffusing the heat generated at the point of cutting. The lubricating attachment also permits greater feeds and speeds, and helps lengthen the life of the cutting tools. (3) A drum-scoring attachment for machining coarse leads ranging from 1/2 to 2 in. in 1/32-in. increments. (4) A gear-type taper attachment for cutting tapers within a range of 5 to 45 deg from the horizontal.

Some manufacturers use a combination unit which can be adapted for thread cutting, drum scoring, or angular turning. The threads may be either Metric or National form. The angles may be cut either on the horizontal or vertical.

Figures 15–20 to 15–23 illustrate some of the operations that may be performed on the vertical-turret lathe. It will be noticed that in each of these examples the article being machined is quite large. Jobs of this kind are usually difficult to machine on an ordinary engine lathe, but offer no problems when they are done on a vertical-turret lathe.

Fig. 15–20. Machining a railroad-car wheel on a vertical-turret lathe. (Bullard Co.)

Fig. 15–21. Machining a mining-conveyor-belt pulley on a vertical-turret lathe. (Bullard Co.)

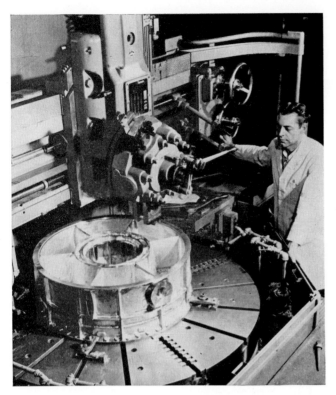

Fig. 15–22. Machining a compressor-intake casting for a jet engine on a vertical-turret lathe. (Bullard Co.)

Fig. 15–23. Machining the grooves of an elevator sheave on a vertical-turret lathe. (Bullard Co.)

Chapter 16 MILLING MACHINES

A milling machine is one that is designed to remove metal or other material from a piece of work with a revolving cutter as the work is fed against it. The cutter, of which there are many kinds and sizes, is held on an arbor or is attached directly to the spindle of the machine. A great variety of

Fig. 16–1. Nomenclature of plain milling machine. (Cincinnati Milling Machine Co.)

A. Column	G. Vertical feed-engaging lever	N. Speed-change crank
B. Knee	H. Rear-table feed-engaging lever	P. Spindle reverse
C. Table	J. Front-table feed-engaging lever	Q. Table-traverse handwheel
D. Spindle	K. Overarm positioning crank	R. Start-stop push buttons
E. Overarm	L. Overarm clamps	S. Knee clamp
F. Starting lever	M. Speed dial	

operations may be performed, producing work both regular and irregular in shape. A plain milling machine is shown in Fig. 16–1.

1. What are the principal parts of a milling machine?

Ans. The principal parts of a milling machine are (1) the column, (2) the knee, (3) the table, (4) the spindle, and (5) the overarm.

2. What is the function of the column?

Ans. The column is the main casting of the milling machine which encloses and supports all other parts of the mill.

3. What is the function of the knee?

Ans. The knee is a unit that is attached to the front of the column and is designed to be moved up or down on sliding ways. It also encloses the feed-change gearing and attached to it are the controls for operating the feed mechanism.

4. What is the purpose of the table?

Ans. The table is attached to the top of the knee. It may be moved from left to right, and forward and back. On universal models, the table may also be swiveled 45 deg to left or right. The table is used to hold the work while it is being machined. The work may be clamped directly to the surface of the table or held in a vise or other devices which have been attached to the table.

5. What is the purpose of the spindle?

Ans. The spindle is a large shaft that is located in the upper part of the column. In the front end of the spindle is a tapered hole into which may be inserted various cutting tools, and arbors for holding other cutting tools.

6. What is the overarm?

Ans. The overarm, which is attached to the top of the column above the spindle, is used to support the arbor. It may be moved forward or back as

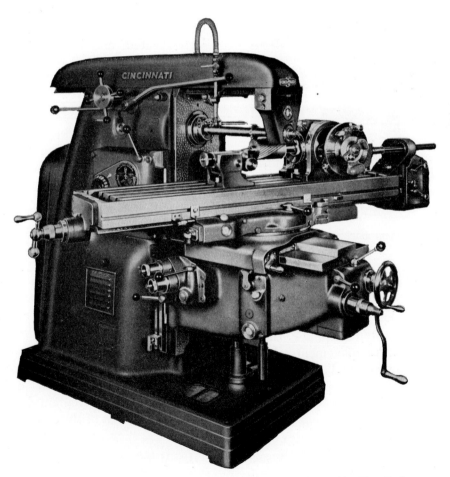

Fig. 16–2. Universal milling machine. (Cincinnati Milling Machine Co.)

required and clamped in position. The overarm may be rectangular, or cylindrical, in shape according to the design of the manufacturer.

7. What are the different types of milling machines?

Ans. Milling machines may be grouped into three classifications. The column and knee type, the manufacturing type, and the planer type. The most common type of milling machine used in the toolroom is the column and knee variety.

Fig. 16–3. Vertical-spindle milling machine. (Cincinnati Milling Machine Co.)

8. What is a plain milling machine?

Ans. The plain milling machine, shown in Fig. 16–1, is one in which the longitudinal travel of the table is fixed at right angles to the spindle. In this machine, the table has three movements: longitudinal (at right angles to the spindle), transverse (parallel to the spindle), and vertical (up and down). It is the practice to take heavy cuts at fast speeds and coarse feeds, in the classes of work for which the medium and larger sizes of plain milling machines are adapted. The ability to perform such work is the chief value of this machine and is made possible by the machine's rigid construction.

9. What is a universal milling machine?

Ans. The universal milling machine (Fig. 16–2) is a development that embodies all the principal features of the other types of milling machines. It is designed to handle practically all classes of milling-machine work. The table has the same movements as the plain milling machine, but, in addition, it can be swiveled on the saddle so that it moves at an angle to the spindle in the horizontal plane. Angular, spiral, and helical cuts may be made when the machine is fitted with an attachment known as an *index head*. The universal type of milling machine is used to cut helical gears, twist drills, milling cutters, and various kinds of straight and tapered work. The universal milling machine is regarded by many as one of the most important machines in the toolroom.

10. What is the vertical-spindle milling machine?

Ans. The vertical-spindle milling machine, shown in Fig. 16–3, embodies the principles of the drilling machine. The spindle and table are similarly located, and the cutter is mounted in the spindle. The spindle has a vertical movement, and the table has vertical, longitudinal, and transverse movements. The vertical-spindle milling machine is used for face milling, profiling, die sinking, and for various odd-shaped jobs. Owing to the position of the spindle, this type of machine can be used advantageously in boring holes.

11. What is a manufacturing milling machine?

Ans. The manufacturing milling machine, shown in Fig. 16–4, is used primarily for the production of small parts for typewriters, sewing machines, and other similar machines. The spindle is supported in bearings located in the adjustable head, which can be raised or lowered. The capacity of the machine is limited for work of great height, because the table cannot be raised or lowered, the only adjustment being in the head. Furthermore, there is no transverse table feed, the only transverse movement being obtained by a slight adjustment of the spindle.

12. What is a planer milling machine?

Ans. The planer milling machine, shown in Fig. 16–5, is designed for the heaviest classes of slab

Fig. 16–4. Manufacturing milling machine. (Cincinnati Milling Machine Co.)

and gang milling. It bears a marked resemblance to the planer, from which it derives its name. The spindle is mounted in bearings carried in a vertically adjustable slide similar to that of a planer and is in a corresponding position. The class of work produced on the planer mill is identical to that of the column and knee-type machine. Therefore the same principles are involved.

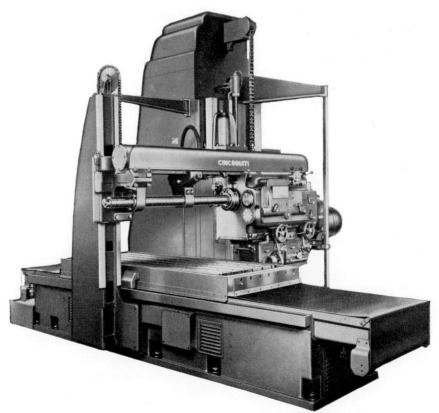

Fig. 16–5. Planer milling machine. (Cincinnati Milling Machine Co.)

13. What is a precision horizontal-boring, drilling, and milling machine?

Ans. A precision horizontal-boring, drilling, and milling machine (Fig. 16–6) is a large machine into which is built high precision and great strength, to ensure accuracy in the machining of jigs and fixtures as well as rigidity for heavy mill-ing operations. It is a multipurpose machine that is used for performing any or all of the operations indicated by its name, at a single setting of the piece of work. This saves time in resetting the work and, what is more important, ensures accuracy in the relation of the machined surfaces to each other.

Fig. 16–6. Precision horizontal-boring, drilling, and milling machine. (New Britain Machine Co.)

Fig. 16–7. Precision jig-boring machine. (Kurt Orban Company, Inc.)

14. What is a precision jig-boring machine?

Ans. A precision jig borer (Fig. 16–7) is a machine designed for the precision boring of jigs and fixtures which are used in the mass production of parts for automobiles, aircraft, machine tools, and so forth. This type of machine is similar in many respects to a vertical-spindle milling machine, but it is more massive in construction and is provided with vernier controls so that the table may be accurately set within 0.00015 in. of a required dimension in either direction.

15. What is a thread mill?

Ans. A thread mill (Fig. 16–8) is a machine that is designed for the sole purpose of cutting external threads. All kinds of external threads may be cut on this machine, using rotary cutters.

16. What is a spline mill?

Ans. A spline mill is a machine that is used to mill slots and keyways with either open or closed ends. The word *spline* is another name for a key that is inserted in a slot. In some cases, a number of equally spaced splines are cut around a shaft, as shown in Fig. 16–9.

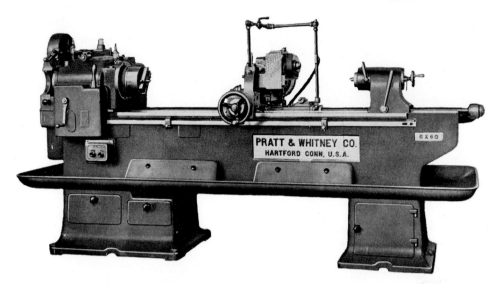

Fig. 16–8. Thread mill. (Pratt & Whitney Co.)

Fig. 16–9. Machining splines on a shaft in a spline mill.

17. What is a tool and die milling machine?

Ans. A tool and die milling machine (Fig. 16–10) is designed for the production of metal patterns, die-casting dies, small drop-forging dies, plastic molds, and so forth. By means of the automatic tracer mechanism, it is possible to reproduce intricate shapes accurately. Ordinary operations such as drilling, reaming, boring, and slotting are also performed on this machine.

Many mechanisms known as *attachments* have been designed to increase the scope of milling machines. Each one is intended to make an otherwise difficult job easy. The intelligent use of such attachments make for increased operating efficiency, convenience, and accuracy.

18. What are some of the advantages of the vertical-milling attachment?

Fig. 16–10. Tool and die milling machine. (Cincinnati Milling Machine Co.)

Ans. The vertical-milling attachment (Fig. 16–11) is used for vertical-milling operations with large end mills and face mills. The spindle head can be swiveled accurately to any degree required for angular milling.

19. What is a universal milling attachment?

Ans. A universal milling attachment (Fig. 16–

Fig. 16–11. Vertical-milling attachment. (Cincinnati Milling Machine Co.)

12), as its name implies, is fully universal because its spindle may be set at any angle in both planes. The spindle speed is faster than the regular spindle. It may be 1 2/3 or 3 1/2 times as fast as the

Fig. 16–12. Universal milling attachment. (Cincinnati Milling Machine Co.)

regular spindle. This attachment is especially advantageous when it is desired to set the spindle at an angle to the table, as in milling angular strips, table ways, and so forth, for with the spindle in this position, the full length of the table travel is available, and an ordinary end mill, instead of an angular cutter, may be used for milling the required angle.

20. *What is a rotary attachment?*

Ans. A rotary attachment (Fig. 16–13) is used on a variety of circular milling such as circular T slots, segment outlines, and so forth, and on many

Fig. 16–13. Rotary attachment with hand feed. (Cincinnati Milling Machine Co.)

tool and die-making jobs that require splining, slotting, or irregular-form milling. In addition to the hand-feed unit, rotary attachments are also available as power-fed units, as in Fig. 16–14. Both styles are graduated on the circumferences of the

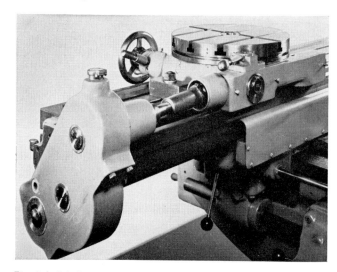

Fig. 16–14. Rotary attachment with power feed. (Cincinnati Milling Machine Co.)

tables, and both have adjustable dials on the worm shaft.

21. What is a slotting attachment?

Ans. A slotting attachment (Fig. 16–15) is largely used in toolmaking, such as forming box tools for screw machines, making templates, and splining keyways. The working parts consist of a tool slide, driven from the machine spindle by an adjustable crank that allows the stroke to be set for different lengths. The attachment may be set at any angle between zero and 90 deg, either side of the center line, the position being indicated on the circumference of the head. The tool is held in place by a clamp bolt and a stop that swings over the top of the tool shank, making it impossible for the tool to be pushed up.

Fig. 16–16. Rack-milling attachment. (Cincinnati Milling Machine Co.)

23. What is a high-speed milling attachment?

Ans. A high-speed milling attachment (Fig. 16–17) consists primarily of a pair of gears for increasing the normal speed of the milling-machine spindle, and an auxiliary spindle that drives the cutter. It is used in order to obtain the correct speed for

Fig. 16–15. Slotting attachment. (Cincinnati Milling Machine Co.)

22. What is a rack-milling attachment?

Ans. A rack-milling attachment (Fig. 16–16) is used for cutting teeth in racks. It can also be used in connection with the universal spiral-index centers for cutting worms, on universal milling machines, and for other miscellaneous operations. The cutter is mounted on the end of a spindle that extends through the attachment case parallel to the table T slots. This spindle is driven from the machine spindle by a train of hardened-steel bevel and spur gears.

Fig. 16–17. High-speed milling attachment. (Cincinnati Milling Machine Co.)

small milling cutters, which should be run more rapidly than the fastest spindle speed of the milling machine, when cutting keyways, slots, etc.

24. What is a universal spiral milling attachment?

Ans. A universal spiral milling attachment (Fig. 16–18) is a device that is designed principally for the milling of helical and spiral gear teeth. It is also suitable for vertical and angular milling, for cutting worms and coarse-pitch screw threads, milling cutters, twist drills, etc.

Fig. 16–18. Universal spiral milling attachment. (Cincinnati Milling Machine Co.)

25. What is a micrometer spindle and table-setting attachment?

Ans. A micrometer spindle and table-setting attachment is used to facilitate the performing of extremely accurate boring and milling jobs. It is of particular advantage in making jigs, fixtures, and dies, and doing other toolroom work where accurate adjustments are required. Measuring bars are used in connection with micrometer heads and dial gages. These bars may be used in combinations to obtain various adjustments. Figure 16–19 shows one of these attachments.

26. What is an index head?

Ans. An index head (Fig. 16–20), also called a *dividing head*, is used for obtaining equally spaced divisions on the periphery of work such as gears, drills, reamers, cutters, and so forth, and also for doing helical, spiral, and general taper work.

27. What types of vises are used on a milling machine?

Ans. The small plain vise (Fig. 16–21) is used for light milling operations. The bed slides are made of cast iron, and the jaws are made of tool steel, hardened and ground. The lever clamping action is quick and powerful. It is fastened to the table by means of T bolts that pass through the slots in the ends of the vise.

Fig. 16–19. Micrometer spindle and micrometer table-setting attachment. (Cincinnati Milling Machine Co.)

Fig. 16–20. Index head. (Cincinnati Milling Machine Co.)

Fig. 16–21. Plain vise. (Cincinnati Milling Machine Co.)

The flanged vise (Fig. 16–22) is a medium-sized vise for holding work up to 7 in. in width. For greater rigidity, slots are provided so that it may be held securely at various angles on the table.

Fig. 16–22. Flanged vise. (Cincinnati Milling Machine Co.)

The swivel vise (Fig. 16–23) is the same as the flanged vise in the upper part, but the base is held to the table with a swivel, allowing the vise to be turned or swiveled at any angle. The entire circumference of the base is graduated in degrees.

The toolmaker's universal vise (Fig. 16–24) is of great advantage to the toolmaker, as a job can be set at any angle in the horizontal or vertical plane.

28. What is a magnetic chuck?

Ans. A magnetic chuck (Fig. 16–25) is a device

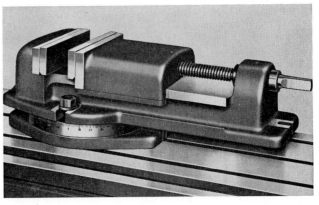

Fig. 16–23. Swivel vise. (Cincinnati Milling Machine Co.)

Fig. 16–24. Toolmaker's universal vise. (Cincinnati Milling Machine Co.)

that may be used to hold work on the milling-machine table. It is especially convenient for thin parts that are difficult to hold in a vise.

29. What is a spring chuck?

Ans. A spring chuck (Fig. 16–26) is a convenient tool for holding wire, small rods, straight-shank drills, mills, and so forth. It consists of a collet holder which is made of steel and ground to fit a standard tapered hole. It has a hole through its entire length. Also, it has a spring collet which is

Fig. 16–25. Magnetic chuck. (Brown & Sharpe Mfg. Co.)

held in place in the holder by a cap nut that forces it against the tapered seat and closes the chuck concentrically.

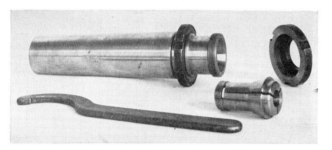

Fig. 16–26. Spring chuck. (Brown & Sharpe Mfg. Co.)

Other types of collets are shown in Fig. 16–27. These are used for holding cutters and tools, depending upon the nature of the work. Style No. 1 has a tang. The inside is a No. 4 B&S taper. The outside is a No. 7 B&S taper. Style No. 2 is tapped

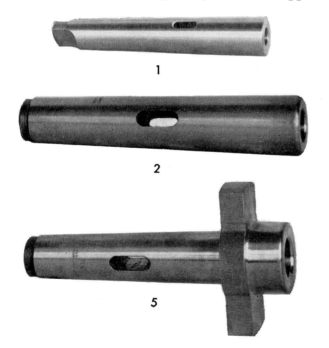

1

2

5

Fig. 16–27. Collets. (Brown & Sharpe Mfg. Co.)

on the small end to receive a drawbar which holds it securely in place. It is available in many sizes and combinations of Brown and Sharpe tapers. Style No. 5 is also tapped on the small end. The inside is a No. 10 B&S taper. The outside is a No. 12 B&S taper. Because it is used for large cutters, this collet is provided with a tenon to help in driving it.

30. What is a milling-machine arbor?

Ans. A milling-machine arbor is a shaft that is designed to hold rotary cutters. Figure 16–28 shows the type of arbor that is used in milling ma-

Fig. 16–28. Cutter arbor for standardized spindle. (Brown & Sharpe Mfg. Co.)

chines having a standardized spindle end. Figure 16–29 shows the type of arbor used in milling machines having a threaded-nose spindle. Other

Fig. 16–29. Cutter arbor for threaded-nose spindle. (Brown & Sharpe Mfg. Co.)

types of arbors are designed for particular cutters, such as the arbor for face-milling cutters (Fig. 16–30); the arbor for shell-end mills (Fig. 16–31); the fly-cutter arbor (Fig. 16–32); and the adapter for holding arbors, collets and end mills having tapered shanks (Fig. 16–33).

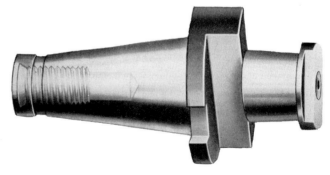

Fig. 16–30. Arbor for face-milling cutters. (Brown & Sharpe Mfg. Co.)

Many kinds of cutters are used on a milling machine. Most kinds are considered standard and may be had in many sizes. Cutters are also de-

Fig. 16–31. Arbor for shell end mills. (Brown & Sharpe Mfg. Co.)

Fig. 16–32. Fly-cutter arbor. (Brown & Sharpe Mfg. Co.)

Fig. 16–33. Cutter adapter. (Brown & Sharpe Mfg. Co.)

signed for a particular job. High-speed steel is the material most favored for cutters. They are also available with carbide tips or cutting edges.

Cutters should be kept sharp. The cutting edges are bound to become worn with use, so they should always be inspected before starting a job. Cutters that are sharpened frequently usually last longer than those that are allowed to become quite dull.

A lubricant is helpful when milling steel, both as a coolant and for producing a good finish. The lubricant may be oil or an emulsion of oil and water.

31. What are plain-milling cutters?

Ans. Plain-milling cutters (Fig. 16–34) are made with cutting edges on the periphery of the cutter only. They are used for cutting keyways, slots, and

for flat surfaces that are narrower than the width of the cutter. Plain-milling cutters that are more than 3/4 in. in width are usually made with spiral

Fig. 16–34. Plain-milling cutter. (Brown & Sharpe Mfg. Co.)

teeth, as in Fig. 16–35. The helical plain cutter (Fig. 16–36) is especially desirable where an uneven surface, or one with holes in it, is to be milled.

Fig. 16–35. Plain spiral-tooth milling cutter. (Brown & Sharpe Mfg. Co.)

Fig. 16–36. Helical plain-milling cutter. (Union Twist Drill Co.)

32. What are side-milling cutters?

Ans. Side-milling cutters (Fig. 16–37) are cutters with teeth on both sides as well as on the periphery. They are used for cutting slots that must be accurate in width. They are also used for straddle milling in which case two or more cutters are mounted on an arbor with spacers between them, as when milling two sides of a casting or two sides of the head of a bolt, as in Fig. 16–38.

Fig. 16–37. Side-milling cutter. (Pratt & Whitney Co.)

Fig. 16–38. Straddle-milling a bolthead with side-milling cutters.

together as in Fig. 16–40. Large side-milling cutters, 8 in. in diameter or larger, are usually made with inserted teeth, as in Fig. 16–41.

Fig. 16–39. Staggered-tooth side-milling cutter. (Union Twist Drill Co.)

Fig. 16–40. Form milling with seven cutters. (Cincinnati Milling Machine Co.)

Fig. 16–41. Face-milling cutter with inserted teeth. (Brown & Sharpe Mfg. Co.)

The staggered-tooth side-milling cutter (Fig. 16–39) is used when deep cuts are required. It is possible, with this type of cutter, to operate at higher speed and feed than with an ordinary cutter. Cutters of various sizes are sometimes grouped

33. *What are slitting saws?*

Ans. Slitting saws (Fig. 16–42) are very thin cutters varying in thickness from 1/32 to 3/16 in. They are used to cut deep slots and to cut material into required lengths. The cutter is thinner at the center than at the edge, to provide clearance and to prevent the cutter from binding in the slot.

Fig. 16–42. Slitting saws. (Pratt & Whitney Co.)

Another form of slitting saw is shown in Fig. 16–43. This style of cutter is preferred when deep slots must be cut at high speed. They are also used for cutting slots in the heads of screws.

Fig. 16–43. Slitting saws with side chip clearance. (Brown & Sharpe Mfg. Co.)

34. *What are angular cutters?*
Ans. Angular cutters may be single, as in Fig.

Fig. 16–44. Angular cutter. (Union Twist Drill Co.)

16–44, or double, as in Fig. 16–45. They are used in the cutting of teeth in flat and rotary cutters and for cutting the flutes of drills and reamers.

Fig. 16–45. Double-angle cutter. (Union Twist Drill Co.)

35. *What are form cutters?*
Ans. Form cutters are designed to cut definite shapes. Examples of these are the convex cutter (Fig. 16–46), the concave cutter (Fig. 16–47), and corner-rounding cutters (Fig. 16–48).

36. *What are end mills?*
Ans. An end mill is a tool similar to a reamer in appearance. It has cutting edges on its periphery

Fig. 16–46. Convex cutter. (Union Twist Drill Co.)

Fig. 16–47. Concave cutter. (Brown & Sharpe Mfg. Co.)

Fig. 16–48. Corner-rounding cutters. (Union Twist Drill Co.)

and on the end. It is used for milling slots, flat surfaces, profiles. It is available in many styles and in sizes from 1/8 to 2 in. in diameter. Figure 16–49 shows a spiral end mill with a straight shank. Fig-

Fig. 16–49. Straight-shank spiral end mill. (Union Twist Drill Co.)

Fig. 16–50. Milling-machine standard tapered-shank end mill. (Brown & Sharpe Mfg. Co.)

ure 16–50 shows a spiral end mill with a milling-machine standard tapered shank. Figure 16–51 shows a spiral end mill with a Brown and Sharpe tapered shank. Figure 16–52 shows a spiral double-end end mill. Figure 16–53 shows a two-lipped end mill, and Fig. 16–54 shows a National Standard shell end mill.

Fig. 16–51. Spiral end mill with Brown and Sharpe tapered shank. (Brown & Sharpe Mfg. Co.)

Fig. 16–52. Spiral double-end end mill. (Union Twist Drill Co.)

Fig. 16–53. Two-lipped tapered-shank end mill. (Union Twist Drill Co.)

Fig. 16–54. Shell end mill. (Union Twist Drill Co.)

37. What is a T-slot cutter?

Ans. A T-slot cutter (Fig. 16–55) is one that is used to cut T-shaped slots similar to those in the milling-machine table. It is available in many sizes.

Fig. 16–55. T-slot cutter. (Union Twist Drill Co.)

38. What is a Woodruff key seat cutter?

Ans. A Woodruff key seat cutter (Fig. 16–56) is similar in appearance to a T-slot cutter, but is designed for the specific purpose of milling circular-shaped slots to fit standard Woodruff keys. They are available in 27 sizes.

Fig. 16–56. Woodruff key seat cutter. (Pratt & Whitney Co.)

39. What is an involute spur-gear cutter?

Ans. An involute spur-gear cutter (Fig. 16–57) is a cutter that is designed to cut teeth in gears and racks. They are available in many sizes to cut teeth from 1 to 48 diametral pitch. Each of these different sizes of cutter is made in eight different forms depending upon the number of teeth in the required gear.

Fig. 16–57. Involute spur-gear cutter. (Pratt & Whitney Co.)

40. What is a straddle sprocket cutter?

Ans. A straddle sprocket cutter (Fig. 16–58) is used to cut the teeth of sprocket wheels. The double form of the cutter makes it possible to cut a complete tooth with each pass of the cutter.

Fig. 16–58. Straddle sprocket cutter. (Brown & Sharpe Mfg. Co.)

41. What is a cam lock?

Ans. A cam lock is a device in cutter adapters designed to give positive locking, drive, and quick-release to end mills and to other adapters that are held in them. Figure 16–59 shows how this device works.

42. How can a right-hand end mill be distinguished from one that is left-handed?

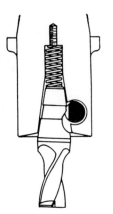
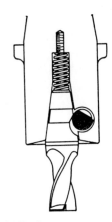

1. START: Adapter or end mill shank inserted in adapter. Note how it floats on spring ready to be gripped by cam lock.

2. GRIP: Cam starts rotation and seats itself accurately because of floating condition of shank.

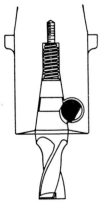
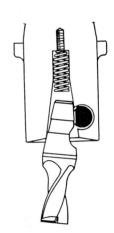

3. LOCK: Cam lock adapter or end mill securely locked in taper as the slight rise on cam grips the specially shaped slot in shank.

4. RELEASE: As cam is rotated backward, end mill or adapter is released.

Fig. 16–59. Cam lock. By following these four quick steps, you can save many minutes in changing end mills or adapters. The positive lock prevents a mill or adapter from being pulled out, either by the cut or vibration. The positive drive prevents slipping. A simple turn of a wrench locks or releases the mill. (Brown & Sharpe Mfg. Co.)

Ans. To distinguish between right- and left-hand end mills, hold the shank of the cutter in the hand with the shank end toward you. If it cuts when it revolves to the right (clockwise), it is a right-hand cutter, and if it cuts when it revolves to the left (counterclockwise), it is a left-hand cutter. Helical end mills are usually designed so that right-hand cutters have left-hand helices and left-hand cutters have right-hand helices. The purpose of this is to counteract the tendency of a cutter to pull out of the machine spindle when cutting.

43. How should a Woodruff keyway cutter be set central with the work?

Ans. A method for setting a Woodruff keyway

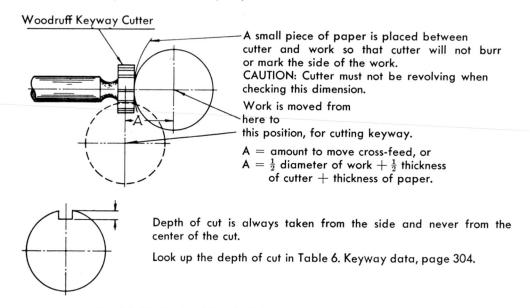

Fig. 16–60. Setting Woodruff keyway cutter central with work.

cutter central with the work is shown and explained in Fig. 16–60.

44. Explain how a cutter that is held on an arbor may be set central with the work.

Ans. In Fig. 16–61(*a*), the keyway is improperly cut. Notice that it is off center. This would make it difficult to fit a key into the job when assembled with mating part.

Cutters are sometimes set central with a shaft by using the sight method, in which the cutter is forced into the work a few thousandths and fed across the work. A small oval, which should not exceed the width of the cutter by more than 1/16 in., is thus formed. The cutter is then set so that an equal portion of the oval is visible on each side of the cutter [see Fig. 16–61(*b*)]. This may be measured with a rule, if desired. The cutting edge of the cutter may also be lined up with the center line of the work by sight, as shown in Fig. 16–61(*c*).

45. What is a dividing head?

Ans. A dividing head, also called an *index head* (Fig. 16–62), is a device used to divide the periph-

ery of a piece of work into any number of equal parts and to hold the work in the required position while the cuts are being made. The most essential parts of the index head are the worm and worm wheel, index plates, sector arms, and change gears.

The worm wheel has 40 teeth and the worm has

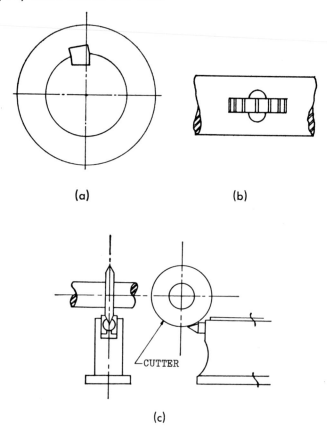

Fig. 16–61. Setting cutter held on arbor central with work.

a single thread. The worm wheel is keyed to the spindle, and when the worm, which is turned by the index crank, is turned 40 times, the spindle is revolved once. Fractional parts of a turn are obtained by means of the index plates which are furnished with each head. The sector arms are used to mark off the number of holes on the index plate which are required to make a fractional part of a turn of the index crank, without having to count them each time the index crank is moved. The change gears control the movement of the index plates and the spindle in differential indexing and helical milling. Rapid, plain, and differential indexing are the three methods most commonly used.

Fig. 16–62. Dividing head. (Brown & Sharpe Co.)

46. What is rapid indexing. Explain how it is used?

Ans. In rapid indexing, the worm and worm wheel are disengaged and the spindle is moved by hand. The required number of divisions on the work is made by means of the rapid-index plate (Fig. 16–63) located on the nose of the spindle. This plate usually has 24 equally spaced holes, and only the numbers which will divide evenly into 24 can be indexed (that is, 2, 3, 4, 6, 8, 12, and 24). An index pin placed in one of the holes of the rapid-index plate locates the spindle in the proper position, and a clamping device locks it while the cut is being made. This method is used when a large number of duplicate parts are being milled.

RULE: Divide 24 by the number of divisions required, and the result equals the number of holes

to move in the rapid-index plate. This may be written as the following formula (N equals the number of divisions required):

$$\text{No. of holes to move} = \frac{24}{N}$$

EXAMPLE: Index for a hexagon-head screw.

$$24 \div 6 = 4$$

To index for a hexagon-head screw, machine one side and move four holes in the rapid-index plate for each of the other sides.

CAUTION: After you have finished rapid indexing, see that the worm and worm wheel are fully engaged, so that the machine is again set for plain indexing.

Fig. 16–63. Cutaway view of dividing head illustrating rapid-indexing details.

47. What is plain indexing? Explain how it is used.

Ans. Plain indexing is a method of indexing for numbers beyond the range of rapid indexing. In this operation, the index-head spindle is moved by turning an index crank attached to a worm which meshes with the worm wheel. The worm wheel has 40 teeth and the worm has a single thread. For each turn of the index crank, the worm wheel moves one tooth, or 1/40 of a revolution. To cause the spindle to make one turn, the index crank must make 40 turns, or in other words, the ratio between the revolutions of the index crank and those of the spindle is 40:1. A wide range of divisions may be indexed by using this method.

The number of turns or fractional parts of a turn

of the index crank necessary to cut any required number of divisions may be easily determined by the following rule.

RULE: Divide 40 by the number of divisions required, and the result will equal the number of turns of the index crank. Expressed as a formula (where N equals the number of divisions required and T equals the turns of the index crank), this is

$$\frac{40}{N} = T$$

EXAMPLE 1: Index for 5 divisions.

$$\frac{40}{N} = \frac{40}{5} = 8T \quad \text{Eight turns for each division}$$

EXAMPLE 2: Index for 8 divisions.

$$\frac{40}{N} = \frac{40}{8} = 5T \quad \text{Five turns for each division}$$

EXAMPLE 3: Index for 10 divisions.

$$\frac{40}{N} = \frac{40}{10} = 4T \quad \text{Four turns for each division}$$

Figure 16–64 shows an index head set up for a plain-indexing job.

Fig. 16–64. An example of plain indexing: milling a hexagon.

When the number of divisions required does not divide evenly into 40, the index crank must be moved a fractional part of a turn. This is done by using index plates. The plates furnished with a Brown and Sharpe index head have circles containing the number of holes listed below. **Learn the number of holes in each of these circles.**

Plate 1: 15, 16, 17, 18, 19, 20
Plate 2: 21, 23, 27, 29, 31, 33
Plate 3: 37, 39, 41, 43, 47, 49

As another example, let us index for 18 divisions.

$$\frac{40}{N} = \frac{40}{18} = 2\frac{4}{18}T$$

The whole number indicates the complete turns of the index crank. The denominator of the fraction represents the index circle to use and the numerator represents the number of holes to move in that circle. Since there is an index circle which contains 18 holes, index for 18 equally spaced divisions by moving the index crank two complete turns and four holes in the 18-hole circle.

When the denominator is smaller or larger than the number of holes contained in any of the index circles, it can be increased or reduced by multiplying or dividing both terms of the fraction by a number which will give a fraction whose denominator is the same as the number of holes in one of the index plates.

For example, assume that it is necessary to index for 1 1/3 turns of the index crank. Select an index circle on one of the index plates in which the number of holes is a multiple of 3, and it will be found that the 15, 18, 21, 27, 33, or 39 hole circle may be used. Divide the number of holes in the selected circle by 3, and obtain the common multiple for both terms of the fraction. Assuming that the 27-hole circle was selected, the common multiple would be obtained by dividing 27 by 3, giving a result of 9. Multiplying each term of the fraction by 9, we have

$$\tfrac{1}{3} \times \tfrac{9}{9} = \tfrac{9}{27}$$

The denominator indicates the number of holes in the circle and the numerator indicates the number of holes to move the index crank pin in that circle. When the index-crank pin is moved 9 holes in the 27-hole circle, one-third of a turn has been made.

When the number of divisions to be indexed exceeds 40, both terms of the fraction may be divided by a common divisor to obtain an index circle which is available. If 160 divisions are required, for example, the fraction to be used is

$$\frac{40}{N} \text{ or } \frac{40}{160}$$

Since there is no 160-hole circle, this fraction

can be reduced to 1/4 by dividing each term of the fraction by 40. The only index circle in the standard index plates which is a multiple of 4 is the 16-hole circle. By multiplying each term of the fraction by 4 as follows,

$$\tfrac{1}{4} \times \tfrac{4}{4} = \tfrac{4}{16}$$

it is found that to make 160 equal divisions, the index crank is moved 4 holes around the 16-hole circle for each division.

EXAMPLE 1: Index for 6 divisions.

$$\frac{40}{N} = \frac{40}{6} = 6\tfrac{2}{3}\,T$$

It is decided to use a 15-hole circle, so the fraction is changed:

$$\tfrac{2}{3} \times \tfrac{5}{5} = \tfrac{10}{15}$$

Ans. For each division, turn the crank 6 full turns and 10 holes of the 15-hole circle.

EXAMPLE 2: Index for 9 divisions.

$$\frac{40}{N} = \frac{40}{9} = 4\tfrac{4}{9}\,T$$

It is decided to use an 18-hole circle, so the fraction is changed:

$$\tfrac{4}{9} \times \tfrac{2}{2} = \tfrac{8}{18}$$

Ans. For each division, turn the crank 4 full turns and 8 holes of the 18-hole circle.

EXAMPLE 3: Index for 65 divisions.

$$\frac{40}{N} = \frac{40}{65} = \frac{8}{13}\,T$$

It is decided to use a 39-hole circle, so the fraction is changed:

$$\tfrac{8}{13} \times \tfrac{3}{3} = \tfrac{24}{39}$$

Ans. For each division, turn the crank for 24 holes of the 39-hole circle.

EXAMPLE 4: Index for 136 divisions.

$$\frac{40}{N} = \frac{40}{136} = \frac{5}{17}\,T$$

Ans. There is a 17-hole circle, so for each division, turn the crank for 5 holes of the 17-hole circle.

CAUTION. In setting the sector arms to space off the proper number of holes in the index circle, **do not** count the hole the index-crank pin is in.

48. What is differential indexing? Explain how it is used.

Ans. The differential method of indexing is used in indexing for numbers beyond the range of plain indexing. This is accomplished by connecting the index plate to the spindle by means of a gear train, so that the index plate can rotate in relationship to the movement of the spindle. By a proper arrangement of the gearing, the index plate can be made to move fast or slow, and in the same direction (positive) or in the opposite direction (negative) to the index crank. This causes the movement of the index plate to be either greater or less than the actual movement of the index crank. Before differential indexing is attempted, gearing and the forming of gear ratios should be understood (see Chap. 10, "Gearing," pages 92 to 105).

The standard change gears (12 in all) that are furnished with each index head have the following number of teeth: 24 (two gears), 28, 32, 40, 44, 48, 56, 64, 72, 86, and 100. Special gears having 46, 47, 52, 58, 68, 70, 76, and 84 teeth may also be furnished. It is desirable to memorize the number of teeth in each of the change gears.

When the required number of divisions cannot be indexed by plain indexing, an approximate number of divisions which can be indexed by the plain-indexing method is selected. The difference between the movement of the spindle thus secured and the necessary movement is corrected by the use of change gears. The proper gearing is found in the following manner (N equals the required number of divisions; n equals the selected number of divisions):

Step 1. Select some number, either greater or less than the required number for which plain indexing can be used. Determine the number of turns of the crank for plain indexing, using the formula

$$\frac{40}{n} = T$$

Step 2. Determine the gear ratio by using the formula

$$\text{Gear ratio} = (n - N) \times \frac{40}{n}$$

Step 3. Select suitable gears, if possible, from the standard change gears furnished with the index head. With some ratios, simple gearing may be used, with others, compound gearing may be necessary. In each case, state the idlers to be used.

EXAMPLE 1: With a gear ratio of 3:8, the gears for simple gearing may be selected as follows:

Multiply each number of the ratio by a number that will make each equal to the number of teeth in one of the standard change gears, as

$$\frac{3}{8} \times \frac{8}{8} = \frac{24}{64} \quad \begin{array}{l}\text{Tooth gear}\\\text{Tooth gear}\end{array}$$

EXAMPLE 2: With a gear ratio of 16:33, the gears for compound gearing may be selected as follows: Factor each number of the ratio and then multiply the numerators and denominators by a number or numbers that will make them equal to the number of teeth in standard change gears, as

$$\frac{16}{33} = \frac{\overset{24}{\cancel{7}}}{\underset{72}{\cancel{3}}} \times \frac{\overset{64}{\cancel{16}}}{\underset{44}{\cancel{11}}} = \frac{24}{72} \times \frac{64}{44}$$

In differential indexing, the numerators of the fractions indicate the driving gears and the denominators indicate the driven gears. Idler gears control the direction of rotation of the index plate and are arranged as follows:

Simple gearing: One idler for positive motion of index plate.
                   Two idlers for negative motion of index plate.

Compound gearing: One idler for negative motion of index plate.
                     No idlers for positive motion of index plate.

Table 16–1 illustrates, in three steps, how to determine the proper gears to use for the differential indexing of 57 divisions.

In Case 1, an approximate number greater than the required number was selected. Note that when the approximate number is greater than the required number, the index plate must turn in the positive direction. Using simple gearing, this requires one idler gear.

In Case 2, an approximate number smaller than the required number was used. Notice that when the approximate number is less than the required number, the index plate must turn in the negative direction. Using simple gearing, two idler gears are required.

In Case 3, an approximate number smaller than the required number was used. Notice that, in this case, compound gearing is necessary, and that since the approximate number is less than the required number, the index plate must turn in the negative direction. This requires one idler gear.

These examples show that the approximate number may be greater or less than the required

Table 16–1. DETERMINING THE PROPER GEARS FOR THE DIFFERENTIAL INDEXING OF 57 DIVISIONS

Steps	Case 1	Case 2	Case 3
1. Plain indexing	$\frac{40}{N} = \frac{40}{57} \quad \frac{40}{60} = \frac{2}{3}$ $\frac{2}{3} \times \frac{7}{7} = \frac{14}{21}$ 14 holes 21 circle	$\frac{40}{N} = \frac{40}{57} \quad \frac{40}{56} = \frac{5}{7}$ $\frac{5}{7} \times \frac{3}{3} = \frac{15}{21}$ 15 holes 21 circle	$\frac{40}{N} = \frac{40}{57} \quad \frac{40}{54} = \frac{20}{27}$ 20 holes 27 circle
2. Gear ratio	$(n - N) \times \frac{40}{n} =$ $(60 - 57) \times \frac{40}{60} =$ $\cancel{3} \times \frac{2}{\cancel{3}} = \frac{2}{1}$	$(n - N) \times \frac{40}{n} =$ $(56 - 57) \times \frac{40}{56} =$ $-1 \times \frac{5}{7} = -\frac{5}{7}$	$(n - N) \times \frac{40}{n} =$ $(54 - 57 \times \frac{40}{54} =$ $-\cancel{3} \times \frac{20}{\cancel{27}} = -\frac{20}{9}$ 9
3. Select gears	$\frac{2}{1} \times \frac{24}{24} = \frac{48}{24} \quad \begin{array}{l}\text{Driver}\\\text{Driven}\end{array}$ 1 idler	$-\frac{5}{7} \times \frac{8}{8} = \frac{-40}{56} \quad \begin{array}{l}\text{Driver}\\\text{Driven}\end{array}$ 2 idlers	$-\frac{20}{9} = \frac{\overset{64}{\cancel{4}} \times \overset{40}{\cancel{5}}}{\underset{48}{\cancel{3}} \times \underset{24}{\cancel{3}}} \quad \begin{array}{l}\text{Driver}\\\text{Driven}\end{array}$ 1 idler

number and that the speed and the direction of rotation of the index plate can be controlled by the change gears. The difference between the ap-

Fig. 16–65. An example of differential indexing with simple gearing. (Brown & Sharpe Co.)

Fig. 16–66. Dividing head geared for differential indexing; compound gearing. (Brown & Sharpe Co.)

proximate number and the required number is limited only by the index-hole circles and change gears which are available.

Figure 16–65 shows a dividing head geared for differential indexing, an example of simple gearing.

Figure 16–66 shows a dividing head geared for differential indexing, an example of compound gearing.

A chart similar to the one in Fig. 16–67 is frequently used in the toolroom to determine the proper indexing for various divisions.

The following exercises are provided to help the student to become familiar with the use of the index head.

EXERCISES

1. Briefly describe the index head and explain its purpose.
2. Describe the following parts of an index head and explain the purpose of each: (*a*) worm and worm wheel, (*b*) index plates, (*c*) sector arms, and (*d*) change gears.
3. What is the usual index-head ratio? Explain what it means.
4. Name and explain briefly three kinds of indexing in common use.
5. Explain how the sector arms should be set for indexing 12 divisions.
6. Explain what must be done in changing from rapid indexing to plain indexing.
7. Explain what must be done to change the index head from plain indexing to differential indexing.
8. List the number of holes in each of the standard index plates and the number of teeth contained in the standard change gears furnished with a Brown and Sharpe index head.
9. Explain the meaning of the following terms: (*a*) gears, (*b*) gear ratio, (*c*) gear train, (*d*) idler gear, (*e*) simple gear ratio, and (*f*) compound gear ratio.
10. Determine the indexing for the following equally spaced divisions: 8, 12, 24, 37, 43, 56, 61, 96, 129, 173.

49. Describe the operation of graduating on a milling machine.

Ans. Flat rules and verniers may be graduated (divided into regular intervals) on a milling ma-

PLAIN & DIFFERENTIAL INDEXING

Gear on Spindle 64 T. — Idler 24 T. — No. 1 Hole — No. 2 Hole — 2nd Gear on Stud 32 T. — 1st Gear on Stud 56 T. — Gear on Worm 40 T. — GEARED FOR 107

NUMBER OF DIVISIONS	INDEX CIRCLE	NO. OF TURNS OF INDEX	GRADUATION	NUMBER OF DIVISIONS	INDEX CIRCLE	NO. OF TURNS OF INDEX	GRADUATION	NUMBER OF DIVISIONS	INDEX CIRCLE	NO. OF TURNS OF INDEX	GRADUATION	NUMBER OF DIVISIONS	INDEX CIRCLE	NO. OF TURNS OF INDEX	GRADUATION
2	Any	20		13	39	$3\frac{3}{39}$	14	26	39	$1\frac{21}{39}$	106	40	Any	1	
3	39	$13\frac{13}{39}$	65	14	49	$2\frac{42}{49}$	169	27	27	$1\frac{13}{27}$	95	41	41	$\frac{40}{41}$	3*
	33	$13\frac{11}{33}$	65		21	$2\frac{18}{21}$	170	28	49	$1\frac{21}{49}$	83	42	21	$\frac{20}{21}$	9*
	18	$13\frac{6}{18}$	65	15	39	$2\frac{26}{39}$	132		21	$1\frac{9}{21}$	85	43	43	$\frac{40}{43}$	12*
4	Any	10			33	$2\frac{22}{33}$	132	29	29	$1\frac{11}{29}$	75	44	33	$\frac{30}{33}$	17*
5	Any	8			18	$2\frac{12}{18}$	132	30	39	$1\frac{13}{39}$	65	45	27	$\frac{24}{27}$	21*
6	39	$6\frac{26}{39}$	132	16	20	$2\frac{10}{20}$	98		33	$1\frac{11}{33}$	65		18	$\frac{16}{18}$	21*
	33	$6\frac{22}{33}$	132	17	17	$2\frac{6}{17}$	69		18	$1\frac{6}{18}$	65	46	23	$\frac{20}{23}$	172
	18	$6\frac{12}{18}$	132	18	27	$2\frac{6}{27}$	43	31	31	$1\frac{9}{31}$	56	47	47	$\frac{40}{47}$	168
7	49	$5\frac{35}{49}$	140		18	$2\frac{4}{18}$	43	32	20	$1\frac{5}{20}$	48	48	18	$\frac{15}{18}$	165
	21	$5\frac{15}{21}$	142	19	19	$2\frac{2}{19}$	19	33	33	$1\frac{7}{33}$	41	49	49	$\frac{40}{49}$	161
8	Any	5		20	Any	2		34	17	$1\frac{3}{17}$	33	50	20	$\frac{16}{20}$	158
9	27	$4\frac{12}{27}$	88	21	21	$1\frac{19}{21}$	18*	35	49	$1\frac{7}{49}$	26				
	18	$4\frac{8}{18}$	87	22	33	$1\frac{27}{33}$	161		21	$1\frac{3}{21}$	28				
10	Any	4		23	23	$1\frac{17}{23}$	147	36	27	$1\frac{3}{27}$	21				
11	33	$3\frac{21}{33}$	126	24	39	$1\frac{26}{39}$	132		18	$1\frac{2}{18}$	21				
12	39	$3\frac{13}{39}$	65		33	$1\frac{22}{33}$	132	37	37	$1\frac{3}{37}$	15				
	33	$3\frac{11}{33}$	65		18	$1\frac{12}{18}$	132	38	19	$1\frac{1}{19}$	9				
	18	$3\frac{6}{18}$	65	25	20	$1\frac{12}{20}$	118	39	39	$1\frac{1}{39}$	3				

GRADUATIONS IN TABLE INDICATE SETTING FOR ARMS OF SECTOR WHEN INDEX CRANK MOVES THROUGH ARC "A," EXCEPT CASES MARKED * WHEN THE INDEX CRANK MOVES THROUGH ARC "B."

NUMBER OF DIVISIONS	INDEX CIRCLE	NO. OF TURNS OF INDEX	GRADUATION	GEAR ON WORM	NO.1 HOLE 1ST GEAR ON STUD	NO.1 HOLE 2ND GEAR ON STUD	GEAR ON SPINDLE	IDLERS NO.1 HOLE	IDLERS NO.2 HOLE
51	17	$\frac{14}{17}$	33*	24			48	24	44
52	39	$\frac{30}{39}$	152						
53	49	$\frac{35}{49}$	140	56	40	24	72		
	21	$\frac{15}{21}$	142	56	40	24	72		
54	27	$\frac{20}{27}$	147						
55	33	$\frac{24}{33}$	144						
56	49	$\frac{35}{49}$	140	56			40	24	44
	21	$\frac{15}{21}$	142	56			40	24	44
57	49	$\frac{35}{49}$	140	56			40	24	44
	21	$\frac{15}{21}$	142	56			40	24	44
58	29	$\frac{20}{29}$	136						
59	39	$\frac{26}{39}$	132	48			32		44
	33	$\frac{22}{33}$	132	48			32		44
	18	$\frac{12}{18}$	132	48			32		44
60	39	$\frac{26}{39}$	132						
	33	$\frac{22}{33}$	132						
	18	$\frac{12}{18}$	132						
61	39	$\frac{26}{39}$	132	48			32	24	44
	33	$\frac{22}{33}$	132	48			32	24	44
	18	$\frac{12}{18}$	132	48			32	24	44
62	31	$\frac{20}{31}$	127						
63	39	$\frac{26}{39}$	132	24			48	24	44
	33	$\frac{22}{33}$	132	24			48	24	44
	18	$\frac{12}{18}$	132	24			48	24	44
64	16	$\frac{10}{16}$	123						
65	39	$\frac{24}{39}$	121						
66	33	$\frac{20}{33}$	120						
67	49	$\frac{28}{49}$	112	28				48	44
	21	$\frac{12}{21}$	113	28				48	44
68	17	$\frac{10}{17}$	116						

NUMBER OF DIVISIONS	INDEX CIRCLE	NO. OF TURNS OF INDEX	GRADUATION	GEAR ON WORM	NO.1 HOLE 1ST GEAR ON STUD	NO.1 HOLE 2ND GEAR ON STUD	GEAR ON SPINDLE	IDLERS NO.1 HOLE	IDLERS NO.2 HOLE
69	20	$\frac{12}{20}$	118	40				56	24	44
70	49	$\frac{28}{49}$	112						
	21	$\frac{12}{21}$	113						
71	27	$\frac{15}{27}$	110	72				40	24
	18	$\frac{10}{18}$	109	72				40	24
72	27	$\frac{15}{27}$	110						
	18	$\frac{10}{18}$	109						
73	49	$\frac{28}{49}$	112	28				48	24	44
	21	$\frac{12}{21}$	113	28				48	24	44
74	37	$\frac{20}{37}$	107						
75	15	$\frac{8}{15}$	105						
76	19	$\frac{10}{19}$	103						
77	20	$\frac{10}{20}$	98	32				48	44
78	39	$\frac{20}{39}$	101						
79	20	$\frac{10}{20}$	98	48				24	44
80	20	$\frac{10}{20}$	98						
81	20	$\frac{10}{20}$	98	48				24	24	44
82	41	$\frac{20}{41}$	96						
83	26	$\frac{10}{26}$	98	32				48	24	44
84	21	$\frac{10}{21}$	94						
85	17	$\frac{8}{17}$	92						
86	43	$\frac{20}{43}$	91						
87	15	$\frac{7}{15}$	92	40				24	24	44
88	33	$\frac{15}{33}$	89						
89	27	$\frac{12}{27}$	88	72				32	44
	18	$\frac{8}{18}$	87	72				32	44
90	27	$\frac{12}{27}$	88						
	18	$\frac{8}{18}$	87						
91	39	$\frac{18}{39}$	91	24				48	24	44
92	23	$\frac{10}{23}$	86						

Fig. 16–67. Chart for plain and differential indexing.

chine, by using a pointed tool and an index head. The tool is held stationary in a fly-cutter holder (Fig. 16–68). This is mounted in the spindle of the machine, or it may be fastened to the spindle of a vertical-milling machine or rack-cutting attachment. The work is clamped to the table parallel to the T slots. The index-head spindle is geared to the table feed screw with gears having a 1:1 ratio. The table is moved longitudinally by turning the index crank. Fractional parts of a turn are obtained by means of the index plates, the same as in plain indexing. The lines are cut by moving the table transversely under the point of the tool. The movement of the table is controlled with the hand feeds.

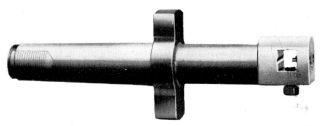

Fig. 16–68. Fly-cutter holder. (Brown & Sharpe Mfg. Co.)

Figure 16–69 shows the milling-machine setup for graduating. Notice how the gears are arranged. When the index crank is turned one revolution, the spindle turns 1/40 of a revolution, and through the 1:1 ratio causes the lead screw to move 1/40 of a revolution. Since the usual lead of the lead screw is 0.250 in., one turn of the index crank will move the table 1/40 of 0.250 in., which equals 0.00625 in.

When the table is to be moved a required distance, divide the required distance by the actual distance the table is advanced in one turn of the index crank, namely, 0.00625 in., and the result will be the number of turns of the index crank that are necessary to move the table the required distance. This may be written as a formula, as follows:

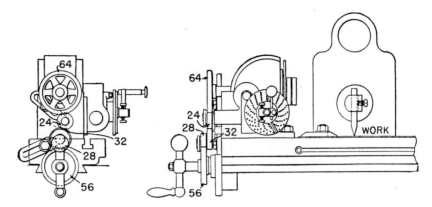

Fig. 16–69. Milling-machine setup for graduating. The numbers on the illustration indicate the number of teeth on each gear.

$T = W/0.00625$, in which T equals the number of turns of the index crank, W equals the width of the required division, and 0.00625 equals the distance that the table moves in one turn of the index crank.

EXAMPLE 1: Determine the indexing for lines 1/32 in. (0.03125) apart.

$$T = \frac{W}{0.00625} = \frac{0.03125}{0.00625} = 5$$

Ans. Turn the index crank 5 full turns for each division.

EXAMPLE 2: Determine the indexing for lines 0.0481 in. apart.

$$T = \frac{W}{0.00625} = \frac{0.04810}{0.00625} = 7\frac{435}{625}$$

By a method of calculation known as continued fractions, 435/625 may be reduced to a fraction suitable for indexing, and although not an equivalent fraction, the amount of error is small. For detailed instructions in combining fractions and continued fractions, see *Practical Shop Mathematics*, Vol. II, pages 279 to 325, by Wolfe and Phelps, McGraw-Hill Book Company, Inc. Briefly, the procedure is as follows:

```
435|625|1
380|435|2        |1|2| 3| 2|  5
 55|190|3     |1|0|1|2| 7|16| 87| × 5 = 435
 50|165|2     |0|1|1|3|10|23|125| × 5 = 625
  5| 25|5        |1|2| 3| 2|  5
   | 25|
 ──|───|
   |  0|
```

It can be seen that 87/125 is an actual equivalent of 435/625 but that 16/23 represents a convenient fraction. In this case, to index for gradua-tions 0.0481 in. apart, the crank should be given 7 full turns and 16 holes of a 23-hole circle.

TO FIND THE ERROR IN EACH DIVISION

The error in each division is equal to the difference between the distance the table should move and the distance the selected indexing actually moves it.

$$\frac{87}{125} \times \frac{0.00625}{1} = 0.0043500 \quad \text{Distance table should move}$$

$$\frac{16}{23} \times \frac{0.00625}{1} = \frac{0.0043478}{0.0000022} \quad \begin{array}{l}\text{Distance table actually}\\ \text{moves}\\ \text{Error in each division}\end{array}$$

TO FIND THE ERROR IN EACH INCH

The error in each inch is equal to the number of divisions in 1 in. multiplied by the error in each division.

$$1.000 \div W = \text{number of divisions in 1 in.}$$
$$1.000 \div 0.0481 = 20.79 \text{ divisions in 1 in.}$$

The error in each division multiplied by the divisions in 1 in. is equal to the error in 1 in.

$$0.0000022 \times 20.79 = 0.000045 \quad \text{Error in 1 in.}$$

50. Describe the use of the angular-indexing table.

Ans. As a preliminary step, the following information seems pertinent. The symbol for degrees is °. The symbol for minutes is ′. The symbol for seconds is ″.

> One circle equals 360°
> One right angle equals 90°
> One degree equals 60′
> One minute equals 60″

It requires 40 turns of the index crank of the dividing head to move the spindle through one revolution, or 360°. Therefore, one turn of the index crank will move the spindle 1/40 of 360°, or 9°.

$$9° = 9 \times 60' \text{ or } 540'$$
$$9° = 9 \times 60' \times 60'' \text{ or } 32,400''$$

In angles given only in degrees, divide the required number of degrees by 9 to obtain the required turns of the index crank. In angles involving

Table 16–2. ANGULAR INDEXING TABLE

Value	H*	C†	Value	H	C	Value	H	C	Value	H	C	Value	H	C	Value	H	C	Value	H	C	Value	H	C
0.0204	1	49	0.1395	6	43	0.2609	6	23	0.3846	15	39	0.5106	24	47	0.6279	27	43	0.7500	12	16	0.8718	34	39
0.0213	1	47	0.1429	3	21	0.2632	5	19	0.3871	12	31	0.5116	22	43	0.6296	17	27	0.7500	15	20	0.8723	41	47
0.0233	1	43	0.1429	7	49	0.2653	13	49	0.3878	19	49	0.5122	21	41	0.6316	12	19	0.7551	37	49	0.8750	14	16
0.0244	1	41	0.1463	6	41	0.2667	4	15	0.3888	7	18	0.5128	20	39	0.6326	31	49	0.7561	31	41	0.8776	43	49
0.0256	1	39	0.1481	4	27	0.2683	11	41	0.3902	16	41	0.5135	19	37	0.6341	26	41	0.7568	28	37	0.8780	36	41
0.0270	1	37	0.1489	7	47	0.2703	10	37	0.3913	9	23	0.5151	17	33	0.6364	21	33	0.7576	25	33	0.8788	29	33
0.0303	1	33	0.1500	3	20	0.2727	9	33	0.3939	13	33	0.5161	16	31	0.6383	30	47	0.7586	22	29	0.8824	15	17
0.0323	1	31	0.1515	5	33	0.2759	8	29	0.3953	17	43	0.5172	15	29	0.6410	25	39	0.7619	16	21	0.8837	38	43
0.0345	1	29	0.1538	6	39	0.2766	13	47	0.4000	6	15	0.5185	14	27	0.6452	20	31	0.7647	13	17	0.8888	16	18
0.0370	1	27	0.1579	3	19	0.2777	5	18	0.4000	8	20	0.5217	12	23	0.6471	11	17	0.7674	33	43	0.8888	24	27
0.0408	2	49	0.1613	5	31	0.2791	12	43	0.4043	19	47	0.5238	11	21	0.6486	24	37	0.7692	30	39	0.8919	33	37
0.0426	2	47	0.1622	6	37	0.2821	11	39	0.4054	15	37	0.5263	10	19	0.6500	13	20	0.7742	24	31	0.8936	42	47
0.0435	1	23	0.1628	7	43	0.2857	14	49	0.4074	11	27	0.5294	9	17	0.6512	28	43	0.7755	38	49	0.8947	17	19
0.0465	2	43	0.1633	8	49	0.2857	6	21	0.4082	20	49	0.5306	26	49	0.6522	15	23	0.7760	36	47	0.8966	26	29
0.0476	1	21	0.1666	3	18	0.2903	9	31	0.4103	16	39	0.5319	25	47	0.6531	32	49	0.7777	21	27	0.8974	35	39
0.0488	2	41	0.1702	8	47	0.2927	12	41	0.4118	7	17	0.5333	8	15	0.6552	19	29	0.7777	14	18	0.8980	44	49
0.0500	1	20	0.1707	7	41	0.2941	5	17	0.4138	12	29	0.5349	23	43	0.6585	27	41	0.7805	32	41	0.9000	18	20
0.0513	2	39	0.1724	5	29	0.2963	8	27	0.4146	17	41	0.5366	22	41	0.6596	31	47	0.7826	18	23	0.9024	37	41
0.0526	1	19	0.1739	4	23	0.2973	11	37	0.4186	18	43	0.5385	21	39	0.6666	10	15	0.7838	29	37	0.9032	28	31
0.0541	2	37	0.1765	3	17	0.2979	14	47	0.4194	13	31	0.5405	20	37	0.6666	12	18	0.7872	37	47	0.9048	19	21
0.0555	1	18	0.1795	7	39	0.3000	6	20	0.4211	8	19	0.5454	18	33	0.6666	14	21	0.7879	26	33	0.9070	39	43
0.0588	1	17	0.1818	6	33	0.3023	13	43	0.4242	14	33	0.5484	17	31	0.6666	18	27	0.7895	15	19	0.9090	30	33
0.0606	2	33	0.1837	9	49	0.3030	10	33	0.4255	20	47	0.5500	11	20	0.6666	22	33	0.7907	34	43	0.9130	21	23
0.0612	3	49	0.1852	5	27	0.3043	7	23	0.4286	9	21	0.5510	27	49	0.6666	26	39	0.7931	23	29	0.9149	43	47
0.0625	1	16	0.1860	8	43	0.3061	15	49	0.4286	21	49	0.5517	16	29	0.6735	33	49	0.7949	31	39	0.9184	45	49
0.0638	3	47	0.1875	3	16	0.3077	12	39	0.4324	16	37	0.5532	26	47	0.6744	29	43	0.7959	39	49	0.9189	34	37
0.0645	2	31	0.1892	7	37	0.3103	9	29	0.4348	10	23	0.5555	10	18	0.6757	25	37	0.8000	12	15	0.9231	36	39
0.0666	1	15	0.1905	4	21	0.3125	5	16	0.4359	17	39	0.5555	15	27	0.6774	21	31	0.8000	16	20	0.9259	25	27
0.0690	2	29	0.1915	9	47	0.3158	6	19	0.4375	7	16	0.5581	24	43	0.6809	32	47	0.8049	33	41	0.9268	38	41
0.0698	3	43	0.1935	6	31	0.3171	13	41	0.4390	18	41	0.5610	23	41	0.6829	28	41	0.8065	25	31	0.9302	40	43
0.0732	3	41	0.1951	8	41	0.3191	15	47	0.4419	19	43	0.5625	9	16	0.6842	13	19	0.8085	38	47	0.9310	27	29
0.0741	2	27	0.2000	3	15	0.3226	10	31	0.4444	8	18	0.5641	22	39	0.6875	11	16	0.8095	17	21	0.9333	14	15
0.0769	3	39	0.2000	4	20	0.3243	12	37	0.4444	12	27	0.5652	13	23	0.6897	20	29	0.8108	30	37	0.9355	29	31
0.0811	3	37	0.2041	10	49	0.3256	14	43	0.4468	21	47	0.5676	21	37	0.6923	27	39	0.8125	13	16	0.9362	44	47
0.0816	4	49	0.2051	8	39	0.3265	16	49	0.4483	13	29	0.5714	12	21	0.6939	34	49	0.8140	35	43	0.9375	15	16
0.0851	4	47	0.2069	6	29	0.3333	5	15	0.4490	22	49	0.5714	28	49	0.6957	16	23	0.8148	22	27	0.9388	46	49
0.0870	2	23	0.2093	9	43	0.3333	6	18	0.4500	9	20	0.5745	27	47	0.6969	23	33	0.8163	40	49	0.9394	31	33
0.0909	3	33	0.2105	4	19	0.3333	7	21	0.4516	14	31	0.5757	19	33	0.6977	30	43	0.8181	27	33	0.9412	16	17
0.0930	4	43	0.2121	7	33	0.3333	9	27	0.4545	15	33	0.5789	11	19	0.7000	14	20	0.8205	32	39	0.9444	17	18
0.0952	2	21	0.2128	10	47	0.3333	11	33	0.4595	17	37	0.5806	18	31	0.7021	33	47	0.8235	14	17	0.9459	35	37
0.0968	3	31	0.2162	8	37	0.3333	13	39	0.4615	18	39	0.5814	25	43	0.7027	26	37	0.8261	19	23	0.9474	18	19
0.0976	4	41	0.2174	5	23	0.3404	16	47	0.4634	19	41	0.5854	24	41	0.7037	19	27	0.8276	24	29	0.9487	37	39
0.1000	2	20	0.2195	9	41	0.3415	14	41	0.4651	20	43	0.5862	17	29	0.7059	12	17	0.8293	34	41	0.9500	19	20
0.1020	5	49	0.2222	6	27	0.3448	10	29	0.4667	7	15	0.5882	10	17	0.7073	29	41	0.8298	39	47	0.9512	39	41
0.1026	4	39	0.2222	4	18	0.3469	17	49	0.4681	22	47	0.5897	23	39	0.7097	22	31	0.8333	15	18	0.9524	20	21
0.1034	3	29	0.2245	11	49	0.3478	8	23	0.4694	23	49	0.5918	29	49	0.7143	15	21	0.8367	41	49	0.9535	41	43
0.1053	2	19	0.2258	7	31	0.3488	15	43	0.4706	8	17	0.5926	16	27	0.7143	35	49	0.8372	36	43	0.9565	22	23
0.1064	5	47	0.2308	9	39	0.3500	7	20	0.4737	9	19	0.5946	22	37	0.7179	28	39	0.8378	31	37	0.9574	45	47
0.1081	4	37	0.2326	10	43	0.3514	13	37	0.4762	10	21	0.5957	28	47	0.7209	31	43	0.8387	26	31	0.9592	47	49
0.1111	2	18	0.2340	11	47	0.3529	6	17	0.4783	11	23	0.6000	9	15	0.7222	13	18	0.8421	16	19	0.9630	26	27
0.1111	3	27	0.2353	4	17	0.3548	11	31	0.4815	13	27	0.6000	12	20	0.7234	34	47	0.8462	33	39	0.9655	28	29
0.1163	5	43	0.2381	5	21	0.3590	14	39	0.4828	14	29	0.6047	26	43	0.7241	21	29	0.8485	28	33	0.9677	30	31
0.1176	2	17	0.2414	7	29	0.3617	17	47	0.4839	15	31	0.6060	20	33	0.7273	24	33	0.8500	17	20	0.9697	32	33
0.1212	4	33	0.2424	8	33	0.3636	12	33	0.4848	16	33	0.6087	14	23	0.7297	27	37	0.8511	40	47	0.9730	36	37
0.1220	5	41	0.2432	9	37	0.3659	15	41	0.4865	18	37	0.6098	25	41	0.7317	30	41	0.8519	23	27	0.9744	38	39
0.1224	6	49	0.2439	10	41	0.3673	18	49	0.4872	19	39	0.6111	11	18	0.7333	11	15	0.8537	35	41	0.9756	40	41
0.1250	2	16	0.2449	12	49	0.3684	7	19	0.4878	20	41	0.6122	30	49	0.7347	36	49	0.8571	18	21	0.9767	42	43
0.1277	6	47	0.2500	4	16	0.3704	10	27	0.4884	21	43	0.6129	19	31	0.7368	14	19	0.8571	42	49	0.9787	46	47
0.1282	5	39	0.2500	5	20	0.3721	16	43	0.4894	23	47	0.6154	24	39	0.7391	17	23	0.8605	37	43	0.9796	48	49
0.1290	4	31	0.2553	12	47	0.3750	6	16	0.4898	24	49	0.6170	29	47	0.7407	20	27	0.8621	25	29			
0.1304	3	23	0.2558	11	43	0.3784	14	37	0.5000	8	16	0.6190	13	21	0.7419	23	31	0.8649	32	37			
0.1333	2	15	0.2564	10	39	0.3793	11	29	0.5000	9	18	0.6207	18	29	0.7436	29	39	0.8666	13	15			
0.1351	5	37	0.2581	8	31	0.3810	8	21	0.5000	10	20	0.6216	23	37	0.7442	32	43	0.8696	20	23			
0.1379	4	29	0.2593	7	27	0.3830	18	47	0.5102	25	49	0.6250	10	16	0.7447	35	47	0.8710	27	31			

* H is the number of holes to move in the index circle.

† C is the index circle.

degrees and minutes, reduce the angles to minutes and divide by 540. In angles involving degrees, minutes, and seconds, reduce the angles to seconds and divide by 32,400. Carry the division to the fourth decimal place, and the result will be the number of turns of the index crank necessary to index the angle.

To find the index circle and the number of holes to move in that circle which must be used for the decimal part of a turn, look for the required decimal number or the nearest decimal number to it in Table 16–2. The index circle is listed under C and the number of holes to move in that circle is listed under H. The following examples show applications of the use of Table 16–2. In each case, refer to Fig 16–70, also.

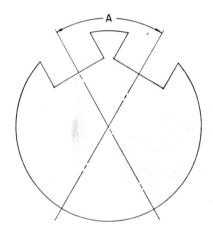

Fig. 16–70. Problem for angular indexing.

EXAMPLE 1: Angle $A = 24°\ 45'$.

$$24° = 24 \times 60' = 1,440'$$
$$45' = 45'$$
$$\overline{1,485'}$$
$$1,485 \div 540 = 2.7500$$

In the angular-indexing table, opposite 0.7500, 12 is under H and 16 is under C. Total indexing equals 2 turns and 12 holes of the 16-hole circle.

EXAMPLE 2: Angle $A = 18°26'$.

$$18° = 18 \times 60' = 1,080'$$
$$26' = 26'$$
$$\overline{1,106'}$$
$$1106 \div 540 = 2.0481$$

Required decimal = 0.0481
Nearest decimal = 0.0476
                  _____
                   0.0005

$$540 \times 0.0005 = 0.27'$$
$$0.27 \times 60'' = 16.2''\ \text{error}$$

In the angular-indexing table, opposite 0.0476, 1 is under H and 21 is under C. Total indexing equals 2 turns and 1 hole of the 21-hole circle.

EXAMPLE 3: Angle $A = 24°54'23''$.

$$24° = 24 \times 60' \times 60'' = 86,400''$$
$$54' = 54 \times 60'' = 3,240''$$
$$23'' = 23''$$
$$\overline{89,663''}$$

$$89,663 \div 32,400 = 2.7674$$

In the angular-indexing table, opposite 0.7674, 33 is under H and 43 is under C. Total indexing equals 2 turns and 33 holes of the 43-hole circle.

EXAMPLE 4: Angle $A = 39°51'21''$.

$$39° = 39 \times 60' \times 60'' = 140,400''$$
$$51' = 51 \times 60'' = 3,060''$$
$$21'' = 21''$$
$$\overline{143,481''}$$

$$143,481 \div 32,400 = 4.4284$$

Nearest decimal = 0.4286
Required decimal = 0.4284
                   _____
                    0.0002

$$32,400'' \times 0.0002 = 6.48''\ \text{error}$$

In the angular-indexing table, opposite 0.4286, 9 is under H and 21 is under C. Total indexing equals 4 turns and 9 holes of the 21-hole circle.

51. If an angular-indexing table is not available, or if greater accuracy is required than can be obtained by the use of the angular-indexing table, the correct indexing may be determined as follows. In some cases, differential indexing must be used.

EXAMPLE 1: Index for 25°: N equals degrees in given angle.

$$\frac{N°}{9°} = T \qquad \frac{N°}{9°} = \frac{25°}{9°} = 2\tfrac{7}{9}T \qquad 2\tfrac{7}{9} \times \tfrac{2}{2} = 2\tfrac{14}{18}T$$

Index 2 turns and 14 holes in 18-hole circle.

EXAMPLE 2: Index for 12°12': N' equals minutes in given angles.

$$\frac{N'}{540'} = T \qquad 12° = 12 \times 60' = 720'$$
$$12' = 12'$$
$$\overline{732'}$$

$$\tfrac{732}{540} = 1\tfrac{192}{540} = 1\tfrac{1}{3}\ \text{approx} \qquad 1\tfrac{1}{3} \times \tfrac{5}{5} = 1\tfrac{5}{15}T$$

Index 1 turn and 5 holes in 15-hole circle.

Gearing:

$$1\frac{1}{3} = \frac{4}{3} \quad \frac{\cancel{122}}{\underset{\underset{\underset{3}{18}}{54}}{\cancel{540}}} \times \frac{3}{\cancel{4}} \times \frac{\cancel{40}}{1} = \frac{122}{3} = 40\frac{2}{3} \text{ turns}$$

$40\frac{2}{3} - 40 = \frac{2}{3}$ gear ratio

$$\frac{2}{3} \times \frac{24}{24} = \frac{48}{72} \quad \begin{matrix}\text{Driving gear}\\\text{Driven gear}\end{matrix} \quad 1 \text{ idler}$$

EXAMPLE 3: Index for $29°25'16''$. Check error in arc. N'' equals seconds in given angle.

$$\frac{N''}{32,400''} = T \qquad \begin{matrix} 29° = 29 \times 60' \times 60'' = 104,400''\\ 25' = \qquad 25' \times 60'' = \quad 1,500''\\ 16'' = \qquad\qquad\qquad\quad \underline{\quad 16''}\\ \qquad\qquad\qquad\qquad\qquad 105,916''\end{matrix}$$

$105,916''/32,400'' = 3\ 3/16$ turns approximately, or 3 turns and 3 holes in a 16-hole circle.

Gearing:

$$3\frac{3}{16} = \frac{51}{16} \qquad \frac{105,916}{32,400} \times \frac{16}{51} \times \frac{40}{1} = 41\frac{473}{20,655} \text{ turns}$$

$$41\frac{473}{20,655} - 40 = 1\frac{473}{20,655} = \frac{21,128}{20,655} \text{ gear ratio}$$

$$\begin{array}{r|r|r} 20,655 & 21,128 & 1\\ 20,339 & 20,655 & 43\\ \hline 316 & 473 & 1\\ 314 & 316 & 2\\ \hline 2 & 157 & 78\\ 2 & 156 & 2\\ \hline & 1 & \end{array}$$

	1	43	1	2	78	2
0	1	44	45	134	10,497	21,128
1	0	1	43	44	131	10,262	20,655
	1	43	1	2	78	2

$$\frac{45}{44} = \frac{\underset{\underset{64}{8}}{\cancel{72}} \times \cancel{20}^{5}}{\cancel{4} \times \cancel{11}} = \frac{72}{64} \times \frac{40}{44} \quad \begin{matrix}\text{Driving gears}\\\text{Driven gears}\end{matrix}$$

Check for error:

$$41\frac{473}{20,655} = 41\frac{1}{44} \text{ approx}$$

$$\frac{1,805}{44} \times \frac{1}{40} \times \frac{51}{16} \times \frac{32,400''}{1} = 105,915.55''$$

$105,916'' - 105,915.55'' = 0.45''$ error

52. *Describe the process of helical and spiral milling.*

Ans. When the spindle of an index head is geared to the lead screw of a milling machine so that the work revolves on its axis as the table moves along the ways, a helical or spiral cut is produced. When the cut is made on cylindrical work, it is called a *helical cut*, and when made on a tapered piece, it is called a *spiral cut*. Helical-milling cutters, helical gears, twist drills, counterbores, and similar work are produced in this way.

Before a helical cut can be made, the lead of the helix, the angle of the helix, and the diameter of the work must be known. The lead is equal to the distance the table advances when the work makes one revolution. Any change in the gearing connecting the index-head spindle and the lead screw will change the lead of the helix. The helix angle is the angle the cut makes with the axis of the work, and changes with any change in the lead or in the diameter of the work. **The table must be set at the helix angle.**

The index-head spindle is geared to the lead screw of the table by means of a train of change gears, as shown in Fig. 16–71. These gears are called *the gear on the screw (D), the first gear on the stud (C), the second gear on the stud (B),* and

Fig. 16–71. Milling machine geared for helical milling. (Cincinnati Milling Machine Co.)

the gear on the worm (A). The gear on the screw and the first gear on the stud are the driving gears and the second gear on the stud and the gear on the worm are the driven gears. This may be expressed as a ratio:

$$\frac{\text{Driven gears}}{\text{Driving gears}} = \frac{2d \times \text{worm}}{1st \times \text{screw}} = \frac{A \times B}{C \times D}$$

By using different combinations of change gears, the distance that the table moves while the spindle revolves once may be changed. In other words, the lead that is cut depends directly on the gears that are used. Usually (though not always) the gear ratio is such that the work is advanced more than 1 in. while it makes one revolution. Therefore, the lead is expressed in inches per revolution rather than in revolutions per inch, as in threads. For example, a helix is said to have an 8-in. lead rather than that its pitch is one-eighth turn per inch.

The table feed screw usually has four threads per inch and a lead of 1/4 in. Motion is transferred from the lead screw to the spindle through the worm and worm wheel, which have a 40:1 ratio. When the spindle makes one revolution, the table moves 10 in. along the ways if even gearing (1:1 ratio) is used. One revolution of spindle times index-head ratio times gear ratio times lead of lead screw equals lead of machine, or

$$1 \times \frac{40}{1} \times \frac{1}{1} \times \frac{1}{4} \text{ in.} = \text{lead of machine}$$

The standard lead of a milling machine is 10 in. and all change gears are figured on this basis. Any change in gear ratio makes a corresponding change in the lead.

EXAMPLE 1: Using 1:4 ratio:

$$1 \times \frac{\overset{\overset{5}{\cancel{10}}}{\cancel{40}}}{1} \times \frac{1}{\cancel{4}} \times \frac{1}{\underset{2}{\cancel{4}}} \text{ in.} = \frac{5}{2} = 2.500 \text{ in. lead}$$

EXAMPLE 2: Using 2:1 ratio:

$$1 \times \frac{\overset{10}{\cancel{40}}}{1} \times \frac{2}{1} \times \frac{1}{\cancel{4}} \text{ in.} = 20 \text{ in. lead}$$

The compound ratio of the driven to the driving gears equals the ratio of the lead of the required helix to the lead of the machine. Expressing this in fraction form,

$$\frac{\text{Driven gears}}{\text{Driving gears}} = \frac{\text{lead of required helix}}{\text{lead of machine}}$$

Or since the product of each class of gears determines the ratio and the lead of the machine is 10 in.,

$$\frac{\text{Driven gears}}{\text{Driving gears}} = \frac{\text{lead of required helix}}{10}$$

The compound ratio of the driven to the driving gears may always be represented by a fraction whose numerator is the lead to be cut, and whose denominator is 10. That is, if the required lead is 20, the ratio is 20:10. To express this in units instead of tens, divide both terms of the ratio by 10. This is often a convenient way to think of the ratio, a lead of 40 giving a ratio of 4:1, a lead of 25 a ratio of 2.5:1, and so forth.

To illustrate the usual calculations, assume that a helix of 12-in. lead is to be cut. The compound ratio of the driven to the driving gears equals the desired lead divided by 10, or it may be represented by the fraction 12/10. Resolving this into two factors to represent the two pairs of change gears,

$$\tfrac{12}{10} = \tfrac{3}{2} \times \tfrac{4}{5}$$

Both terms of the first factor are multiplied by a number (24 in this case) that will make the resulting numerator and denominator correspond with the number of teeth of two of the change gears furnished with the machine (such multiplications not affecting the value of a fraction).

$$\tfrac{3}{2} \times \tfrac{24}{24} = \tfrac{72}{48}$$

Treating the second factor similarly,

$$\tfrac{4}{5} \times \tfrac{8}{8} = \tfrac{32}{40}$$

Selecting 72, 32, 48, and 40 teeth gears,

$$\frac{12}{10} = \frac{72 \times 32}{48 \times 40}$$

The numerators of the fractions represent the driven gears, and the denominators the driving gears. The 72-tooth gear is the worm gear, the 40 is first on the stud, the 32 is second on the stud, and the 48 is the screw gear. The two driven gears or the two driving gears may be transposed without changing the helix. That is, the 72-tooth gear could be used as the second on the stud and the 32-tooth gear could be used as the worm gear, if desired. A third combination could also be made.

Determine the gears to be used in cutting a lead of 27 in.

$$\frac{27}{10} = \frac{3}{2} \times \frac{9}{5} = \left(\frac{3}{2} \times \frac{16}{16}\right)\left(\frac{9}{5} \times \frac{8}{8}\right) =$$

$$\frac{48}{32} \times \frac{72}{40} \quad \begin{array}{l}\text{Driven gears} \\ \text{Driving gears}\end{array}$$

Reversing the procedure, determine the lead that would be cut by the gears, with 48, 72, 32, and 40 teeth, the first two being used as the driven gears.

$$\text{Helix to be cut} = \frac{10 \times 48 \times 72}{32 \times 40} = 27 \text{ in. to one revolution}$$

The milling-machine table must always be set to the angle of the job.

The angle of the helix depends upon the lead of the helix and the diameter to be milled. In the sketch in Fig. 16–72, let A equal the circumference (circum) and C the lead of helix. The greater the lead of the helix for a given diameter, the smaller the helix angle, and the greater the diameter for a given lead, the greater the helix angle. Any change in the diameter of the work or in the lead will make a corresponding change in the helix angle.

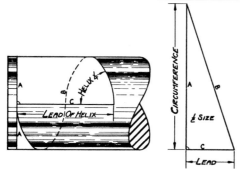

Fig. 16–72. Determining the relationship of the circumference and lead.

$$\frac{\text{Circum}}{\text{Lead}} = \frac{SO}{SA} = \text{tangent of helix angle}$$
$$\text{Lead} = \text{circum} \times \text{cotangent of helix angle}$$
$$\frac{\text{Lead}}{10} = \text{gear ratio}$$
$$\text{Gear ratio} \times 10 \text{ in.} = \text{lead cut}$$

Required lead minus lead that gears will cut equals the error in lead.

EXAMPLE 1: Find gearing required to mill the flutes on a 3-in.-diameter cutter when the helix angle is 35°8'.

Referring to Fig. 16–73,

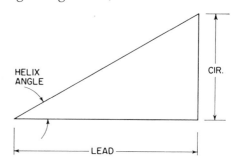

Fig. 16–73. Problem outline for calculating the helix angle.

Lead = circum ($\pi \times D$) $\times$ cotangent of helix angle
Lead = 3.1416 × 3 × 1.4211 = 13.3935

$$\text{Gear ratio} = \frac{\text{lead}}{10} = \frac{13.3935}{10} \times \frac{10,000}{10,000} = \frac{133,935}{100,000}$$

100,000	133,935	1
67,870	100,000	2
32,130	33,935	1
30,685	32,130	17
1,445	1,805	1
1,440	1,445	4
5	360	72
	360	
	0	

1	2	1	17	1	4	72	
0	1	1	3	47	1	75	371	26,785	× 5 = 133,935
1	0	1	2	3	53	56	277	20,000	× 5 = 100,000
1	2	1	17	1	4	72	

$$\frac{75}{56} = \frac{48}{64} \quad \frac{100}{56}$$
$$\frac{75}{56} = \frac{\cancel{3} \times \cancel{25}}{\cancel{4} \times \cancel{14}} = \frac{48}{64} \times \frac{100}{56} \quad \begin{array}{l}\text{Driven gears} \\ \text{Driving gears}\end{array}$$
$$64 \quad 56$$

$$\frac{75}{56} \times \frac{10}{1} = \frac{750}{56} = 13.3928 \text{ in. lead}$$

13.3935	Required lead
13.3928	Lead cut
0.0007	Error in lead

Set table at the helix angle.

EXAMPLE 2: Find helix angle and gearing required for a lead of 3.140 in. on 1 1/2 in. diameter.

$$\frac{\text{Circum}}{\text{Lead}} = \text{tangent of helix angle}$$

$$\frac{3.1416 \times 1.5}{3.140} = \frac{4.7124}{3.140} = 1.50076$$

1.50076 is the tangent of 56°19'24".

$$\text{Gear ratio} = \frac{\text{lead}}{10} = \frac{3.140}{10} = \frac{314}{1000}$$

$$
\begin{array}{r|r|r}
314 & 1,000 & 3 \\
290 & 942 & 5 \\
\hline
24 & 58 & 2 \\
20 & 48 & 2 \\
\hline
4 & 10 & 2 \\
4 & 8 & 2 \\
\hline
0 & 2 &
\end{array}
$$

$$
\begin{array}{c|c|c|c|c|c|c|c}
 & 3 & 5 & 2 & 2 & 2 & & 2 \\
\hline
1\,|\,0 & 1 & 5 & 11 & 27 & 65 & 157 & \times 2 = 314 \\
0\,|\,1 & 3 & 16 & 35 & 86 & 207 & 500 & \times 2 = 1{,}000 \\
\hline
 & 3 & 5 & 2 & 2 & 2 & 2 &
\end{array}
$$

$$
\frac{27}{86} = \frac{3 \times 9}{2 \times 43} = \frac{24}{64} \times \frac{72}{86} \quad
\begin{array}{l} \text{Driven gears} \\ \text{Driving gears} \end{array}
$$

$$
\frac{27}{86} \times \frac{10}{1} = \frac{135}{43} = 3.13953 \text{ in. lead cut}
$$

Required lead minus lead cut equals error.

$$3.140 - 3.13953 = 0.00007 \text{ in.}$$

The helical-milling situation of Fig. 16–74 shows how the indexing head and the rack-cutting attachment are set up to mill a helical groove or thread in a worm. The worm shown has a triple thread, 2 in. pitch diameter, 0.500 pitch, 1.500 lead, and a helix angle of 76°34′30″. The gear ratio and the table setting for this worm are found as follows:

$$\frac{\text{Lead}}{10} = \text{gear ratio} \qquad \frac{1.5}{10} \times \frac{10}{10} = \frac{15}{100}$$

$$
\frac{15}{100} = \frac{3 \times 5}{4 \times 25} = \frac{24}{64} \times \frac{40}{100} \quad
\begin{array}{l} \text{Driven gears} \\ \text{Driving gears} \end{array}
$$

When using the rack-cutting attachment, the cutter is held at a 90-deg angle with the work and the table is set at the complement of the helix angle.

$$
\begin{array}{r}
90° = 89° \; 59' \; 60'' \\
76° \; 34' \; 30'' \\
\hline
13° \; 25' \; 30''
\end{array}
$$

53. Describe the process of short-lead milling.

Ans. When very small leads are required, the di-

Fig. 16–74. Cutting a worm with small lead with the rack-cutting attachment. (Brown & Sharpe Mfg. Co.)

viding head, worm, and worm wheel may be disengaged and the gearing connected directly from the dividing-head spindle to the table lead screw. With even gearing, when the dividing-head spindle revolves once, the lead screw (which has four threads per inch) makes one revolution and the table is moved a distance equal to the lead, or 0.250 in. The rack-cutting attachment, shown cutting a worm in Fig. 16–74, is used with this method.

EXAMPLE: Find the gears to cut a lead of 0.3492 in.

$$\frac{\text{Lead}}{0.250} = \text{gear ratio} \qquad \frac{0.3492}{0.250} \times \frac{10{,}000}{10{,}000} = \frac{3{,}492}{2{,}500}$$

$$
\begin{array}{r|r|r}
2{,}500 & 3{,}492 & 1 \\
1{,}984 & 2{,}500 & 2 \\
\hline
516 & 992 & 1 \\
476 & 516 & 1 \\
\hline
40 & 476 & 11 \\
36 & 440 & 1 \\
\hline
4 & 36 & 9 \\
 & 36 &
\end{array}
$$

$$
\begin{array}{c|c|c|c|c|c|c|c}
 & 1 & 2 & 1 & 1 & 11 & 1 & 9 \\
\hline
0\,|\,1 & 1 & 3 & 4 & 7 & 81 & 88 & 873 \quad \times 4 = 3{,}492 \\
1\,|\,0 & 1 & 2 & 3 & 5 & 58 & 63 & 625 \quad \times 4 = 2{,}500 \\
\hline
 & 1 & 2 & 1 & 1 & 11 & 1 & 9
\end{array}
$$

$$\frac{88}{63} = \frac{\overset{64}{\cancel{8}} \times \overset{44}{\cancel{11}}}{\underset{72}{\cancel{9}} \times \underset{28}{\cancel{7}}} = \frac{64}{72} \times \frac{44}{28} \quad \begin{array}{l} \text{Driven gears} \\ \text{Driving gears} \end{array}$$

$$\frac{88}{63} \times \frac{0.250}{1} = 0.349206 \text{ in. lead cut}$$

Required lead minus lead cut equals error.

$$0.349206 - 0.3492 = 0.000006 \text{ in. error}$$

The regular means of indexing cannot be used in short-lead milling. Have the number of teeth in the gear on the spindle some multiple of the number of divisions required. The gears may then be swung out of mesh and the gear on the spindle advanced the number of teeth necessary to index the work one division.

Sometimes it is necessary to mill a few teeth on a cylindrical shaft or plunger. If a rack-cutting attachment is not available, the work may be done as shown in Fig. 16–75. The shaft is supported on a parallel and clamped in a vise, and the teeth are indexed by means of the graduated dial on the cross-feed screw, the movement being equal to the linear pitch, or 3.1416 divided by the diametral pitch. Before indexing, care should be taken to remove backlash from the screw.

Fig. 16–75. Cutting a rack with only a few teeth. (Brown & Sharpe Mfg. Co.)

54. *Describe some of the methods of milling cams.*

Ans. Figure 16–76 shows a cylindrical cam being milled with an end mill, producing a helical slot with parallel sides. The dividing-head centers are brought in line with the center of the machine spindle. The table is set at right angles to the spindle and the angle of the helix is obtained by the combination of change gears used. Either right-hand or left-hand helices may be cut in this way by leaving out, or adding, an extra idler gear. When this method is used for cylindrical-cam milling, the gears are calculated and placed the same as for helical milling, as shown in Fig. 16–71.

Fig. 16–76. Milling cylindrical-path cam. (Cincinnati Milling Machine Co.)

The cam-cutting attachment in Fig. 16–77 is used for cutting face, peripheral, or cylindrical cams from a flat cam former. The cam former is made from a disk about 1/2 in. thick, on which the required outline is laid out. The disk is machined or filed to the required shape. The table of the machine remains clamped in one position during the cutting, and the necessary rotative and longitudinal movements are contained in the mechanism itself. The rotative movement is obtained by a worm driving a wheel fixed to the spindle of the attachment. The cam former is secured to the face of the worm wheel, and as the wheel revolves, the cam former depresses the sliding rack, which in turn drives a pinion geared to another rack in the sliding bed of the attachment. This gives the necessary longitudinal movement on the face of the worm wheel.

The path cam, illustrated in Fig. 16–78, is machined by another method. The work is held in the

Fig. 16–77. Cam-cutting attachment. (Brown & Sharpe Mfg. Co.)

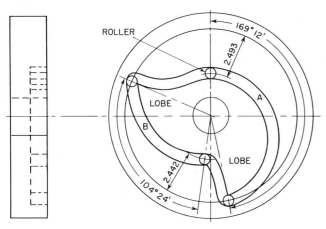

Fig. 16–78. Path cam.

horizontal plane in the dividing head, and an end mill is used in the vertical-spindle attachment.

In Fig. 16–78, we have a cam with two lobes (a lobe is a projecting part of a cam wheel), one (*A*) having a rise of 2.493 in. in 169°12′ and the other (*B*) having a rise of 2.442 in. in 104°24′.

The lead in 360° of lobe *A* equals

$$\frac{360°}{169° \, 12′} \times 2.493 \text{ in.} = 5.304 \text{ in.}$$

The lead in 360° of lobe *B* equals

$$\frac{360°}{104° \, 24′} \times 2.442 \text{ in.} = 8.421 \text{ in.}$$

To gear up the dividing head to cut lobe *A*,

$$\frac{\text{Lead of lobe}}{\text{Lead of machine}} = \frac{\text{driven}}{\text{drivers}} = \frac{\text{second} \times \text{worm}}{\text{first} \times \text{screw}}$$

$$\frac{5.304}{10} = \frac{35}{66} \text{ (approx)} \quad \text{By continued fractions}$$

$$\frac{35}{66} = \frac{\overset{28}{\cancel{7}} \times \overset{40}{\cancel{5}}}{\underset{44}{\cancel{11}} \times \underset{48}{\cancel{6}}} = \frac{28}{44} \times \frac{40}{48}$$

To gear up the dividing head to cut lobe *B* (NOTE: use two idlers),

$$\frac{8.421}{10} = \frac{16}{19} \text{ (approx)} = \frac{16 \times 4}{19 \times 4} = \frac{64}{76}$$

The path of the roller should first be rough-drilled. The parts of the cam, other than lobes *A* and *B*, can be scribed, drilled, and then milled to the scribed lines.

A method often followed in cutting peripheral cams, especially those for use on automatic screw machines, is that of using the dividing head and a vertical-spindle milling attachment. This is illustrated in Fig. 16–79. The dividing head is geared to the table feed screw, the same as in cutting an ordinary helix, and the cam blank is fastened to the end of the dividing head. An end mill is used in the vertical-spindle milling attachment, which is set to mill the periphery of the cam at right angles to its sides. In other words, the axes of the dividing-head spindle and attachment spindle must always be parallel, in order to mill cams by

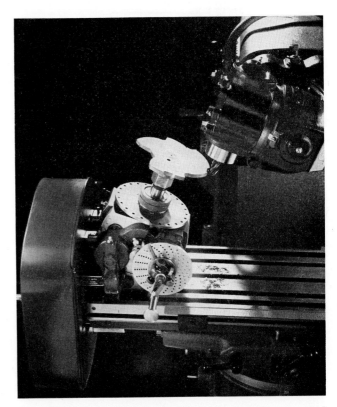

Fig. 16–79. Milling a face cam. (Brown & Sharpe Mfg. Co.)

this method. The cutting is done by the teeth on the periphery of the end mill. The principle of this method may be explained in the following way:

Suppose the dividing head is elevated to 90 deg, or at right angles to the surface of the table (see Fig. 16–80), and is geared for a given lead. It is apparent that as the table advances and the blank is turned, the distance between the axes of the dividing-head spindle and the attachment spindle becomes less. In other words, the cut becomes deeper and the radius of the cam is shortened, producing a spiral lobe with a lead which is the same as that for which the machine is geared.

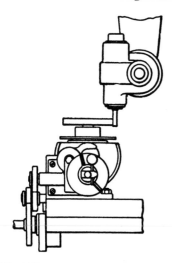

Fig. 16–80. Milling a cam in a horizontal position.

Now suppose the same gearing is retained and the dividing head is set at zero degrees, or parallel to the surface of the table, as shown in Fig. 16–81. It is apparent, also, that the axes of the dividing-head spindle and the attachment spindle are parallel to each other. Therefore, as the table advances

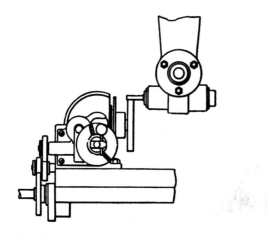

Fig. 16–81. Milling a cam in a vertical position.

and the blank is turned, the distance between the axes of the dividing-head spindle and the attachment spindle remains the same. As a result, the periphery of the blank, if milled, is concentric, or the lead is zero.

If, then, the dividing head is elevated to any angle between zero and 90 deg, as shown in Fig. 16–82, the amount of lead given to the cam will be between that for which the machine is geared and zero. Hence it is clear that cams with a very large range of different leads can be obtained with one set of change gears, and the problem of milling the lobes of a cam is reduced to a question of finding the angle at which to set the dividing head to obtain any given lead.

Fig. 16–82. Milling a cam in an angular position.

To cut the smallest possible lead with the dividing head geared to the lead screw, place a 24-tooth gear on worm, an 86-tooth gear first on stud, a 24-tooth gear second on stud, and a 100-tooth gear on worm. Calculate the lead as follows:

$$\frac{24}{86} \times \frac{24}{100} \times \frac{40}{4} = 0.66976, \text{ or } 0.67$$

in which 40 equals the number of turns of the index crank to one spindle revolution and 4 equals the number of threads per inch on the lead screw.

EXAMPLE: To find the angle to set the dividing head and vertical-spindle attachment, divide the lead of the cam by the lead of the machine. The lead of the machine must always be greater than the lead of the cam.

To find the lead of the cam, that is, the theoretical continuous rise in one complete revolution, if the rise in 27 deg is 0.127 in., calculate as follows:

360 deg divided by angle in which rise occurs times rise equals rise in 360 deg.

$$\frac{360}{27} \times 0.127 = 1.693 \text{ rise in 360 deg} = \text{lead of cam}$$

To calculate the leads, gears, and angles to incline the dividing head and vertical-spindle attachment, for a cam having a 0.470 in. rise in 85 deg, 0.750 in. rise in 75 deg, and 0.358 in. rise in 58 deg (see Fig. 16–83) proceed as follows:

0.470 in. rise in 85 deg $= \frac{360}{85} \times 0.470 = 1.99$ lead

0.750 in. rise in 75 deg $= \frac{360}{75} \times 0.750 = 3.600$ lead

0.358 in. rise in 58 deg $= \frac{360}{58} \times 0.358 = 2.222$ lead

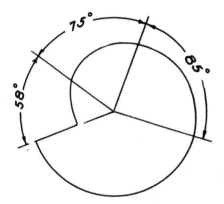

Fig. 16–83. Face cam.

The machine must be geared with a greater lead than that of the cam having the greatest lead. As an example, use as the lead 3.657 in. and gear the machine as follows:

$$\frac{3.657}{10.000} \text{ by continued fractions} = \text{approx } \frac{64}{175} = \frac{\overset{32}{\cancel{4}}}{\underset{56}{7}} \times \frac{\overset{64}{\cancel{16}}}{\underset{100}{25}}$$

Place the 32-tooth gear on the worm, the 56-tooth gear the first on the stud, the 64-tooth gear the second on the stud, and place the 100-tooth gear on the lead screw.

The sine of the angle at which to incline the dividing head is found by dividing the lead of the cam by the lead of the machine. The size of the angle can then be found in a table of sines.

Lead of cam having 0.470 in. rise in 85 deg $= \dfrac{1.99}{3.657}$
$= 0.54415$
$= \sin 32° 58'$

Lead of cam having 0.750 in. rise in 75 deg $= \dfrac{3.600}{3.657}$
$= 0.9844$
$= \sin 79° 52'$

Lead of cam having 0.358 in. rise in 58 deg $= \dfrac{2.222}{3.657}$
$= 0.6076$
$= \sin 37° 25'$

Note, in the above work, that the machine is geared the same for all leads and that the dividing head and vertical-spindle attachment are inclined at different angles to mill the different leads.

A cylindrical cam is milled and the gears calculated in the same manner as a helical groove is milled, an end mill being used instead of a milling cutter.

All toolrooms have, or can obtain, a chart showing the many different leads and gears used to cut these leads.

55. What is meant by the cutting speed of a milling cutter?

Ans. The cutting speed of a milling cutter is the rate at which the cutter engages the work—usually expressed in surface speed in feet per minute. No definite rule can be made for the speed at which a milling cutter should be run, because too many factors, such as the depth of cut, amount of feed, the kind of material to be cut, type of job, condition of machine and cutter, and finish required, must be considered. With cutters made of high-speed steel, the feeds in Table 16–3 are usually satisfactory:

Table 16–3. FEEDS FOR HIGH-SPEED STEEL CUTTERS

Material	Fpm
SAE 6470 high-speed steel	40– 50
SAE 1095 tool steel	60– 80
SAE 1015 machine steel	80–100
Cast iron	80–100
Brass	150–200

A cutter should never be run at a speed which would cause excessive heat and dull or burn the cutting edge.

The following formulas may be used in figuring the speed of a milling cutter.

$$\text{Rpm} = \frac{\text{cutting speed} \times 12}{3.1416 \times \text{dia}}$$

EXAMPLE 1: What is the speed of the spindle for a 1 1/4 in. cutter running 40 fpm?

$$\text{Rpm} = \frac{40 \times 12}{3.1416 \times 1.25} = 122$$

$$\text{Cutting speed} = \frac{3.1416 \times \text{dia} \times \text{rpm}}{12}$$

EXAMPLE 2: Find the cutting speed of a 1 1/2 in. end mill running 382 rpm.

$$\text{Cutting speed} = \frac{3.1416 \times 1.5 \times 382}{12} = 150$$

Table 16–4 may be used to find directly the rpm of cutters of different diameters for the more common surface speeds.

Table 16–4. CUTTING SPEEDS

Dia, in.	Feet per second															
	40	45	50	55	60	65	70	75	80	90	100	110	120	130	140	150
	Revolutions per minute															
$\frac{1}{4}$	611	688	764	840	917	993	1,070	1,146	1,222	1,375	1,528	1,681	1,833	1,986	2,139	2,292
$\frac{5}{16}$	489	550	611	672	733	794	856	917	978	1,100	1,222	1,345	1,467	1,589	1,711	1,833
$\frac{3}{8}$	407	458	509	560	611	662	713	764	815	917	1,019	1,120	1,222	1,324	1,426	1,528
$\frac{7}{16}$	349	393	437	480	524	568	611	655	698	786	873	960	1,048	1,135	1,222	1,310
$\frac{1}{2}$	306	344	382	420	458	497	535	573	611	688	764	840	917	993	1,070	1,146
$\frac{5}{8}$	244	275	306	336	367	397	428	458	489	550	611	672	733	794	856	917
$\frac{3}{4}$	204	229	255	280	306	331	357	382	407	458	509	560	611	662	713	764
$\frac{7}{8}$	175	196	218	240	262	284	306	327	349	393	437	480	524	568	611	655
1	153	172	191	210	229	248	267	287	306	344	382	420	458	497	535	573
$1\frac{1}{8}$	136	153	170	187	204	221	238	255	272	306	340	373	407	441	475	509
$1\frac{1}{4}$	122	138	153	168	183	199	214	229	244	275	306	336	367	397	428	458
$1\frac{3}{8}$	111	125	139	153	167	181	194	208	222	250	278	306	333	361	389	417
$1\frac{1}{2}$	102	115	127	140	153	166	178	191	204	229	255	280	306	331	357	382
$1\frac{5}{8}$	94.0	106	118	129	141	153	165	176	188	212	235	259	282	306	329	353
$1\frac{3}{4}$	87.3	98.2	109	120	131	142	153	164	175	196	218	240	262	284	306	327
$1\frac{7}{8}$	81.5	91.7	102	112	122	132	143	153	163	183	204	224	244	265	285	306
2	76.4	85.9	95.5	105	115	124	134	143	153	172	191	210	229	248	267	287
$2\frac{1}{4}$	67.9	76.4	84.9	93.4	102	110	119	127	136	153	170	187	204	221	238	255
$2\frac{1}{2}$	61.1	68.8	76.4	84.0	91.7	99.3	107	115	122	138	153	168	183	199	214	229
$2\frac{3}{4}$	55.6	62.5	69.5	76.4	83.3	90.3	97.2	104	111	125	139	153	167	181	194	208
3	50.9	57.3	63.7	70.0	76.4	82.8	89.1	95.5	102	115	127	140	153	166	178	191
$3\frac{1}{4}$	47.0	52.9	58.8	64.6	70.5	76.4	82.3	88.2	94.0	106	118	129	141	153	165	176
$3\frac{1}{2}$	43.7	49.1	54.6	60.0	65.5	70.9	76.4	81.9	87.3	98.2	109	120	131	142	153	164
$3\frac{3}{4}$	40.7	45.8	50.9	56.0	61.1	66.2	71.3	76.4	81.5	91.7	102	112	122	132	143	153
4	38.2	43.0	47.7	52.5	57.3	62.1	66.8	71.6	76.4	85.9	95.5	105	115	124	134	143
$4\frac{1}{2}$	34.0	38.2	42.4	46.7	50.9	55.2	59.4	63.6	67.9	76.4	84.9	93.4	102	110	119	127
5	30.6	34.4	38.2	42.0	45.8	49.7	53.5	57.3	61.1	68.8	76.4	84.0	91.7	99.3	107	115
$5\frac{1}{2}$	27.8	31.3	34.7	38.2	41.7	45.1	48.6	52.1	55.6	62.5	69.5	76.4	83.3	90.3	97.2	104
6	25.5	28.6	31.8	35.0	38.2	41.4	44.6	47.8	50.9	57.3	63.7	70.0	76.4	82.8	89.1	95.5

Chapter 17 GAGES AND GAGE BLOCKS

In a previous chapter, a number of measuring tools used in toolmaking and similar types of work were discussed. In addition to those tools, many other devices are commonly employed in industry, not only by skilled persons such as toolmakers, but also by those who measure the size of articles manufactured by mass-production methods. Tools for this kind of measuring are called gages. Some of them are made for general use, that is, they may be adapted to measure a wide range of sizes, but most gages are made for a definite measuring operation with close limits. They are usually made of tool steel, hardened and ground.

1. What are some of the common types of gages?

Ans. The most common types of gages include the ring gage, plug gage, snap gage, caliper gage, receiving gage, master gage, indicating gage, thickness gage, and radius gage.

Fig. 17–1. Ring gages. (Brown & Sharpe Mfg. Co.)

2. What is a ring gage?

Ans. A ring gage (Fig. 17–1) is one that is cylindrical in shape with a hole that is of the exact size specified for the part to be measured. In using a ring gage, it should fit over the part being checked without the use of force and without any noticeable side movement. The surface being measured may be cylindrical or conical in shape.

3. What is a plug gage?

Ans. A plug gage (Fig. 17–2) is used to test the accuracy of holes. It should engage the hole to be checked without using pressure and should be able to stand up in the hole without falling through,

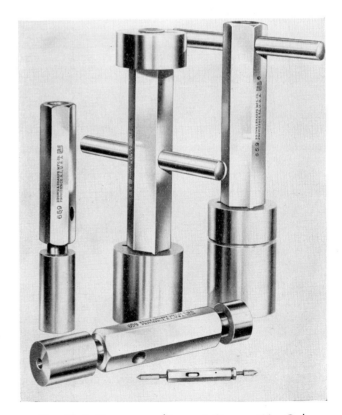

Fig. 17–2. Plug gages. (Brown & Sharpe Mfg. Co.)

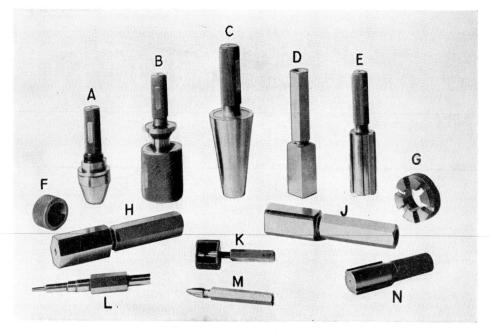

Fig. 17-3. Miscellaneous plug gages. (Brown & Sharpe Mfg. Co.)

just able to slowly slide through. The shape of the plug may also be conical, as gages *A* and *C;* square, as gage *D;* hexagon, as gage *H;* or one of the several others shown in Fig. 17-3.

4. *What is a snap gage?*

Ans. A snap gage (Fig. 17-4) is one that is made with openings to fit over a part to be checked. The part may be cylindrical or flat. Snap gages are made double-ended for measuring two dimensions,

and also single-ended. An adjustable type of snap gage is shown in Fig. 17-5. They are made in many sizes with openings ranging from 1/4 to 12 in. The lower anvils of the gage may be adjusted as much as 1/4 in. to a required dimension. Gages with two anvils are sometimes referred to as "go" and "not go" gages. When this is the case, the inner anvil is raised slightly higher than the front one. For example, to measure a shaft with a dimension of 1.500 with a 0.003 limit more or less would call for the inside opening to be 1.498 and the outside opening to be 1.503. In order to pass inspection, the shaft should "go" through the outer setting of the gage, but should "not go" through the inner setting.

Fig. 17-4. Snap gages. (Brown & Sharpe Mfg. Co.)

Fig. 17-5. Adjustable snap gage. (Taft-Peirce Mfg. Co.)

5. *What is a caliper gage?*

Ans. A caliper gage (Fig. 17-6) is similar to a snap gage but is designed to measure an internal

Fig. 17–6. Caliper gage. (Brown & Sharpe Mfg. Co.)

dimension with one end and an external dimension with the other end.

6. *What is a receiving gage?*

Ans. A receiving gage is one whose inside measuring surfaces are designed to check a specific article for shape and size. An example of this type of gage is shown at G in Fig. 17–3.

7. *What is a taper test gage?*

Ans. A taper test gage is a device consisting of a base upon which are located two hardened steel plates which may be readily adjusted to a special or standard taper. It may then be used to test other tapers.

8. *What is a master gage?*

Ans. A master gage is a precise duplicate of the article to be measured. Gages used by workmen are checked for accuracy with the master gage.

9. *What is an indicating gage?*

Ans. An indicating gage is one that exhibits visually the variations in the uniformity of dimensions or contour, the amount of variation being indicated by a lever on a graduated dial. There are many types of indicating gages and new uses for them are constantly being devised.

The most common type of indicator is shown in Fig. 17–7. While it is commonly referred to in the shop as a *dial indicator,* it is more properly called a *test set.* It consists of a sturdy steel base with T slots on its top and bottom surfaces, a steel column which may be securely fastened to the base, an adjustable clamp which fits on the column, an indicator-holding rod, and a dial indicator. This is a general-purpose gage used in all departments of a toolroom. One of the most common uses for it is in setting a piece of work in a four-jaw lathe chuck accurately.

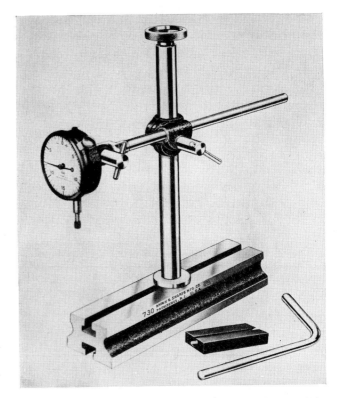

Fig. 17–7. Test set with dial indicator. (Brown & Sharpe Mfg. Co.)

Dial indicators are made in five standard sizes, ranging from 1 1/4 to 3 5/8 in. in diameter. The size of the graduations on the face of the dial may vary from 0.00005 to 0.001 in. Some dials are of the balanced type, as in Fig. 17–8. In this case, the graduations are numbered consecutively on both

Fig. 17–8. Balanced dial without revolution counter and double dial. (Federal Products Corp.)

sides of zero. Continuous dials have the graduations numbered continuously around the dial, as in Fig. 17–9. Indicators usually have a range of 2 1/2 revolutions of the indicator hand. Some indicators have a revolution counter built in, which indicates how many revolutions the indicator hand has made (from one to ten) on the face of the continuous dial. Another desirable feature is a double dial which permits setting zero at any required position around the edge of the dial, independent of the revolution counter.

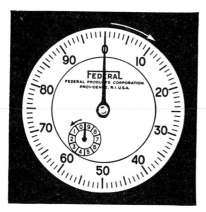

Fig. 17–9. Continuous dial with revolution counter and double dial. (Federal Products Corp.)

10. What is a hole attachment for a dial indicator?

Ans. A hole attachment (Fig. 17–10) is a device that is attached to the stem of an indicator to test internal and other surfaces that cannot be reached with the regular dial spindle. The horizontal arm is pivoted on its center so that a movement of one end inside of a piece of work will cause a cor-

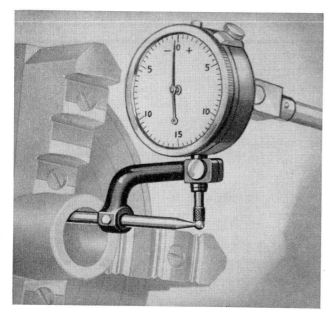

Fig. 17–10. Hole attachment for dial indicator. (Federal Products Corp.)

responding movement of the other end against the contact point of the indicator.

11. What is a right-angle offset attachment for a dial indicator?

Ans. A right-angle offset attachment (Fig. 17–11) is a device that is designed to be attached to the stem of the indicator for the purpose of transferring motion at right angles to the indicator spindle. It is useful in small spaces.

Fig. 17–11. Right-angle offset attachment for dial indicator. (Federal Products Corp.)

12. What are indicator hole gages?

Ans. Indicator hole gages are measuring devices that have a dial indicator built into them to show directly the accurate size of a hole. They are available in many styles and sizes. Figure 17–12 shows a gage which is designed for testing holes ranging in size from 1.250 to 1.500 in. Sizes up to 2.250 in. may be measured by changing the gaging head. Other models of this type of hole gage have measuring capacities from 0.500 up to 12.665 in.

Another type of hole gage has retracting contacts, as in Fig. 17–13. This feature makes possible the accurate measurement of a larger inside hole or recess (see Fig. 17–14). The individual range of each model of this style of gage is much more than the kind shown in Fig. 17–12. The small models have a range of 0.100 in. and the large models a range of 0.500 in.

13. What is a universal test indicator?

Ans. A universal test indicator (Fig. 17–15) is a

Fig. 17–12. Indicator hole gage. (Federal Products Corp.)

testing device that may be used for many types of work. The index point, which comes in contact with the surface of the work, may be readily adjusted with the fingers to suit the job. The movement of the index point is shown on the dial. The

Fig. 17–15. Universal test indicators. (Federal Products Corp.)

graduations on the dial are 0.001 in. on one model and 0.0001 in. on another model. The head of the indicator may be adjusted to many different posi-

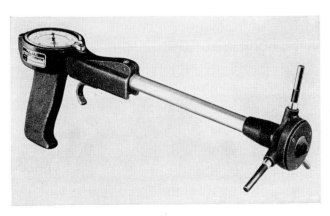

Fig. 17–13. Hole gage with retracting contacts. (Federal Products Corp.)

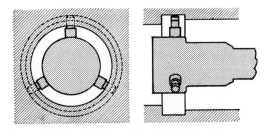

Fig. 17–14. Sketch shows how contacts can be contracted to allow them to pass through small opening and then allowed to expand to contact the larger diameter of recess. (Federal Products Corp.)

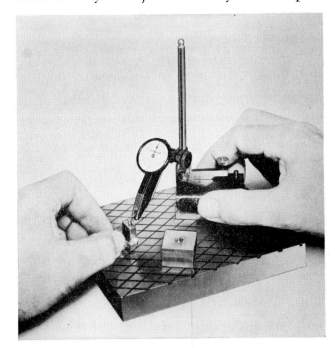

Fig. 17–16. Indicator held in surface gage checks dimension of work by comparing it with gage blocks. (Federal Products Corp.)

tions by means of the universal clamp which holds it to the rectangular shank. It may be attached to a surface gage, as in Fig. 17–16, or to a height gage, as in Fig. 17–17. It may also be attached to the tool post for adjusting or testing work in a lathe, or it may be clamped to the spindle of a mill.

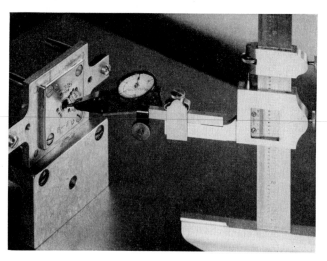

Fig. 17–17. Checking location of hole with indicator attached to height gage. (Federal Products Corp.)

14. What is an indicating inside-caliper gage?
Ans. A type of inside caliper with an indicating gage is shown in Fig. 17–18. The graduations on the dial face are 0.010 in. with a measuring capacity of from 1 to 3 in. Because of the large size of graduations and range, this gage does not measure as accurately as other types of indicating hole gages but is suitable where a speedy check is desirable.

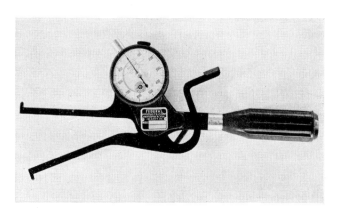

Fig. 17–18. Inside-caliper gage. (Federal Products Corp.)

15. What is an indicating snap gage?
Ans. An indicating snap gage (Fig. 17–19) is similar in design to an ordinary snap gage but has

the advantage of indicating on the dial the exact variation from the required dimension of the work. The adjustable lower anvil permits the gage to be

Fig. 17–19. Indicating snap gage. (Federal Products Corp.)

set with a wide measuring range. The regular models are available in five sizes with a total measuring range of from zero to 6 in. The indicat-

Fig. 17–20. Indicating snap gage attached to bench stand. (Federal Products Corp.)

ing gage dial may be adjusted to any position to suit the convenience of the user. The gage may also be set in a bench stand, as in Fig. 17–20.

Other types of indicating snap gages are the single-purpose gage shown in Fig. 17–21, and an adjustable gage with a retracting anvil, in Fig. 17–22. The latter type is desirable for measuring highly polished surfaces, as it does not mar the finish. Figure 17–23 shows an adjustable backstop

Fig. 17–21. Single-purpose indicating snap gage. (Federal Products Corp.)

Fig. 17–22. Adjustable indicating snap gage with retractable anvil. (Federal Products Corp.)

that helps to locate the work correctly on the anvil of the gage.

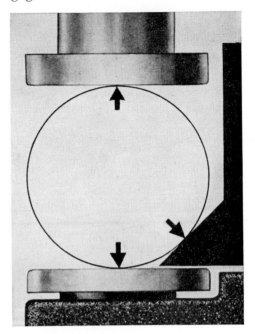

Fig. 17–23. Adjustable backstop for locating work on the anvil of gage. (Federal Products Corp.)

16. *What is a thickness gage?*

Ans. A thickness gage (Fig. 17–24) is actually a set of gages consisting of thin strips of metal of a given thickness in sizes from 0.0015 to 0.025 in. It is used to measure the space between two surfaces.

Fig. 17–24. Thickness gage. (Lufkin Rule Co.)

Another type of thickness gage (Fig. 17–25) is of the indicating variety. These convenient gages are designed to inspect the thickness of paper, plastic, sheet metal, leather, and so forth, with great accuracy. The graduations on the dial are in 0.001 in. with a measuring range of from zero to 0.500 in. Another model is available with graduations of 0.0001 in. with a range of 0.100 in. A gage of this type is being used to measure the thickness of sheet metal in Fig. 17–26.

The indicating outside-caliper gage (Fig. 17–27)

Fig. 17–25. Indicating thickness gage. (Federal Products Corp.)

is also a type of thickness gage. The graduations on the dial are usually 0.010 or 1/64 in. The convenience and speed of measuring encourages the measurement of work that might otherwise go unchecked. The jaws are sometimes designed to suit the shape of a particular piece of work.

17. What is an indicating depth gage?

Ans. An indicating depth gage (Fig. 17–28) is a gage for accurately measuring the depth of holes, slots, and other recesses in a positive and convenient manner. The graduations on the dial are in 0.001 in. with a total measuring range of from zero to 3 in. Figure 17–29 shows a gage of this type being used to measure the depth of a recess.

Fig. 17–26. Measuring the thickness of sheet metal with an indicating thickness gage. (Federal Products Corp.)

Fig. 17–28. Indicating depth gage. (Federal Products Corp.)

Fig. 17–27. Indicating outside-caliper gage. (Federal Products Corp.)

18. What is a radius gage?

Ans. A radius gage (Fig. 17–30) consists of a number of steel blades that are shaped to curved surfaces of definite sizes. The size of the radius of the curve is stamped on each blade. The blades on one end of the gage are used to measure concave corners, those on the other end for convex corners.

Fig. 17–29. Measuring the depth of a recess with an indicating depth gage. (Federal Products Corp.)

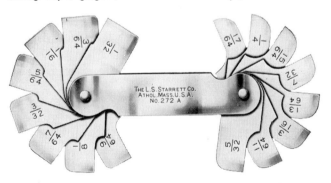

Fig. 17–30. Radius gage. (L. S. Starrett Co.)

19. What is an amplifying comparator gage?

Ans. An amplifying comparator gage (Fig. 17–31) is an instrument that amplifies the variation in the size of two similar parts 10 times. In using it, a gage of the required size is placed under the indicating point, and the dial of the indicator is set at zero. The gage is then removed and the part to be checked is placed under the point. Any deviation shown on the indicator dial indicates 10 times the amount of error between the gage and the work.

It has been said that all important discoveries have been made through the medium of fine meas-

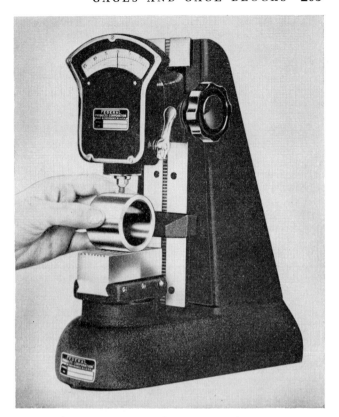

Fig. 17–31. Amplifying comparator gage. (Federal Products Corp.)

urement of time, mass, or length, and of these three, precision measurement of length is the most difficult and has become more and more important, until today it is one of the greatest problems facing the mechanical world.

20. What are the standard units of measurement in industry?

Ans. The standard units of length are the inch and the millimeter which are, respectively, fractional parts of the yard and the meter.

21. What determines the length of an inch?

Ans. An inch is a relative quantity and is an English unit of length that has been definitely established at 1/36 of the British imperial yard, which Great Britain defines as the distance, at 62 degrees Fahrenheit between the central traverse lines in two gold plugs in a bronze bar one inch square and thirty-six inches long.

22. Does the United States of America have a standard yard?

Ans. No. There is no standard yard in the United States of America. All measurements of length are referred to our copy of the International Prototype Meter, which is kept at the Bureau of Standards, Washington, D.C.

The International Prototype Meter is defined as the length at zero degrees centigrade (32 degrees Fahrenheit) between two lines on a platinum-iridium-alloy bar, kept in the International Bureau of Weights and Measures, near Paris, France.

23. What is the authority for the length of the yard in the United States of America?

Ans. In the United States of America, the yard has been defined by Executive order, dated Apr. 15, 1893, as 3,600/3,937 of a meter, or, expressed as a decimal, 0.9144 meter. An inch is defined as 1/36 of a yard or 2.54 centimeters.

A few years ago, the mechanics who worked in machine shops were all-round machinists; that is, they were proficient in the operation of all the machine equipment, as well as being able to perform bench and assembly operations.

Today the all-round machinist has given way (except on tool and gage work) to the highly specialized operator who is instructed and trained to perform a certain operation on a particular piece of apparatus. The tools and gages furnished make it possible for him to make all measurements in accordance with predetermined specifications which are more accurate than was thought possible by the all-round mechanic of yesteryear.

The gradually increasing quantity production of recent years is on such a huge scale that the cut-and-try method of measuring has been discarded, even by the machine shop that builds only one complete apparatus.

24. What are some of the requirements of a precision measuring instrument?

Ans. (1) It must be able to measure externally and internally to within one ten-thousandth (0.0001) of an inch. (2) It must be of such design as to be used directly on the work, to eliminate the possibility of error in transferring accurate measurements. (3) It must give the same result, any number of times, in the hands of different mechanics. (4) It must be self-checking, so error due to wear, accident, or abuse may be readily discovered. (5) The materials from which it is made must be seasoned and stabilized, to reduce to a minimum errors in accuracy due to the changes that take place normally in metals. (6) It must have an

established reputation for accuracy that is accepted by the manufacturer and the customer.

25. What type of gage is considered a universal standard of measurement?

Ans. Johansson-type gage blocks are the standard of precision measurement for the world. They measure accurately in millionths of an inch, an accomplishment considered impossible before their introduction.

26. What are precision gage blocks?

Ans. Precision gage blocks of the Johansson type (Fig. 17–32) are rectangular pieces of tool steel, approximately 3/8 by 1 3/8 in. by specified size, hardened, ground, stabilized, and finished to an accuracy within a few millionths part of an inch from the specified size.

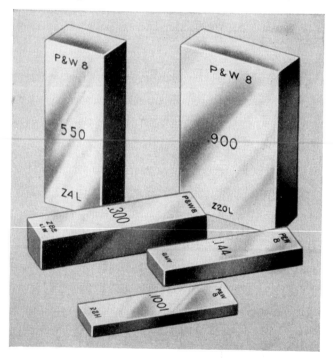

Fig. 17–32. Precision gage blocks. (Pratt & Whitney Co.)

27. What problems in industry have been solved by the use of precision gage blocks?

Ans. Precision gage blocks embody in their commercial manufacture the solution of four universally recognized metallurgical and mechanical problems, namely, flat surfaces in steel, parallel surfaces in steel, accuracy as to dimension in steel, and effective heat-treatment and seasoning of steel.

28. What are some of the characteristics of a flat surface in steel?

Ans. It is considered one of the most remarkable achievements in mechanics to make a flat surface in steel, and by the Johansson methods, a flat surface with an extremely high finish, having the appearance of burnished silver, is produced, which approaches nearer the perfect plane than any other surface produced by the hand of man. These flat-lapped surfaces, when thoroughly cleaned and slid one on the other with a slight inward pressure, will take hold as though magnetized. They have been known to sustain a weight of 200 lb on a direct pull, although the contacting surfaces are less than one-half of a square inch. Scientists have offered atmospheric pressure, molecular attraction, and a minute film of oil on the lapped surfaces as explanations of this phenomenon. Possibly it is a combination of all three.

29. *What are some of the characteristics of parallel surfaces in steel?*

Ans. The degree of parallelism attained in the manufacture of the Johansson gage blocks is well shown by the fact that any block in a given combination may be turned end for end, at will, without affecting the parallelism of the two extreme surfaces of the combination.

30. *Has it been possible to combine parallel surfaces in steel with accurate measurement?*

Ans. The making of one steel surface parallel with another is good, but to make the parallel surface a predetermined distance from another surface with an accuracy in millionths of an inch is a more remarkable achievement. This has been accomplished, and is proven by the way in which an equivalent combination of precision gage blocks checks against one solid block.

31. *What is an important process in making gage blocks?*

Ans. An important operation in the making of gage blocks is the seasoning of the metal. This must be done so that the internal stresses and strains within the metal are relieved. The molecules of the steel may be said to be at rest and because of this, the usual warping or growing is checked.

32. *What is a set of gage blocks?*

Ans. A full set of gage blocks (Fig. 17–33) consists of 81 blocks which have surfaces flat and parallel within 0.000008 in. In addition to the regular blocks, many accessories have been designed to be used with them. A group of accessories is shown in Fig. 17–34, including a foot block, straight edge, scriber, tram points, adjustable holder, and jaws of various sizes.

Another style of precision gage block is the Hoke type, a complete set of which is shown in the first three rows of Fig. 17–35. These blocks are approximately 0.950 in. square and vary in the thickness of each one. There is a hole through the center of each block. This permits the use of internal tie rods, by means of which rapid, compact assembling of various attachments is possible without the use of clamps. Many of these attachments are shown in the back of the box of gage blocks in Fig. 17–35.

Some types of gage blocks have holes near the

Fig. 17–33. A full set of Johansson-type gage blocks. (Brown & Sharpe Co.)

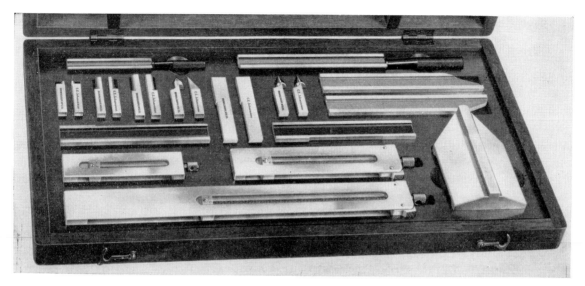

Fig. 17–34. Gage block accessories. (Brown & Sharpe Co.)

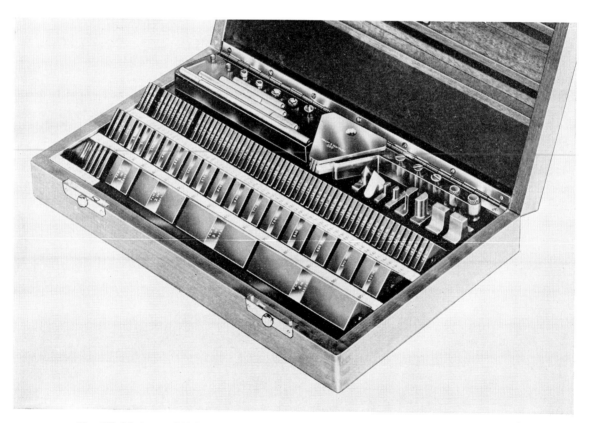

Fig. 17–35. A set of Hoke-type gage blocks and accessories. (Pratt & Whitney Co.)

ends so that they may be joined together by an eccentric clamp after the ends have been wrung together, as in Fig. 17–36. Examples of blocks joined together by eccentric clamps are shown in Figs. 17–37 and 17–38.

Precision gage blocks and an electrolimit height

gage are being used in Fig. 17–39 to check the location of a hole in a master railroad gage.

33. Most styles of precision gage blocks are made in four series. What units are contained in the first series of gage blocks?

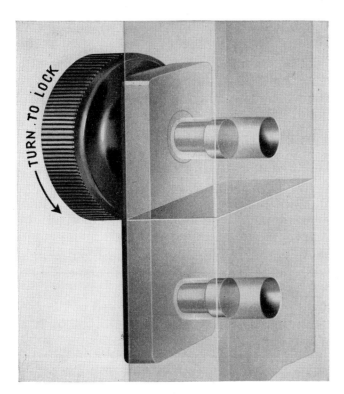

Fig. 17–36. Gage blocks held together with eccentric clamps. (Webber Gage Co.)

Fig. 17–37. Gage blocks combined to form a precision surface gage. (Webber Gage Co.)

Ans. The first series (see Table 17–1) consists of nine blocks, ranging in size from 0.1001 to 0.1009 in. by steps of 0.0001 in.

34. What units are contained in the second series of gage blocks?

Ans. The second series (see Table 17–1) consists of 49 blocks, ranging in size from 0.101 to 0.149 in. by steps of 0.001 in.

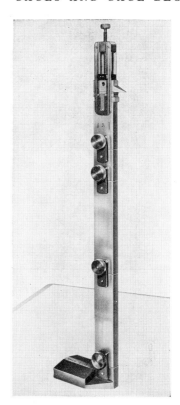

Fig. 17–38. A combination of gage blocks provides a height gage of a size accurate to millionths of an inch. (Webber Gage Co.)

Fig. 17–39. Checking the location of a hole with gage blocks and an electrolimit height gage. (Pratt & Whitney Co.)

35. What units are contained in the third series of gage blocks?

Ans. The third series (see Table 17–1) consists of 19 blocks, ranging in size from 0.050 to 0.950 in. by steps of 0.050 in.

36. What units are contained in the fourth series of gage blocks?

Ans. The fourth series (see Table 17–1) consists of four blocks measuring 1, 2, 3, and 4 in.

37. How are the blocks usually combined?

Ans. The blocks of the third series may be combined with those of the fourth series to give any multiple of 0.050 between 0.050 and 10 in. The second series may be used to obtain dimensions varying by thousandths of an inch, and the first series to obtain dimensions varying by steps of ten-thousandths of an inch.

Table 17–1. PRECISION GAGE BLOCKS

First Series

0.1001	0.1002	0.1003	0.1004	0.1005	0.1006	0.1007	0.1008	0.1009

Second Series

0.101	0.102	0.103	0.104	0.105	0.106	0.107	0.108	0.109	0.110
0.111	0.112	0.113	0.114	0.115	0.116	0.117	0.118	0.119	0.120
0.121	0.122	0.123	0.124	0.125	0.126	0.127	0.128	0.129	0.130
0.131	0.132	0.133	0.134	0.135	0.136	0.137	0.138	0.139	0.140
0.141	0.142	0.143	0.144	0.145	0.146	0.147	0.148	0.149	

Third Series

0.050

0.100	0.200	0.300	0.400	0.500	0.600	0.700	0.800	0.900
0.150	0.250	0.350	0.450	0.550	0.650	0.750	0.850	0.950

Fourth Series

1.000	2.000	3.000	4.000

38. Are all gage blocks of the same quality?

Ans. No. Precision gage blocks are made in three qualities designated as B quality, A quality, and AA quality. At a temperature of 68°F, the blocks have the following accuracy:

Working set (B quality) = 0.000008 in.
Inspection set (A quality) = 0.000004 in.
Laboratory set (AA quality) = 0.000002 in.

39. How does the accuracy of precision gage blocks compare with (1) a human hair, (2) precision tool work, and (3) light waves?

Ans. A human hair is approximately three-thousandths (0.003) of an inch thick. The most accurate work in the mechanical field is that of toolmakers, who work to an accuracy of one ten-thousandth of an inch, which is 30 times finer than a human hair. Light waves are approximately sixteen-millionths of an inch long, which is 250 times finer than a human hair and 6 1/4 times finer than

the accuracy used by a toolmaker. Compared with the accuracy of AA quality gage blocks (0.000002 in.) the above are relatively large amounts. It is seen then that the accuracy of the blocks is 1,500 times finer than a human hair; 50 times finer than a toolmaker works; and 8 times finer than the length of a light wave.

40. What is the procedure for building a definite size of gage with gage blocks?

Ans. The following steps are suggested: (1) Become acquainted with the size of the blocks in the set. (2) Begin with the right-hand figure of the specified size. (3) Continue working from the right to the left. (4) Build the combination with the fewest possible number of blocks.

The following example shows some of the possible combinations for one particular size:

		0.1008	0.1006	0.1007
	0.1009	0.1003	0.1005	0.1004
0.1001	0.1002	0.139	0.138	0.141
0.149	0.147	0.132	0.133	0.130
0.123	0.124	0.100	0.500	0.600
0.900	0.800	0.700	0.300	0.200
1.2721	1.2721	1.2721	1.2721	1.2721

To join one block to another, proceed as follows: (1) Select from the set the first two blocks of the combination. (2) Wipe each of the contacting surfaces of the blocks on the palm of the hand, on the wrist, or on a piece of chamois, and then place the contacting surfaces together. (3) With a slight inward pressure, slide one block on the other. If the contacting surfaces are clean, they will cling together as though they were magnetized. (4) Continue in this manner until the required combination is completed.

41. What is a sine bar?

Ans. A sine bar (Fig. 17–40) consists of a hardened-and-ground steel bar in which two hardened-and-ground plugs of the same diameter are set. For ease in making calculations, the center distance between the plugs is 5, 10, or 20 in. The edges of the bar must be parallel with the center line of the two plugs. A sine bar is always used in conjunction with a true surface, such as a surface plate (Fig. 17–41), from which measurements are taken. The sine bar receives its name from the fact that, in setting a sine bar to a required angle, as in Fig. 17–42, the

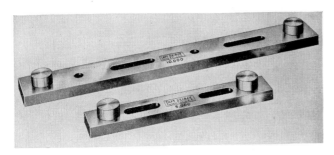

Fig. 17–40. Sine bars. (Taft-Peirce Mfg. Co.)

Fig. 17–41. Surface plate. (Brown & Sharpe Mfg. Co.)

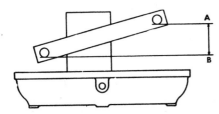

Fig. 17–42. The distance *AB* is equal to the sine of the angle multiplied by the length of the sine bar.

dimension *AB* is calculated by multiplying the sine of the required angle by the length of the sine bar.

42. What are some of the uses of a sine bar?

Ans. The sine bar may be used to set a piece of work to a required angle. In Fig. 17–42, the plug at one end of the sine bar is elevated above the other plug a distance equal to the sine of the required angle, multiplied by the length of the sine bar. The angle in this case is 32°29′ and the sine bar is 5 in. in length. Therefore the distance of one

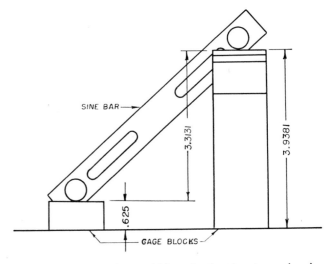

Fig. 17–43. The angle at which a sine bar is set may be determined from the vertical distance between the two plugs of the sine bar.

Fig. 17–44. Angle gage blocks. (Webber Gage Co.)

plug of the sine bar above the other plug equals the sine of 32°29′, which is 0.53705, multiplied by 5, which equals 2.68525 in. The sine bar may be set in position by the use of gage blocks or with the aid of a vernier height gage.

The sine bar may also be used to determine the size of an angle. The vertical distance between the plugs of the 5-in. sine bar in Fig. 17–43 is found to be 3.3131 in. By dividing the distance by 5, it is found that the sine of the required angle is 0.66262 which is shown in a table of sines to represent an angle of 41°30′.

43. What are angle gage blocks?

Ans. Angle gage blocks (Fig. 17–44) are flat pieces of hardened steel measuring 4 in. on the base and 5/8 in. thick. A complete set consists of 16 blocks with angles of:

1°	3°	5°	15°	30°	45°	Degree series
1′	3′	5′	20′	30′		Minute series
1″	3″	5″	20″	30″		Second series

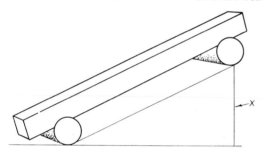
Fig. 17–45. Diagram for sine-bar problem.

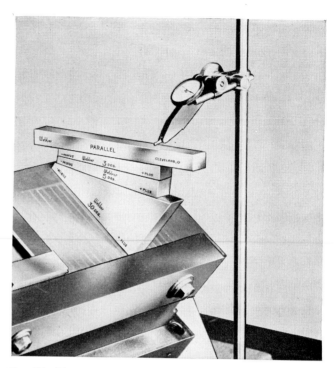
Fig. 17–47. A combination of angle gage blocks is used to adjust a magnetic chuck. (Webber Gage Co.)

Fig. 17–46. An adjustable angle plate is accurately set with angle gage blocks and a universal test indicator attached to a surface gage. (Webber Gage Co.)

Fig. 17–48. The toolhead of a shaper is accurately adjusted to a required angle with angle gage blocks. (Webber Gage Co.)

44. What is the advantage of angle gage blocks as compared to a sine bar?

Ans. A precision angle has always been difficult to set because of the involved trigonometric formula that is used with the sine bar. The chief difficulty lies in the dimension X of Fig. 17–45 which often results in a figure with many decimal places. Gage blocks can only approximate this value. For example, to measure 44°30′ by the sine-bar method, the following steps are required when using a 5-in. sine bar:

The sine for 44° 30′ angle	0.7009093
For dimension X, multiply by 5	3.5045465

Gage blocks necessary to match this dimension:

0.1005	
0.104	Residual error:
0.300	3.5045465
3.000	−3.5045
3.5045	0.0000465

This error cannot be eliminated in sine-bar procedure. However, it can be eliminated with the use of angle gage blocks. With angle gage blocks, a 45° block is wrung on a 30′ block so that the plus end of the 45° block contacts the minus end of the 30′ block which forms an angle of 44°30′. This is a simple procedure, and what is more important, it is absolutely accurate.

A complete set of 16 angle blocks yields 356,400 angles in steps of one second, with an accuracy measured in millionth parts of a circle. At first glance, this ability of a few blocks to measure hundreds of thousands of angles seems impossible. However, the discovery that angles can be measured by subtraction as well as by addition allowed a few blocks to perform this surprising job.

Some applications of the use of angle gage blocks are shown in Figs. 17–46 to 17–48.

Chapter 18 HEAT-TREATMENT

Heat-treatment is a term used in industry to describe a process whereby the physical properties of a metal may be changed by subjecting it to heat. In some instances the procedure is a simple one, while in others it is quite complicated, involving the use of scientific knowledge and equipment. In discussing the subject in this book, steel is the only metal that will be given attention.

There are two principal reasons for heat-treating steel: one is to harden it, the other is to anneal (soften) it.

Before any of these processes is described, it is well to become acquainted with the material itself. To some people, steel is simply a hard metal. To persons in industry, however, the word *steel* brings to mind not just one kind of material, but a great number that may all be classified as steel but which differ from one another in their chemical analysis and physical properties.

1. What is steel?

Ans. Steel is an alloy of iron and carbon. In addition, there are minute percentages of other elements present, including silicon, phosphorus, sulfur, and manganese.

2. How may steels be classified?

Ans. Steels may be roughly classified as straight carbon steels and alloy steels. A straight carbon steel is one that owes its particular properties chiefly to the presence of certain percentages of carbon without substantial amounts of other alloying elements. Straight carbon steels may be classified into three groups, low-carbon, medium-carbon, and high-carbon. An alloy steel is one in which some element other than carbon has been added, to improve or change the physical properties.

3. Of what importance is the element carbon in straight carbon steel?

Ans. Carbon is the element which makes possible the hardening of straight carbon steel.

4. How much carbon must be present in steel before it can be hardened noticeably?

Ans. Steel must contain at least 0.20 percent of carbon before it can be hardened sufficiently for commercial use.

5. What is a low-carbon steel?

Ans. A low-carbon steel is one that does not contain enough carbon to cause it to harden when heated to a high temperature and quenched in oil, water, or brine. The amount of carbon in low-carbon steel may vary from 0.05 to 0.20 percent. Some of the low-carbon steels are machine steel and cold-rolled steel, which are also identified as SAE 1015 steel. Typical of the articles made from low-carbon steel are bolts, nuts, clamps, washers, pressure pads, stripper plates, and similar items where the surface is not subjected to continuous wear. When a hard-wearing surface and a soft core are required, low-carbon steel may be case-hardened by a special process.

6. What is a medium-carbon steel?

Ans. A medium-carbon steel is one that contains from 0.20 to 0.60 percent carbon. Medium-carbon steels are used for a wide variety of work including nuts, bolts, stock guides, flask pins, crankshafts, crane shafts, and so forth. Medium-carbon steels are also used extensively in production manufacturing. A medium degree of hardness (Rockwell 38–46) may be obtained by heat-treatment.

7. What are high-carbon steels?

Ans. High-carbon steels are those which usually contain from about 0.60 to 1.30 percent of carbon. Tool steel (SAE 1095) is a high-carbon steel. It may be heat-treated, hardened, and tempered. The degree of hardness is high; between 52 and 64, Rockwell. Many of the tools and working parts of machines, guide pins, rest buttons, locating pins, dies, punches, gages, bushings, centers, and so forth, all of which are required to withstand a great deal of wear, are made from tool steel.

8. What are alloy steels?

Ans. Alloy steels are those which contain, in addition to carbon and iron, some alloying elements, such as chromium, vanadium, nickel, molybdenum, or tungsten, which give them some peculiar characteristic not possessed by ordinary steel. Alloys are put into steels for the following reasons: to secure greater hardness; to secure greater toughness or strength; to enable the steel to hold its size and shape during hardening; or to enable the steel to retain its hardness at high temperatures.

Chromium is added to steel to increase the depth to which the steel may be hardened. The amount used is from 0.40 to 1.5 percent. Larger amounts, 12 to 25 percent, are used in stainless steels.

Vanadium is added to steel in small quantities, 0.12 to 0.20 percent; it retards internal stress in the steel even when subjected to high temperatures.

Nickel will increase the toughness and strength of steel, but will not increase its capacity for being hardened. The amount added varies from 0.30 to 3.75 percent. For stainless steel, as much as 20 percent is used.

Molybdenum increases greatly the depth of hardness and makes steel tough. It also helps it to remain hard at high temperatures. It is added in small amounts of from 0.10 to 2.00 percent.

Tungsten is used in tool steel to make a fine-grain alloy which tends to maintain a sharp cutting edge on tools. The amount used is 0.50 to 1.50 percent. For high-speed steel, 6 to 18 percent tungsten is added. High-speed steel is used for high-grade cutting tools, milling-machine cutters, drills, reamers, broaches, and many other tools that are required to stay sharp under conditions that would ruin the cutting edge of tools made of ordinary tool steel.

9. What are some of the operations involved in the heat-treatment of steel?

Ans. Normalizing, annealing, quenching, tempering, strain drawing, cyaniding, carburizing, and nitriding.

10. What is the process of normalizing steel?

Ans. Normalizing is the uniform heating of steel above the usual hardening temperatures, followed by cooling freely in air. This treatment is used to put steel back in a normal condition after forging or after an improper heat-treatment.

11. What is the process of annealing?

Ans. Annealing is accomplished by heating the steel slowly above the usual hardening temperature, keeping it at that heat for 1/2 to 2 hr followed by a slow cooling, preferably in a furnace. This operation is for the purpose of softening a piece of work that is too hard to machine or because it is necessary to remachine a job that has been hardened. Annealing is also done to relieve internal strains in a piece of steel that have been set up in it by extensive machining.

12. What is the process of quenching?

Ans. Quenching is the operation of cooling a heated piece of work rapidly, by dipping it in water, brine, or oil.

13. What is the process of tempering steel?

Ans. Tempering, also known as strain drawing (drawing the temper or strain from the steel), is a process whereby a certain degree of hardness is sacrificed, to reduce brittleness and to increase the toughness of a steel tool. This is accomplished by reheating the tool to a low temperature, usually between 375 and 500°F, immediately after quenching. If only the cutting end of the tool has been quenched, the heat retained in the remainder of the tool may, by conduction, reheat the end to the required temperature after which it may be quenched again. In this case, the hardener watches the color of the cutting end of the tool.

A temperature of 375 to 400° is indicated by a pale-yellow color which is suitable for punches, scrapers, centers, cams, and so forth, where maximum hardness is desired. A light-straw color representing about 430° is suitable for hammers, tool bits, and so forth. A medium-straw color corresponding to about 460° is suitable for dies, drills, screw drivers, and so forth. A dark-straw color indicates about 490°, which is often used for chisels. A light-purple color which represents about 520° is suitable for axes, needles, and so forth.

When more than one tool is being tempered, it

Fig. 18–1. Electric pot furnace. (Lindberg Engineering Co.)

Fig. 18–2. Toolroom tempering furnace. (Lindberg Engineering Co.)

is more practical to reheat the tools in a bath of oil or nitrate in a pyrometer-controlled heating pot like the one shown in Fig. 18–1, or in a box-type furnace, which is heated by forced circulation of accurately heated air, shown in Fig. 18–2.

Tools made of high-speed steel are tempered by reheating to much higher temperatures than those specified for ordinary tool steel. The temperatures vary from 1000 to 1200°F.

14. What is the process of cyaniding steel?

Ans. Low-carbon steels do not become hard when heated above their critical points and quenched. However, the surface of the steel may be hardened by cyaniding. This is done by immersing the piece of steel in a molten bath of sodium cyanide from 5 to 30 min, depending on the size of the piece of work, and the depth of penetration desired. It is then quenched in water, brine, or oil, and a very hard skin or casing, 0.010 to 0.015 in. thick, is formed. This is also called *casehardening*.

15. Is it customary to grind a piece of work made of low-carbon steel that has been casehardened by cyaniding?

Ans. No. The hardened case of the steel is only about 0.015 in. thick and this amount is usually removed during the grinding operation.

16. What is the process of carburizing steel?

Ans. Carburizing is another method of giving a hardened case to a piece of steel. The piece of work is placed in a metal box containing a mixture of bone, leather, charcoal, and other carburizing materials. The lid is sealed with fire clay and the box is placed in a furnace for some hours at a temperature of 1700°F. The depth to which the carbon penetrates the steel depends upon the length of time that the work is left in the furnace. After the steel is removed from the furnace and cooled to room temperature, it can be normalized by reheating at 1560 to 1650°F and cooling in air. It can then be hardened by inserting it into a furnace or a lead pot (Fig. 18–3), heating it to the required temperature, and quenching it in the same manner as other high-carbon steel, but only the part that absorbed the carbon will become hard. The inside which did not absorb the carbon will remain soft.

Fig. 18–3. Lead pot. (Bellevue Industrial Furnace Co.)

17. For what type of job is a carburized piece of steel recommended?

Ans. Carburized steel is recommended for work requiring a hard surface and a tough core. The hard surface can be made sufficiently deep so that it may be ground without removing all of the hardened surface. An example of this kind is the wrist pin of an automobile engine. It must have a hard surface to resist wear and a tough core to absorb the shock incident to its use. Many jobs made in the toolroom require this form of heat-treatment.

Carburizing may also be used for special jobs requiring partial hardening, as in the nut shown

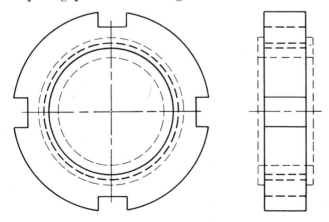

Fig. 18–4. Nut prepared for casehardening.

in Fig. 18–4. In this case, the outside diameter must be hard and the threads are to be kept soft. The operations are as follows: Finish the outside diameter and the thickness of the nut to the required size, leaving a flange on each side 1/8 in. greater than the major diameter of the thread and extending 1/8 in. on each side. Bore the hole for the thread 1/4 in. smaller than the minor diameter of the thread. Mill the slots. Carburize the nut. After carburizing, bore the hole to within 1/16 in. of the required size and face off the flanges. Heat-treat to the required hardness. The threads may now be cut. Inasmuch as the carbon did not penetrate the part of the steel in which the threads are to be cut, the heat-treatment did not harden it.

18. What is the process of nitriding steel?

Ans. Nitriding is a method of putting an extremely hard surface on a piece of steel. The process consists of exposing the steel to hot ammonia gas for some hours. The ammonia breaks down into nitrogen and hydrogen because of the heat, and the nitrogen reacts with the steel to form a nitride case around the steel.

19. What operations are involved in hardening steel?

Ans. Hardening involves both heating and cooling operations. Heating is the bringing of the steel to the desired temperature above the critical range, in order to get the grain structure in the steel into the proper state for hardening. Cooling is the quenching of the steel in some medium such as water, brine, caustic solution, or oil in order to preserve the structure obtained in heating. The quenching medium must have an even temperature.

20. What is meant by the critical point when heating steel?

Ans. The critical point or critical temperature is that at which some definite change takes place in the physical properties of the steel. This point is important because, in heat-treating a piece of steel, it must be heated to a temperature just above its own particular critical point. The critical point varies according to the type of steel being heat-treated. For instance, tool steel and high-speed steel must be heated to 1400° but not more than 1450°F, whereas die steel is heated to between 1550 and 1600°F.

21. How is the exact temperature of a furnace controlled?

Ans. The heat of the furnace can be controlled or regulated by a pyrometer. Figure 18–5 shows a type of pyrometer used on an electric furnace. Not so many years ago, it was the custom for a hardener of steel to watch the color of the work in the furnace, to determine its temperature. There was a big element of chance in this procedure and the U.S. Bureau of Standards has demonstrated conclusively that at temperatures around 2000°F, the old-timers who depended on their eyes were off as much as 200° in judging furnace temperature. Nowadays, scientific instruments such as the pyrometer are in common use for the accurate control of furnace temperatures.

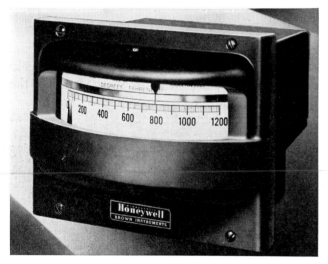

Fig. 18–5. Pyrometer. (Minneapolis-Honeywell Regulator Co., Industrial Division)

22. What are some of the types of furnaces used in heat-treating metals?

Ans. Gas, oil, and electric furnaces are most commonly used. The heat can be easily controlled in these furnaces, which is an important factor. Some steels are heated in open furnaces, while others are heated in pot furnaces. If the pot contains molten lead, it is called a *lead pot* but if it contains molten cyanide, it is called a *cyanide pot.* The pot furnace can also be used for tinning, for melting low-fusion metals, and for other heating purposes. Tools such as dies, punches, springs, and other small steel parts may be hardened uniformly in this type of furnace without danger of oxidizing the steel. The lead pot is especially adapted for jobs where only a portion of the tool is to be hardened. Only the portion of the tool to be hardened is immersed in the lead. The pot furnace is rapid, convenient, and satisfactory.

An automatic heat-treating furnace is shown in Fig. 18–6, which is heated by radiant-heating tubes that are designed for either gas-fired or electric heating elements. The unit operates at temperatures up to 1850°F, and has completely automatic straight-through operation from heating of the parts through cooling or oil quench. The unit is sealed to provide absolute atmosphere control during the entire heat-and-quench cycle, assuring bright, scale-free work on all types of heat-treating processes, such as hardening, carburizing, carbonitriding, and normalizing. The work is loaded directly into the heating zone, and after the proper time at heat, the work tray is automatically transferred onto a quenching rack which holds the load for atmospheric cooling, or lowers it for oil quench, whichever has been pre-selected on the cycle-control panel. As soon as the tray is on the rack, a new load can be put into the heating zone.

A furnace for the bright-tempering of steel is shown in Fig. 18–7. This unit is supplied, during the entire cycle of operation, with a protective atmosphere. After sufficient time at the required temperature, the load is cooled in the furnace until it reaches approximately 400°F. The bright, scale-free work is then cool enough to be removed from the furnace without danger of oxidation.

This type of furnace also produces a controlled oxide coating, which is often desired to reduce corrosion or wear, and to produce an attractive blue-gray or blue-black appearance.

23. Why is charcoal kept on top of the lead in a lead pot?

Ans. Charcoal is kept on top of the molten lead in a lead pot to burn up the oxygen in the air, to prevent oxidation, and to keep the job clean. This prevents surface or skin softness and helps to eliminate scale on the steel.

24. Is it possible to harden one part of a piece of work without hardening it all over?

Ans. Yes. One way is to cover a part of the work with fire clay which insulates the material covered from the full heat of the furnace. Another method, when the shape of the work permits, is to heat the work in a pot of lead or cyanide, immersing only

Fig. 18–6. Automatic furnace heated by radiant-heating tubes with control panel. (Ipsen Industries, Inc.)

Fig. 18–7. Furnace for tempering and controlled oxide coating of steel, with control panel. (Ipsen Industries, Inc.)

that part of the work which is to be hardened. A third way is to heat the part to be hardened with the flame of an oxyacetylene torch. The flame can be directed to the desired part without heating the remainder of the work sufficiently to affect it.

The process of hardening steel in this manner is

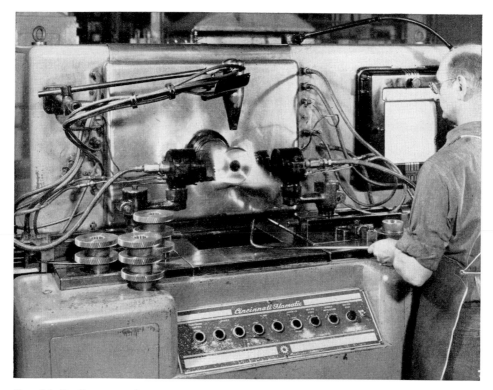

Fig. 18–8. Heat-treating gears in a flame-hardening machine. (Cincinnati Milling Machine Co.)

known as *flame hardening*. It has been developed rather extensively in the last few years, to the point where special machines have been designed for the purpose. Figure 18–8 shows a machine that is designed for the express purpose of flame-hardening gears. Multiple nozzles grouped in a flame head on each side of the machine pour streams of heat on the gear. The temperatures for heating and quenching are maintained and controlled with an accuracy of plus or minus 5 deg, by means of electronic equipment. Another example of a flame-hardening machine is shown in Fig. 18–9. This machine is used to harden the ways of a lathe. A separate flame head with multiple nozzles is used for each side of the lathe bed. Figure 18–10 shows a cross section of the ways of a lathe that have been heat-treated by the flame-hardening process.

Fig. 18–9. Flame-hardening the ways on the bed of a lathe. (Monarch Machine Tool Co.)

Fig. 18–10. Cross section of the ways of a lathe after flame hardening. (Cincinnati Milling Machine Co.)

25. *What are some of the advantages of flame heating?*

Ans. (1) Because it heats quickly, flame heating is convenient when hardness is required only for a limited depth of the material, the reminder retaining its original toughness and ductility. (2) Flame heating makes it possible and practical to harden a part or all of a piece of work that is too large or too inconvenient to place in a furnace. (3) The amount of time required for heating is less with flame heating than with a furnace, and there is no need to wait until a furnace is available.

26. *How are different types of steel designated?*

Ans. The most common system of identification is that adopted by the Society of Automotive Engineers (SAE). In this plan, each grade of steel is given a number containing four digits. The first digit indicates the general group; the second one, the approximate percentage of the principal alloying element used; and the last two, the approximate amount of carbon in the steel. The general groups represented by the first digit are:

1. Carbon steel
2. Nickel steel
3. Nickel chromium steel
4. Molybdenum steel
5. Chromium steel
6. Chromium vanadium steel
7. Tungsten steel
8. Silicon steel

Some examples of this numbering system are: Type SAE 1020 steel is a carbon steel containing 0.20 percent carbon. Type SAE 2317 steel is a nickel-steel alloy containing 3 percent nickel and 0.17 percent carbon. Type SAE 5130 steel is a chromium-steel alloy containing 1 percent chromium and 0.30 percent carbon.

27. *Do all manufacturers use the SAE system of identifying different grades of steel?*

Ans. No. Some companies have developed systems of their own, using numbers or letters.

28. *What is the spark-test method for identifying different kinds of steel?*

Ans. The ends of steel bars are sometimes painted in various colors and color combinations as a means of identifying different grades of steel. For instance, machine steel is painted black; tool steel, aluminum and brown; high-speed steel, aluminum and red. Steels that are not marked may be identified within certain limits by the type of sparks given off when they are held against a revolving grinding wheel. This is known as the *spark-test* method. When testing a piece of steel in this manner, use only enough pressure to maintain a steady contact between the work and the grinding wheel. A satisfactory speed for the grind-

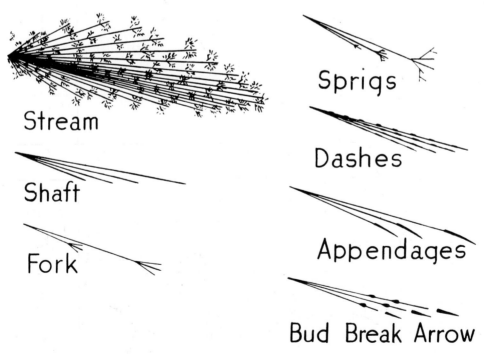

Stream

Shaft

Fork

Sprigs

Dashes

Appendages

Bud Break Arrow

Fig. 18–11. Meaning of the terms used in spark testing. (Linde Air Products Co.)

ing wheel is about 8,000 surface feet per minute. The type of sparks from a piece of steel that has been hardened are practically the same as from a piece of the same grade of steel that has not been hardened. The sparks are seen most easily in diffused daylight.

In general, the presence of various elements in steel have the following effects upon the sparks: Carbon causes the sparks to burst. Manganese tends to brighten the spark and increase the spray around the periphery of the grinding wheel. Chromium darkens the color of the sparks, suppresses the stream and bursts, and causes fine carrier lines. Nickel suppresses the stream slightly and causes forked tongues. Tungsten suppresses the stream and bursts, and causes fine red carrier lines. Mo-

lybdenum causes a detached spearhead at the end of the ray. Figure 18–11 illustrates the meaning of the terms used in spark testing.

The chart of Fig. 18–12 shows sketches of sparks from some of the most commonly used steels. They are of necessity very general but may be used to point out certain characteristics. For example, the difference in the carbon content of steel is indicated by the difference in the number of sparks as shown in the first three sketches. If a piece of machine steel and a piece of high-speed steel were sparked, the difference between them could be easily discerned. However, proficiency in identifying all steels can be gained only by practice and experience. The spark test does not analyze a piece of steel, but simply guides in identifying it.

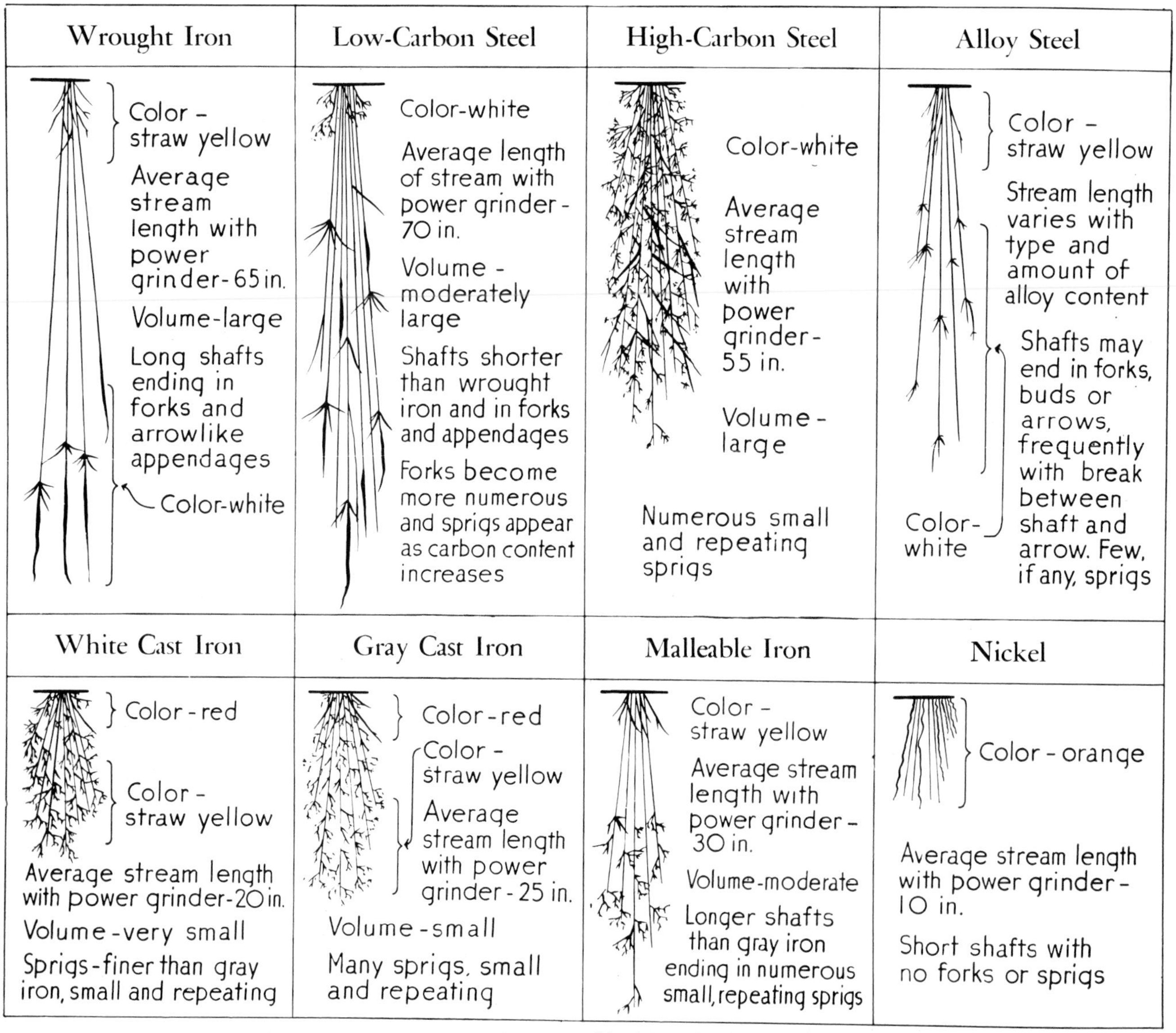

Wrought Iron	Low-Carbon Steel	High-Carbon Steel	Alloy Steel
Color – straw yellow. Average stream length with power grinder-65 in. Volume-large. Long shafts ending in forks and arrowlike appendages. Color-white	Color-white. Average length of stream with power grinder-70 in. Volume-moderately large. Shafts shorter than wrought iron and in forks and appendages. Forks become more numerous and sprigs appear as carbon content increases	Color-white. Average stream length with power grinder-55 in. Volume-large. Numerous small and repeating sprigs	Color – straw yellow. Stream length varies with type and amount of alloy content. Shafts may end in forks, buds or arrows, frequently with break between shaft and arrow. Few, if any, sprigs. Color-white

White Cast Iron	Gray Cast Iron	Malleable Iron	Nickel
Color-red. Color-straw yellow. Average stream length with power grinder-20 in. Volume-very small. Sprigs-finer than gray iron, small and repeating	Color-red. Color-straw yellow. Average stream length with power grinder-25 in. Volume-small. Many sprigs, small and repeating	Color-straw yellow. Average stream length with power grinder-30 in. Volume-moderate. Longer shafts than gray iron ending in numerous small, repeating sprigs	Color-orange. Average stream length with power grinder-10 in. Short shafts with no forks or sprigs

Fig. 18–12. Identification of sparks from various types of metal. (Linde Air Products Co.)

29. How is the hardness of steel determined?

Ans. The hardness of steel may be determined by the file test, and also by the Brinell, Rockwell, and Shore scleroscope hardness-testing machines.

30. What is a file test?

Ans. A file test is a method of determining the hardness of a piece of material by trying to cut into it with the corner of a file. The hardness is indicated by the bite that the file will take. This is the oldest and one of the simplest methods of checking hardness. While this test will not give very definite results—a new file will cut better than an old file—it will give results ranging from quite soft to glass hardness. The principal objection to the use of the file test is that no accurate record of results can be maintained.

31. What is the Brinell system for testing the hardness of a metal?

Ans. In the Brinell test, the hardness of the material tested is indicated by a number which is determined by the resistance it offers to the penetration of a steel ball under pressure. The Brinell hardness number is found by measuring the impression made by the ball when forced into the material being tested under a given pressure. The width of the indentation is measured with a microscope and the hardness number corresponding with this width is found by consulting a Brinell chart. The higher the number, the harder the material. The Brinell tester (Fig. 18–13) is most useful in testing soft and medium-hard materials and for large articles. On hard steel, the impression is so small that it is difficult to read the size of it.

32. What is the Rockwell system for testing the hardness of a metal?

Ans. In the Rockwell hardness test, a 120-deg diamond cone for hard metals, or a 1/16-in. steel ball for the softer materials, is impressed into the surface to be tested by a dead weight acting through a series of levers. The depth of penetration is then measured. The softer the piece of metal, the deeper will be the impression under a given load. The average depth of penetration on the softest steel is only about 0.008 in. The hardness is indicated on a dial gage graduated in the Rockwell B and C hardness scales. The harder the piece of steel, the higher the Rockwell number will be.

Fig. 18–13. Brinell hardness tester. (Steel City Testing Laboratories)

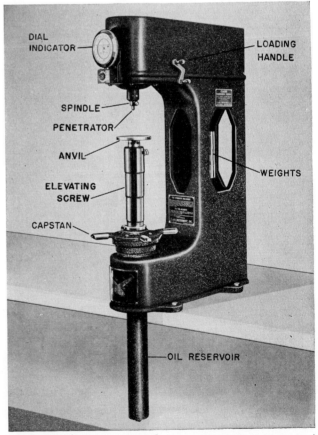

Fig. 18–14. Rockwell hardness tester. (Clark Instrument, Inc.)

Fig. 18–15. Step 1, place the part to be tested on the anvil of the tester. (Clark Instrument, Inc.)

Fig. 18–17. Step 3, trip the major load and re-set. After the dial has been adjusted to zero position, the loading beam is tripped by turning the loading handle which drops the major-load weights. When dial hand stops, return the loading handle to original position. (Clark Instrument, Inc.)

Fig. 18–16. Step 2, apply the minor load and adjust the dial. Turning the wheel of the elevating screw raises the part, making contact with the penetrator. When the large hand of the dial has made three complete turns, the correct minor load of 10 kg has been applied. (Clark Instrument, Inc.)

Fig. 18–18. Step 4, read the hardness number on the dial. (Clark Instrument, Inc.)

Fig. 18–19. Equipment for Rockwell hardness tester. (A) Extension rest for long pieces of stock; second anvil is adjustable. (B) Zero-drag tripping lever in head of tester. (C) Checking anvil with extra-hard disk. (D) V anvil for large cylindrical parts. (E) Eight-inch anvil for extra-large work having a flat bearing surface. (Clark Instrument, Inc.)

For example, to be machinable, steel should not show a reading of more than 35 on the Rockwell C scale while a cutter made of hardened high-speed steel would show a reading of from 63 to 65. When testing hard steels, the diamond point should be used and the hardness number read on the C scale. For nonferrous metals, the steel ball should be used and the hardness number read on the B scale. Figure 18–14 shows the Rockwell tester, and Figs. 18–15 to 18–18 the directions for using it. Some special equipment for use with this machine is shown in Fig. 18–19.

33. What is the Shore scleroscope system for testing the hardness of a metal?

Ans. In the Shore scleroscope hardness test, the piece of work to be tested is placed on the clamping stand of the unit and the large handwheel on the left side of the clamp is revolved to bring the instrument barrel firmly in contact with the test specimen. As pressure is being maintained on the handwheel, the diamond hammer, which is located in the upper end of the glass tube, is released from its elevated position by squeezing the rubber bulb. The height to which the hammer rebounds on its first bounce indicates the hardness of the specimen. The hammer is then raised preparatory to the next test by again squeezing and releasing the bulb. The operator should focus his eyes several points below the general area of the first rebound and take two or three more tests. The top of the hammer rather than its bottom should be observed. The average of several tests is the correct hardness of the specimen. Tests should not be made more than once in the same spot, as the impact of the diamond hammer cold-works that spot, causing subsequent tests on that spot to be high. A direct-reading scleroscope is shown in Fig. 18–20.

Fig. 18–20. Shore scleroscope hardness tester. (Shore Instrument & Mfg. Co.)

Fig. 18–22. Dial-recording Shore scleroscope. (Shore Instrument & Mfg. Co.)

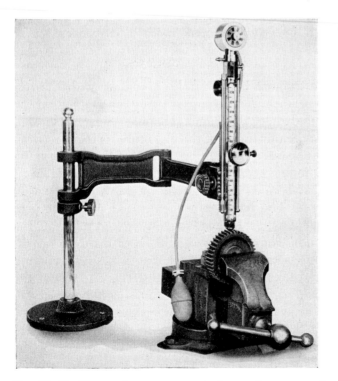

Fig. 18–21. Shore scleroscope mounted on swing arm and post. (Shore Instrument & Mfg. Co.)

In testing various small parts up to 3 in. in height, the instrument is mounted, as shown, on the clamping stand. It may also be mounted on a swing arm and post, illustrated in Fig. 18–21, for testing large, unwieldy parts. Very heavy objects and structures that cannot be conveniently moved may be tested by holding the scleroscope free-hand.

A dial-recording scleroscope is shown in Fig. 18–22. This instrument operates on the same general principle as the other kind, but by an ingenious arrangement of a ball-and-hollow-cone clutch, the degree of hardness is recorded on a dial. The dial hand remains fixed until the knob is turned for another test. It may be used freehand, or in a swing arm and post in the same manner as the regular scleroscope.

A comparison of Brinell, Rockwell, and Shore hardness numbers is shown in Table 18–1 on the next page.

Table 18–1. HARDNESS CONVERSION TABLE
(Approximate)

Brinell		Rockwell		
Dia 3,000 kg, 10-mm ball, mm	Hardness No.	C scale 150 kg, 120-deg cone	B scale 100 kg, 1⁄16-in. ball	Shore
Very hard				
2.20	780	68		96
2.25	745	67		94
2.30	712	65		92
2.35	682	63		89
2.40	653	62		86
2.45	627	60		84
Hard				
2.50	601	58		81
2.55	578	56		78
2.60	555	55		76
2.65	534	53		73
2.70	514	51		71
2.75	495	50		68
2.80	477	48		66
2.85	461	47		64
2.90	444	46		62
2.95	429	44		60
3.00	415	43		58
3.05	401	42		56
Medium hard				
3.10	388	41		54
3.15	375	39		52
3.20	363	38		51
3.25	352	37		49
3.30	341	36		48
3.35	331	35		46
3.40	321	34		45
Tough but can be machined				
3.45	311	32		43
3.50	302	31		42
3.55	293	30		41
3.60	285	29		40
3.65	277	28		38
3.70	269	27		37
3.75	262	26		36
3.80	255	25		35
3.85	248	24	100	34
3.90	241	23	99	33
Soft				
4.00	229	21	98	32
4.10	217	18	96	30
4.20	207	16	95	29
4.30	197	14	93	28
4.40	187	12	91	27
4.50	179	10	89	25
4.60	170	8	87	24
4.70	163	6	85	23
4.80	156	4	83	23
4.90	149	2	81	22

34. How may fractures be prevented when heat-treating an article with sharp edges or one that has adjacent thick and thin sections?

Ans. Fractures may be prevented in cases of this kind by applying fire clay to the thin parts, to permit uniform heating.

35. How long should a piece of steel be left in a furnace when heating?

Ans. Steel should be heated long enough to ensure a good, even heat throughout. The practical rule is to keep or "soak" the part in the furnace one hour for each square inch of cross-sectional area.

36. How may warping be avoided when quenching a long, slender piece of work?

Ans. Warping may be avoided by holding the part vertically over the quenching bath and plunging it straight down.

37. Can a hardened piece of work that has become warped in the process of heat-treating be salvaged?

Fig. 18–23. Sandblasting machine. (American Wheelabrator & Equipment Corp.)

Ans. Yes. A warped piece of work may be straightened under pressure in a straightening press after heating it with an oxyacetylene torch. The work is held between centers and moved back or forth as required to bring the distorted section under the pressure unit. The work is checked for accuracy after each adjustment, with a dial-indicator test gage.

38. During the heat-treating process, scale often forms on the surface of the metal, and dirt may be baked on it. This should be removed before the work is sent to the inspector or to the grinding department. What are some of the ways of cleaning heat-treated parts?

Ans. A stiff wire brush and a scraper are helpful when parts have to be cleaned once in a while, but a more efficient job may be done by sandblasting. A sandblasting machine is shown in Fig. 18–23. In using a sandblast, the operator passes his arms through the sleeves attached to the holes in the front of the machine and manually directs the air blast to the work being cleaned. He is able to see what he is doing by looking through the glass window in the top of the machine.

Another type of metal cleaner is the wet blast (Fig. 18–24). This machine uses a liquid abrasive which is directed toward the surface to be cleaned by the operator. Figure 18–25 shows the interior of a wet blast with the operator aiming the blasting gun toward the work.

Fig. 18–25. Interior of wet-blast machine. (American Wheelabrator & Equipment Corp.)

Metal cleaning is also done by a machine that does not use air or liquid. A machine of this type is the table-style Wheelabrator, shown in Fig. 18–26. Abrasives, in the form of shot or grit of

Fig. 18–24. Wet-blast machine. (American Wheelabrator & Equipment Corp.)

Fig. 18–26. Table-style Wheelabrator metal cleaner. (American Wheelabrator & Equipment Corp.)

various grades, are hurled upon the work. The driving unit is shown in Fig. 18–27. It is capable of throwing 300 lb of abrasive per minute. This type

Fig. 18–27. Driving unit of Wheelabrator. (A) Abrasive funnel, (B) abrasive shot, (C) spacers between side plates, (D) side plates, (E) removable blades, (F) control cage, and iG) impeller. The impeller carries the abrasive to the opening (n the control cage where it discharges to the bladed section of the wheel. (American Wheelabrator & Equipment Corp.)

Fig. 18–28. Tumbling style of metal cleaner. (American Wheelabrator & Equipment Corp.)

of cleaning is considered the most efficient in shops where a large amount of work is cleaned daily.

The driving unit may also be used in a tumbling machine (Fig. 18–28) which is preferred for the speedy cleaning of castings and similar parts that can withstand being tumbled around. A phantom view of the Tumblast showing how the abrasive is driven against the parts to be cleaned, and the manner of elevating the abrasive to be used again, is shown in Fig. 18–29.

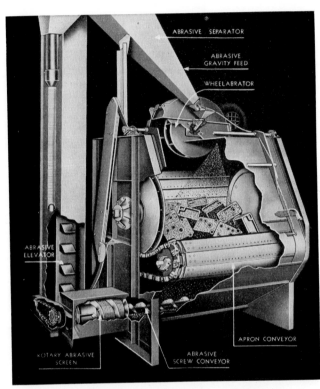

Fig. 18–29. Phantom view of tumbler showing manner of operation. (American Wheelabrator & Equipment Corp.)

Metal parts are also cleaned by wire-wheel brushes mounted on a general-purpose grinding machine (Fig. 18–30) or held in an electric drill. Brushes of this kind are shown in Fig. 18–31.

39. *What are some of the safety rules which should be observed in the heat-treating department?*

Ans. (1) Goggles must be worn when working on a lead, cyanide, or nitrate pot. (2) Cyanide is a deadly poison. Do not leave any of it around. Keep it under lock and key. (3) Do not put anything damp or wet into a heating pot, or an explosion will occur. (4) Do not leave hot tongs where other persons may accidentally be burned by them. (5)

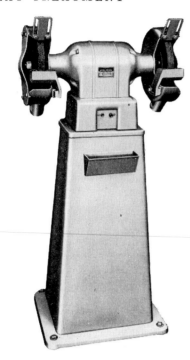

Fig. 18–30. General-purpose grinding machine. (Black & Decker Mfg. Co.)

Fig. 18–31. Wire brushes for use on grinding machine or electric drill. (Black & Decker Mfg. Co.)

Do not pick up a piece of work with the bare hands unless you are sure that it is not hot. (6) Rubber gloves must be worn while sandblasting or wet-blasting.

Some samples of typical heat-treatments for various types of steel are listed below:

Commercial annealing
1. Heat to 1500 to 1550°F.
2. Cool in mica.
3. To eliminate scale, pack in charcoal.

Commercial normalizing
1. Heat to 1425°F.
2. Cool in air.

Cyaniding of low-carbon steel
1. Heat in cyanide 1500 to 1560°F. Soak 10 min.
2. Quench in brine; small parts in oil.
3. Test for hardness with a file.
   Use for a hard surface not subject to continuous wear.
   Do not grind.
   Suitable for clamps, locating gages, pressure and stripper pads, stock guides, bolts, nuts, and washers.

Carburizing of low-carbon steel
1. Carburize at 1700°F.
2. Cool in carburizing box.
3. Reheat to 1650°F.
4. Cool in air.
5. Reheat to 1425°F.
6. Quench in brine.
7. Strain-draw in oil at 350 to 375°F.
8. Hardness of Rockwell 62–64 required.
   Because of soft core, should be used for parts difficult to straighten. This heat-treatment may also be used for selective hardening where it is necessary to machine after hardening, in which case:
   a. Leave stock.
   b. Carburize.
   c. Remove surplus stock.
   d. Harden.
   e. Machine.

SAE 1075 spring steel
1. Heat to 1450°F.
2. Quench in oil.
3. Draw temper at 750°F.
4. Hardness of Rockwell 41–44 required.
   Use for all types of steel springs.

SAE 1095 tool steel
1. Heat to 1400 to 1450°F.
2. Quench in brine.
3. Strain-draw in oil at 350 to 375°F.
4. Draw temper if specified.

5. Hardness: Rockwell 52–64, as required.

Suitable for arbors, ball races, bushings, cams, chuck jaws, gages, locators, rest buttons, V blocks, etc.

Use when the maximum hardness is desired.

For small parts, quench in oil if the required degree of hardness can be obtained.

SAE 3150 die steel

1. Heat to 1620°F.
2. Cool in air (fan-blast)
3. Draw to 1050 to 1075°F.
4. Hardness of Rockwell 42–46 required.

Suitable for hammer-die inserts, hot-heading dies.

SAE 5132 steel

1. Rough-machine.
2. Heat to 1560°F.
3. Quench in brine or caustic solution.
4. Draw to 950 to 1050°F.

5. Cool in air.
6. Finish machining.
7. Hardness of Rockwell 30–34 required.

To be used where accuracy combined with toughness is more important than hardness.

Suitable for armature shafts, large boring bars, large gears, miscellaneous heavy machine parts.

SAE 6470 high-speed steel

1. Preheat to 1450 to 1500°F.
2. Superheat to 2225 to 2240°F.
3. Quench in oil.
4. Double draw in furnace at 1050°F, allowing 3 hr for each draw.
5. Hardness of Rockwell 63–65 required.
6. If necessary, redraw in nitrate at 700 to 800°F for 3 or 4 hr to reduce brittleness.

Suitable for broaches, counterbores, cut-off tools, form tools, milling cutters, reamers, special drills, spot-facers, tool bits.

Chapter 19 ABRASIVES AND GRINDING

WHEELS

To do a good job of grinding, one must understand abrasives and grinding wheels. In this chapter natural and manufactured abrasives are described; and the bonds and abrasives used in making grinding wheels, the different grades and shapes of grinding wheels, and the selection of the proper grinding wheel for different types of jobs are discussed.

ABRASIVES

An **Abrasive** is any material that has the ability to wear away a substance softer than itself. Sand and sandstone are perhaps the oldest abrasives known to mankind. Prehistoric man used sand and sandstone to form or shape edges of tools, and as tools became more and more important for preservation of life, he became more dependent on natural abrasives for maintenance of sharp tools.

Natural abrasives

Emery and **Corundum** are two natural abrasives which were commonly used in industry for the purpose of sharpening edged tools. They occur as a mineral deposit in the earth's crust. These abrasives, formed into wheels, were superior to the old grindstones in that they were capable of faster cutting and could be made coarse or fine. In spite of this, they could not meet the demands of industry because they contained impurities which were difficult to extract and because the percentage of the important cutting element, aluminum oxide, was not constant.

Manufactured abrasives

The only other element known to be harder than emery or corundum is the diamond, but its

cost was prohibitive as far as industrial usage was concerned. In 1891, Dr. Edward G. Acheson set himself to the task of trying to produce artificial diamonds. His experiment consisted of combining powdered coke and corundum clay at extremely high temperatures. After the mass cooled it was found to contain brightly colored crystals, which, upon examination, proved to possess the ability to cut glass and to have a slight cutting effect on diamonds. To this new substance Dr. Acheson gave the name *carborundum* because it was formed from carbon and corundum; later, however, this new substance was found to be composed of silicon and carbon so that the name *silicon carbide,* having the chemical symbol SiC, was given to it.

This new material, silicon carbide, was considered the answer to the quest for a better abrasive, but cost and limited methods of manufacture kept it from being used except as a lapping compound for finishing precious jewels; but with the development of hydroelectric generators and cheap electric power, the cost of production was cut to a point where all industries could afford to use it.

About the same time that Dr. Acheson was experimentally producing silicon carbide, Charles P. Jacobs, an engineer at Ampere, N.J., was conducting similar experiments to produce a better grade of emery. His experiments consisted of trying to extract the impurities of sand, iron, and titanium oxides from clay deposits rich in aluminum oxide by use of a small electric furnace. The result was a product which consisted of about 95 percent pure aluminum oxide and possessed characteristics similar to those of silicon carbide.

Characteristics and manufacture

While these two artificial abrasives are similar, their properties differ widely. Silicon carbide is extremely hard, being rated at 9.87 on the Mohs scale of hardness as compared with 10.0 for the diamond. It is easily fractured by impact, and its excellence depends upon the purity of the ingredients used in making it. It has a specific gravity of 3.18, which is very low in comparison with other abrasives. Aluminum oxide is not as hard as silicon carbide but it is much tougher. On the Mohs scale of hardness, it is rated at 9.6 as compared with 9.87 for silicon carbide and 10.0 for the diamond.

Silicon carbide is suited for grinding materials which have a low tensile strength but which are very hard in nature, such as ceramics, pottery, and tungsten carbide.

Aluminum oxide, because of its toughness, is resistant to shock and therefore suitable for grinding materials of high tensile strength, such as tool steel and high-speed steel.

Artificial abrasives have a distinct advantage over natural abrasives in that purity of product and grain size can be readily controlled. This is important because undersize grains cannot do their share of the work, while oversize grains give a poor finish to the work.

Electric furnaces are used to produce both types of abrasives. Silicon carbide is made in an open troughlike furnace, by fusing a mixture of coke, sawdust, sand, and salt. After the mass has cooled,

the sides of the furnace are let down, exposing a big clinker; this clinker is broken by means of a drop weight, and the pieces put through a crushing machine. As the abrasive particles leave the last crusher, they are magnetically cleaned and washed, after which they pass onto shaker screens. These screens vary from 4 to 220 meshes to the lineal inch. By their vibrating action they sort the grains according to a definite size. If the abrasive passes through a screen having 30 meshes to the lineal inch, but is retained on a screen of 36 meshes, it is called a *No. 30 abrasive.* Abrasives finer than 220 are graded for size by hydraulic or sedimentation methods. After the abrasive has been graded to size, it is dried and placed in storage bins or hoppers for future use. Table 19–1 shows how the various grain sizes are classified.

Table 19–1. GRAIN-SIZE CLASSIFICATION

Very coarse	Coarse	Medium	Fine	Very fine	Flour sizes
8	12	30	70	150	280
10	14	36	80	180	320
	16	46	90	220	400
	20	60	100	240	500
	24		120		600

GRINDING WHEELS

Grinding wheels (see Fig. 19–1) are formed by using a suitable material to cement or bond the abrasive grains together in the desired shape. The hardness or softness of the wheel is dependent on the amount and kind of bonding material used. Since the hardness rating of the abrasive is constant, it is apparent that the bond can have no effect whatever upon it. When speaking of the hardness or softness of the wheel, it is always understood to have reference to the strength of the bond.

Bonds

There are a great many different kinds of bonds. The kinds commonly used are the **vitrified, silicate, shellac, rubber,** and **resinoid.** Of these bonds, the vitrified and silicate are used most. The **vitrified** bond is used in making about 75 percent of all grinding wheels. The reason for this is that its strength and porosity enable it to remove con-

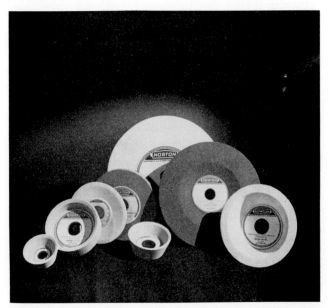

Fig. 19–1. Various types of grinding wheels. (Norton Co.)

siderable stock from the job for each inch of wheel wear; it is not affected by water, acids, or ordinary temperature changes, and it is free from hard and soft spots. In the vitrified process, glass, feldspar, flint, or other ceramic substances are mixed with the abrasive and subjected to heat, which causes the bond to form a glasslike structure between each abrasive particle.

In the **silicate** bond, silicate of soda is used. Besides the amount of bond used, the hardness of this wheel is governed by the amount of tamping or pressing. This produces a wheel which is milder acting than the vitrified wheel and permits the abrasive grains to be released more readily; therefore, they do not heat up so fast. Silicate wheels can be made in larger diameters than vitrified wheels and are generally used for grinding edged tools such as drills, reamers, milling cutters, etc.

Rubber wheels (Fig. 19–2) are made of a mixture of abrasive, rubber, and sulfur; the mass is then pressed into shape and given a mild vulcanizing treatment. Wheels of this bond are used for high-speed grinding operations and, because of their high safety factor, can be made very thin and can be used for cutting off steel stock.

Fig. 19–2. Rubber grinding wheels. (Norton Co.)

Shellac-bonded wheels are made by mixing the abrasive and bond in a heated machine which mixes and completely coats the abrasive with the bonding material. After the wheels are formed, they are placed in an oven, covered with sand, and then baked for a short time at approximately 300°F. Wheels of this bond are used very extensively for grinding mill rolls and jobs where a high-luster finish is required.

Resinoid-bonded wheels are made by mixing powdered resinoid with the abrasive particles and then adding a plastic substance so that the wheels can be molded. The mold is then placed in an electric oven and heated at approximately 300°F for a period ranging from a few hours to 3 or 4 days, depending on the size of the wheel. Upon cooling, the wheel becomes very hard. Wheels of this bond are generally used in foundries for snagging castings or for cleaning up steel billets.

Wheel structure

The amount of puddling or packing that is applied in forming the grinding wheel is very influential in the way the wheel cuts, because it affects the wheel structure (Fig. 19–3), or grain spacing. Two wheels of the same grade and grain size but of different grain spacing will have different cutting actions. Wheels with wide grain spacing should be used on hard, dense material and those with close spacing should be used to secure a good finish on the work. For this reason, wheel life can often be increased without sacrificing grinding quality, using the same grain and grade of wheel but with a different structure.

Wheel grading

As has been previously stated, the amount of bond used in making a grinding wheel determines its hardness. The degrees of hardness are specified by use of the letters of the alphabet. The Norton Company and several other companies use a letter-

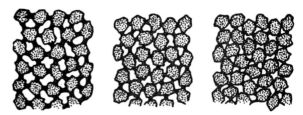

Fig. 19–3. Grain spacing in a grinding wheel: wide, medium, close.

ing system by which letters at the beginning of the alphabet indicate soft wheels and letters at the end of the alphabet indicate hard wheels. The lettering system for the grade of bond is shown in Table 19–3. The Carborundum Company uses a system in the reverse order. Table 19–2 shows the grades and grain sizes commonly used.

Table 19–2. COMMONLY USED GRADES AND GRAIN SIZES

	Surface	Internal	External	Cutter
Grades	F G H I J K P	I J K L	J K L M P*	I J K L
Grain sizes	36–46–60–80 120	34–46 60–120	46–60–80 120	36–46 60

* P for corners.

In the Norton system, a wheel which is marked 3860–K5BE has the following characteristics: 38 represents the kind of abrasive, which in this case is Alundum, or aluminum oxide, abrasive; 60 is the grain size, which, according to Table 19–1, is medium; K indicates the grade of the bond, which, according to Table 19–3, is soft; 5 indicates the wheel structure; the numbers from 0 to 3 indicate close structure; 4 to 6 indicate medium structure; 7 to 12 indicate coarse structure. The last symbol in the wheel marking indicates the kind of bond. BE indicates the vitrified bond. S indicates a silicate bond; T is for the resinoid bond; R for the rubber bond; and I for the shellac bond.

Table 19–3. GRADE OF BOND

Very soft	Soft	Medium	Hard	Very hard
E	H	L	P	T
F	I	M	Q	U
G	J	N	R	W
	K	O	S	Z

Wheel selection

There are several factors which affect the selection of a grinding wheel. They are the kind of material to be ground, the amount of stock to be removed, the accuracy as to size, the kind of finish required, the area of contact between the wheel and the work, and the kind of grinding machine to be used.

The nature of the material to be ground affects the selection of the wheel because, generally speaking, hard, dense materials require wheels possessing a soft bond with silicon carbide abrasive; materials that are soft and tough require a hard bond using aluminum oxide abrasive.

The amount of material to be removed is important in selecting a grinding wheel because, when there is a considerable amount of material to be removed, the grains of a coarse-grain wheel with wide spacing will be capable of taking a bigger, deeper cut without heating the work, but with a slight sacrifice as to surface finish. When the amount of stock to be removed is slight, a wheel of fine grain and narrow spacing will take a smaller bite and give a good finish.

There are other factors which affect the grinding operation, such as the speed of the wheel, the speed of the work, the condition of the grinding machine, and the knowledge and skill of the machine operator.

GRINDING THEORY

Grinding is the act of dressing, shaping, or finishing surfaces by means of a rotating abrasive wheel. In modern machine-shop operation, it has been found by actual test that grinding costs will vary as much as 100 percent on the same work with the same kind of machine in the same factory. This is due to the difference in the handling and skill of operation of the machine by the mechanic. A good mechanic takes into consideration the factors involving the mounting, movement, size, and speed of the work and the mounting, movement, size, speed, and dressing, or truing, of the grinding wheel.

For precision grinding, the work must be held rigidly, to avoid vibration and to produce a good finish. If the work is held between centers, the center holes must be free from nicks, burrs, or dirt. The machine centers must be held securely and be free from nicks. If held in a chuck or fixture, the work must be solidly supported and clamped so as to put the least strain on it. After the work is correctly mounted, the work speed must be selected so that it will move at approximately the right number of surface feet per minute to prevent distortion and excessive wear of the wheel face, and, at the same time, the traverse movement must be at a constant speed to prevent high and low spots on the work. The mechanism for moving the wheel must work smoothly and freely without play or bind to ensure accuracy as to depth of cut.

The grinding-wheel mounting is important, because it must give steady and true motion to the wheel so that after it is trued up it will be free from vibration, will have a steady cutting action, and be capable of producing a good finish after it is properly dressed.

Grinding-wheel speeds

In most modern grinding machines, the speed of the wheel is fixed as built by the manufacturer of the machine. Grinding wheels may be run from 5,000 to 6,000 surface speed in feet per minute (sfpm). In case it is necessary to determine what the surface feet per minute of a wheel is, place a tachometer or speed indicator in the center of the spindle and check the revolutions for one minute; then multiply the diameter of the wheel by 3.1416, which will give the circumference of the wheel in inches. The circumference multiplied by the rpm will give the distance in inches which the wheel would travel in one minute if laid on its periphery and rolled at its given rpm. This result divided by 12 (12 in. to the foot) gives the surface speed in feet per minute.

EXAMPLE: Determine the surface speed in feet per minute of a grinding wheel 7 in. in diameter mounted on a surface grinder. Using a tachometer, the rpm is found to read 3,200. Multiply the diameter of the wheel by 3.1416, by 3,200, and divide by 12:

$$\frac{7 \times 3.1416 \times 3,200}{12} = \frac{70,371.84}{12} = 5,864.3$$

Thus the surface speed in feet per minute equals 5,864.3.

Table 19–4 shows the peripheral or surface speed of grinding wheels in relation to the rpm of the wheels.

By being a good observer, the operator can tell many things about the work and machine. Poor or defective bearings readily show up while the wheel is being dressed, for the diamond will not show a steady red spark as it moves across the face of the wheel.

Chatter or vibration

If the work vibrates, it will be shown by lines on the work parallel to the work axis, known as *chatter*. This may be remedied by changing to a softer wheel, tightening the spindle bearings, checking and repairing bad belt connections, taking a lighter cut, or cutting down on the work speed. If the work shows mottled surfaces, it is generally an indication of vibration due to irregular motion of the grinding wheel. This irregular motion may be caused by the lead core in the wheel being improperly placed, the wheel being waterlogged on one side, the structure of the wheel being of uneven density, or the face of the wheel being improperly trued.

Glazing and loading

Glazing of the wheel is a condition in which the face or cutting edge takes on a glasslike appearance and is caused by the abrasive grains wearing away faster than the bond. As long as the bond is being worn away as fast as the abrasive particles of the wheel are being dulled, the wheel will continue to have good cutting action. To remedy this condition of glazing, use a wheel having a softer bond.

Frequently the material being ground clogs up or becomes imbedded in the pores of the wheel. This condition is known as *loading* or *pinning* and is caused by the work speed being too slow, the wheel action too hard, or crowding the wheel.

The continued use of the wheel after it becomes glazed or loaded puts an added strain on the work supports and wheel-spindle bearings, forces the wheel out of true, and, if continued for long, will produce chatter marks or surface checks on the work.

Dressing

The cutting face of a grinding wheel must be kept in a true, clean, sharp condition, if the grinding operation is to be done efficiently. This requires frequent dressing, or truing, of the wheel. **Dressing** is the operation of cleaning, or fracturing, the cutting surface of a wheel for the purpose of exposing new cutting particles. **Truing** a wheel is the operation of removing material from the cutting face so that the resulting surface runs concentric with the wheel-spindle axis.

The operations of truing and dressing grinding wheels are usually accomplished by using a commercial diamond or piece of tungsten carbide inserted in the conical point of a piece of cold-rolled steel; by a diamond-dust-impregnated cement, formed into a stick and encased in metal tubing;

Table 19-4. REVOLUTIONS PER MINUTE FOR VARIOUS DIAMETERS OF GRINDING WHEELS TO GIVE PERIPHERAL SPEED IN FEET PER MINUTE AS INDICATED *

Diameter of wheel, in.	Peripheral speed in feet per minute											
	4,000	4,500	5,000	5,500	6,000	6,500	7,000	7,500	8,000	8,500	9,000	9,500
	Revolutions per minute											
1	15,279	17,189	19,098	21,008	22,918	24,828	26,737	28,647	30,558	32,467	34,377	36,287
2	7,639	8,594	9,549	10,504	11,459	12,414	13,368	14,328	15,279	16,233	17,188	18,143
3	5,093	5,729	6,366	7,003	7,639	8,276	8,913	9,549	10,186	10,822	11,459	12,115
4	3,820	4,297	4,775	5,252	5,729	6,207	6,685	7,162	7,640	8,116	8,595	9,072
5	3,056	3,438	3,820	4,202	4,584	4,966	5,348	5,730	6,112	6,494	6,876	7,258
6	2,546	2,865	3,183	3,501	3,820	4,138	4,456	4,775	5,092	5,411	5,729	6,048
7	2,183	2,455	2,728	3,001	3,274	3,547	3,820	4,092	4,366	4,538	4,911	5,183
8	1,910	2,148	2,387	2,626	2,865	3,103	3,342	3,580	3,820	4,058	4,297	4,535
10	1,528	1,719	1,910	2,101	2,292	2,483	2,674	2,865	3,056	3,247	3,438	3,629
12	1,273	1,432	1,591	1,751	1,910	2,069	2,228	2,386	2,546	2,705	2,864	3,023
14	1,091	1,228	1,364	1,500	1,637	1,773	1,910	2,046	2,182	2,319	2,455	2,592
16	955	1,074	1,194	1,313	1,432	1,552	1,672	1,791	1,910	2,029	2,149	2,268
18	849	955	1,061	1,167	1,273	1,379	1,485	1,591	1,698	1,803	1,910	2,016
20	764	859	955	1,050	1,146	1,241	1,337	1,432	1,528	1,623	1,719	1,814
22	694	781	868	955	1,042	1,128	1,215	1,302	1,388	1,476	1,562	1,649
24	637	716	796	875	955	1,034	1,115	1,194	1,274	1,353	1,433	1,512
26	588	661	734	808	881	955	1,028	1,101	1,176	1,248	1,322	1,395
28	546	614	682	750	818	887	955	1,023	1,092	1,159	1,228	1,296
30	509	573	637	700	764	828	891	955	1,018	1,082	1,146	1,210
32	477	537	597	656	716	776	836	895	954	1,014	1,074	1,134
34	449	505	562	618	674	730	786	843	898	955	1,011	1,067
36	424	477	530	583	637	690	742	795	848	902	954	1,007

* *Example:* To find the rpm of an 18-in. wheel having a surface speed of 6,000 fpm, read across in the 18 line to the 6,000 column, which gives 1,273 rpm.

or by a piece of silicon carbide mounted as a small wheel on an axle and placed in a cast iron base. In using any of these implements, the point of the dresser is brought into contact with the face of the wheel by means of a special holder, and then moved mechanically or by hand across the face of the wheel at a rate of speed which will produce the desired form or surface on the cutting edge.

A clean, true wheel of the proper bond and abrasive size is a very efficient cutting tool, but, at best, will cause the work to heat up rapidly. In the case of the lathe tool, there is only one cutting point acting on the work, but even so, it is a well-known fact that the cutting tool, work, and chips get quite hot. In the case of a grinding wheel, there are thousands of these cutting points each doing its share of the work but all acting at the same time, so that, since the action of a lathe tool generates heat, the action of a grinding wheel would necessarily develop a much greater heat. For that reason, a flood of lubricant-coolant at the point of contact between the wheel and work is necessary to carry off the heat and to keep the temperature of both the wheel and work as nearly constant as possible. This is especially true where a job is roughed and finish-ground.

Rough grinding

The purpose of roughing the job is to remove internal strains set up by heat-treatment and to remove the excess stock as rapidly as possible in preparation for finishing. Roughing is accomplished by using a slow work speed and a fast traverse, then when finishing, using a high work speed and slow traverse. In both cases, use a flood of good coolant.

The following are suggestions, originally made by well-known grinding-wheel and machine manufacturers, which, if generally adopted, should do much to eliminate grinding accidents.

Care of grinding wheels

1. Handle all wheels with the greatest care in storing or delivery. Wheels are frequently cracked by rough usage long before they are ever placed on a grinding machine.
2. Wheels should be stored in a dry place.
3. Before a wheel is placed on the spindle, it should be sounded for cracks. A solid wheel, when tapped by a nonmetallic object, gives off a dull ringing sound. A cracked wheel gives off a dull thudding sound.
4. Make sure that the grinding wheel is equipped with blotting-paper gaskets on each side.
5. Never crowd a wheel on the spindle; the hole in the wheel should be 0.003 to 0.005 in. oversize to permit it to slide easily on the spindle and squarely against the flange.
6. Never mount a wheel without flanges, which should be properly relieved and of suitable proportions.
7. Don't screw the wheel nut too tight. The nut should be set up only tight enough so that the flanges hold the wheel firmly.
8. Keep the wheel clean and true by frequent dressing, but don't remove any more stock than is necessary to put the wheel in proper condition.
9. If a wheel vibrates excessively after it has been properly trued, there is something wrong. Stop the machine and call an instructor.
10. Large wheels, that is, wheels over 12 in., require special balancing. Don't attempt to balance them yourself.

REVIEW QUESTIONS

1. What is meant by the term *abrasive?*
2. Name two natural abrasives.
3. Name two artificial abrasives.
4. Why are artificial abrasives used more than natural abrasives?
5. What are the characteristics of silicon carbide?
6. Name four materials on which silicon carbide should be used.
7. On what kinds of material should aluminum oxide be used?
8. Why is control of the abrasive grain size important?
9. How is the abrasive grain size determined?
10. How are the abrasive particles formed into a wheel?
11. What determines the hardness or softness of a wheel?
12. Name five commonly used bonds.
13. Which bond is used most frequently? Give five reasons.
14. What are the advantages of the silicate bond?
15. Silicate-bonded wheels are generally used for what purpose?
16. Rubber-bonded wheels are used for what purpose?
17. How does the wheel structure affect the grinding operation?
18. How are the degrees of hardness of the wheels specified?
19. What is the difference between the Norton and Carborundum methods of rating hardness?
20. Into what five groups are the degrees of hardness divided?
21. What six factors govern the wheel selection for a given job?
22. Give four methods of overcoming chatter.
23. What is the difference between glazing and loading?
24. What is the difference between dressing and truing?
25. Why is it necessary to keep the face of the wheel clean and true?
26. For general toolroom work, which abrasive is most generally used, and why?
27. How might the grade and structure of the grinding wheel produce chatter?

Chapter 20 GRINDING MACHINES

A grinding machine is a machine which employs a grinding wheel for producing cylindrical, conical, or plane surfaces accurately and economically and to the proper shape, size, and finish. The surplus stock is removed either by feeding the work against the revolving wheel or by forcing the revolving wheel against the work.

There is a great variety of grinding machines, but it is the purpose of this text to treat only of those machines which are regularly used in tool and die shops. The machines which are generally used are the cutter grinder, cylindrical grinder, surface grinder, internal grinder, tool grinder, and thread grinder. These machines are usually classified as to size by the largest piece of work which they can completely machine, as 6- by 18-in. external grinder, or are specified by numbers, such as Brown and Sharpe No. 13, Rivet No. 104 internal, and No. 3 abrasive surface grinder.

CUTTER GRINDER

A cutter grinder is a machine that holds the cutter while a rotating abrasive wheel is applied to the edges for the purpose of sharpening it. These machines vary in design from simple machines having a limited purpose to complex universal machines that can be adapted to any cutter-grinding requirements.

Figure 20–1 is an illustration of a universal cutter grinder that is of particular value for grinding and resharpening all kinds of cutters that may be held in spring chucks or collets. The work head, on the left, may be moved from left to right (longitudinally), and swiveled around through 235 deg. The wheel head, on the right, may be moved up or down, to left or right, or back and forth.

Another type of cutter grinder is shown in Fig. 20–2. This machine is designed to hold work in a chuck or collets, and also between centers. The

Fig. 20–1. Universal cutter and tool grinder. (Cincinnati Grinders, Inc.)

A. Work head	F. Wheel head
B. Work head spindle	G. Wheel head spindle
C. Longitudinal slide	H. Vertical slide
D. Turntable	J. Longitudinal slide
E. Indexing mechanism	K. Transverse slide

work head may be moved to a required position on the table, and swiveled from side to side. The wheel head may be moved up and down, back and forth, or swiveled around through 220 deg.

The universal cutter grinder is capable of grinding cutters of various shapes by using special attachments and specially formed grinding wheels. Generally the flaring cup, plain, and dish or saucer wheels are used on cutter grinders (Fig. 20–3).

Fig. 20–2. Cutter and tool grinder. (Landis Tool Co.)

In selecting a grinding wheel for general-purpose cutter grinding, select a soft, free-cutting wheel and take very light cuts so that the temper is not drawn from the edge of the teeth. Generally speaking, wheels of grain size from 30 to 60 and J or K bond are best adapted for high-speed cutters. The shape of the wheel depends on the shape of the cutter to be sharpened.

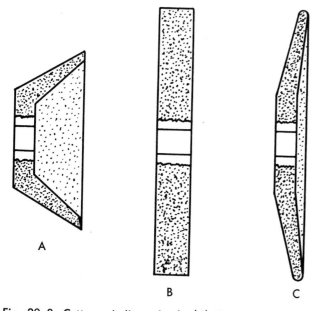

Fig. 20–3. Cutter grinding wheels. (A) Flaring cup wheel, (B) plain wheel, and (C) dish or saucer wheel.

Sharpening of cutters

Plain-milling cutter. To sharpen the teeth of a plain-milling cutter, the cutter is generally mounted on a lathe mandrel and supported between centers, as shown in Fig. 20–4, or the cutter

Fig. 20–4. Sharpening a plain-milling cutter. (Norton Co.)

is mounted on a special stub arbor and held in a universal swivel fixture (Fig. 20–5). After the cutter has been mounted in the machine, a tooth rest is mounted on the table or work head and adjusted to the tooth to be first sharpened.

Tooth rests are of two kinds, plain and hook (Fig. 20–6). They consist of a piece of spring steel about 0.030 in. thick, 1/2 to 1 1/2 in. wide, and from 1 to 3 in. long, brazed or riveted in a piece of round, 3/8-in. cold-rolled steel. They are held by means of a forged clamping fixture (Fig. 20–7), by bolting the fixture either to the worktable or the grinding-wheel head. The table and tooth rest are adjusted so that the grinding wheel follows the original land on the back of the tooth and gives the proper clearance. The cutter is then fed to the rotating grinding wheel until sparks indicate contact between it and the wheel; then the table is moved back and forth, traversing the cutter until the wheel has finished cutting. Next, the cutter is revolved backward 180 deg against the spring tension of the tooth rest and, without changing the depth of cut, a trial cut is taken on this opposite tooth to check for taper. If no taper is apparent, the cutter is revolved backward and the next tooth is sharpened. This process is repeated until all teeth have been sharpened and ground concentric.

Side-milling cutter. The peripheral teeth of a

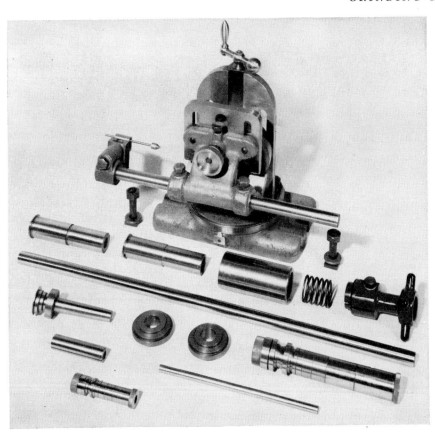

Fig. 20-5. Universal head or swivel fixture and accessories used with it. (Brown & Sharpe Mfg. Co.)

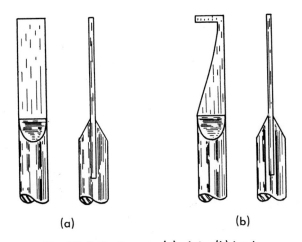

Fig. 20-6. Tooth rests: (a) plain; (b) hook.

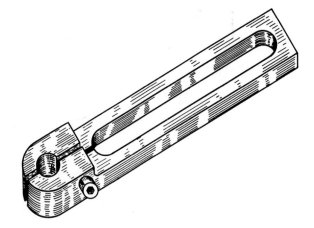

Fig. 20-7. Clamp for tooth rests.

side-milling cutter are sharpened the same way as those of a plain-milling cutter. To sharpen the side teeth, the cutter is generally mounted on a stub expansion arbor and placed in the universal swivel fixture (Fig. 20-8). The swivel fixture is then adjusted so that the side teeth will be ground about 1 deg out of parallel with the side of the cutter and have a side clearance of from 3 to 5 deg. The gen-

eral practice is to give the teeth of roughing cutters a side clearance of 5 deg and finishing cutters, 3 deg. It is important in all cutter grinding to grind all teeth to the same height, so that each tooth will do its share of cutting. For that reason, after the teeth have all been sharpened, a very light cut is taken on each tooth to insure uniform height.

Slabbing cutters. These cutters, which are of

Fig. 20–8. Grinding side teeth of side-milling cutter. (Norton Co.)

considerable length relative to their diameters, are sharpened the same way as a plain-milling cutter, if they have straight teeth.

Helical-tooth cutters. These are ground and mounted the same as other cutters, but the tooth rest must be mounted in a fixed position relative to the grinding wheel. Generally, the tooth rest is mounted on the wheel head, as shown in Fig. 20–9.

This is done so that the cutter is forced to slide over the tooth rest, causing the cutter to turn in such a manner that the tooth being ground will have the same helical shape as when it was originally milled. When the cutter and tooth rest are properly mounted and the grinding ready to start, the tooth should be pressed lightly against the tooth rest and held there while the table is moved longitudinally. If this is not done, the tooth will leave the rest and the cutter will be damaged.

Formed cutters. This type of cutter is sharpened by grinding the face of the teeth radially, that is, by grinding the face of the teeth with a dish or saucer wheel so that the face of the tooth comes on the radius of the cutter.

The machine is set up for grinding the formed cutter by bringing the centers in line with the face of the grinding wheel. If this is not done, the cutter will not have the correct shape.

The cutter, mounted on a mandrel, is placed between the centers and the face of the tooth brought against the grinding wheel. The tooth rest is then set against the back of the tooth. Move the table longitudinally, clear the wheel from the work, start the wheel, and take a trial cut. To adjust the work to the wheel while grinding, revolve the cutter by moving the tooth rest toward the grinding wheel. This practice keeps the faces of the teeth radial and maintains the correct shape of the tooth.

Fig. 20–9. Tooth rest is mounted on wheel head when grinding helical-tooth cutter. (Brown & Sharpe Mfg. Co.)

Fig. 20–10. Using a master form for spacing and support while sharpening a gear cutter. (Norton Co.)

Various methods are used to control the proper spacing of the teeth. In Fig. 20–10, a master form, having the same number of teeth as the gear cutter to be sharpened, is placed securely on the end of the mandrel. The tooth rest is then placed in turn under each tooth of the master form.

Angular cutter. To sharpen an angular cutter, the cutter is mounted on a stub expansion arbor and placed in a swivel fixture (Fig. 20–11). The fixture is then swiveled to the desired clearance angle and the tooth rest set on the exact center line of the cutter. Adjust the grinding wheel to the cutter by raising or lowering the table so it will grind the tooth supported by the tooth rest and allow the tooth immediately above to clear the grinding wheel, as illustrated. The tooth rest should never be set above or below center as this will cause a change in the actual angle ground on the cutter from the one at which the machine has been set, this is often the cause of angular cutters not being accurate.

Fig. 20–11. Grinding an angular cutter. (Norton Co.)

End mills. These, whether they are straight or helical, are ground the same as milling cutters. The end teeth are ground the same as the side teeth of a side-milling cutter. The end mill is held between centers. The tooth rest is set on the wheel-spindle slide (see Fig. 20–12), or it may be held in the V block of the universal head, as in Fig. 20–13.

Concave- and convex-shaped cutters. This type may be sharpened with the aid of a radius-grinding attachment. The edge of the grinding wheel is first dressed to the radius of the cutter. As shown in Fig. 20–14, the wheel head is swiveled to bring the wheel in position to face the cutter. The cutter is held on a mandrel by the work holders. The work slide and the base are then adjusted so that, as the swivel is turned, the grinding wheel contacts the

Fig. 20–12. Grinding an end mill between centers. (Brown & Sharpe Mfg. Co.)

Fig. 20–13. Grinding an end mill held in the V block of the universal head. (Brown & Sharpe Mfg. Co.)

surface of the cutting edge of the cutter perfectly. Note the position of the tooth rest.

Wheel shapes

As was previously mentioned, there are three wheel shapes commonly used for cutter grinding. They are the **disk, flaring-cup,** and **saucer** wheels. The saucer wheel is used for grinding formed cutters; the disk wheel is used for grinding the clearance on cutters having narrow lands on the teeth;

Fig. 20–14. Sharpening the edges of a concave cutter with a radius-grinding attachment. (Brown & Sharpe Mfg. Co.)

the flaring-cup wheel is used for grinding clearance on teeth having wide lands, and for gumming out slitting saws and the spacing between the teeth of milling cutters.

In actual practice, the grinding wheel revolves downward toward the cutting edge, so that the action of the wheel forces the tooth against the tooth rest, as in Fig. 20–15. This practice results in a burr or wire edge being left on the tooth, which should be oil-stoned off.

A keener cutting edge, free from burr, is obtained if the cutter to be sharpened is reversed, as

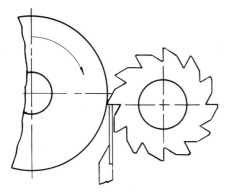

Fig. 20–15. In this arrangement, the grinding wheel rotates off the cutting edge.

in Fig. 20–16. The disadvantage is that it is more difficult to maintain the tooth rest in position, because the rotation of the grinding wheel tends to carry the cutter around.

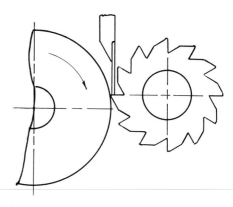

Fig. 20–16. In this arrangement, the grinding wheel rotates on to the cutting edge.

Important facts to remember when sharpening cutters

1. Keep the cutter tooth firmly against the tooth rest.
2. Make sure the grinding wheel follows the original land on the tooth.
3. Mount the tooth rest correctly.
4. Keep the cutting surface of the grinding wheel clean.
5. Don't remove any more stock from the tooth than that required to sharpen it.
6. Be careful not to draw the temper of the tooth.

Safety Rules for cutter grinders

The following safety rules for cutter grinders must be observed at all times:

1. Always wear goggles on all cutter-grinder work.
2. Under no circumstances is the machine to be started unless the grinding wheel is adequately guarded. Use a guard of the proper size and adjust it closely to the wheel, allowing the minimum amount of wheel exposure with which to work.
3. In mounting wheels on cutter grinders, use standard wheel bushings and safety washers. Use paper washers on large wheels.
4. When hand-dressing wheels, be careful to allow ample hand clearance between the wheel and the table or other parts of the machine.
5. Hand-dressing operations should be performed

with a light pressure, especially when dressing thin wheels. A slip of the hand or a broken wheel may cause severe lacerations.

6. Any changes of guards, dogs, centers, setup, tooth rests, or other parts of a machine are not to be made while the machine is running.

7. When grinding spot-facers, counterbores, and so forth, on a draw collet, use a special, automatic safety guard, or shut the machine down to remove the work.

8. In backing off drills, spiral reamers, and so forth, see that the tooth rest is properly adjusted in relation to the wheel and work, to prevent slippage and consequent spinning of stock. Ask the instructor about this.

9. Care should be taken in handling sharp tools, such as reamers, drills, cutters, and counterbores, as severe lacerations may result from stock slipping through the hands.

10. Towels are not to be used in holding small tools such as spot-facers, counterbores, and similar tools that become warm while grinding. Ask the instructor how to take care of work of this class.

11. Exhaust hoods are supplied as a safeguard for the health of grinder operators. See that they are properly adjusted at all times and that they are not abused.

REVIEW QUESTIONS
Cutter Grinding

1. What is a cutter grinder?
2. Name three manufacturers of universal cutter-grinding machines used in the shop.
3. What kinds of cutters can be sharpened on the universal cutter-grinding machine?
4. What kinds of grinding wheels are suitable for general-purpose cutter grinding?
5. What is a tooth rest, and why is it used in cutter grinding?
6. How are plain-milling cutters held for sharpening?
7. After the work and tooth rests are correctly mounted, how is the tooth sharpened?
8. Name three shapes of wheels used for cutter grinding.
9. How are the teeth of side-milling cutters sharpened?
10. How are slabbing cutters, having helical teeth, sharpened?

11. What caution should be exercised in sharpening the teeth of helical-tooth cutters?
12. How are the teeth of formed-tooth cutters ground?
13. Why are formed-tooth cutters ground radially on the face?
14. What is the shape of the wheel used for formed-tooth grinding?
15. How are end mills generally ground?
16. Why is it important to prevent burning of the cutting edge in cutter grinding?
17. What causes burning of the cutting edge in cutter grinding?
18. Name the two types of tooth rests most generally used.

CYLINDRICAL GRINDING
Shop terms: External, OD grinding
Internal, ID grinding

External grinders

External grinding, as commonly thought of, is the act of grinding the outside diameter of a piece of work while it is revolving on its axis, for the purpose of reducing it to size, and leaving a fine finish. However, external grinders are also used to produce external cams, eccentrics, and special forms on the outside diameter of work. They are machines upon which may be performed many of the operations done on a lathe, but much more accurately. The big advantage lies in the fact that, after a job has been heat-treated (hardened), a good surface finish and extreme accuracy as to size can be obtained. Where these two factors are important, the extra cost involved in grinding can be overlooked. If parts can be designed so that the amount of stock to be removed is within grinding limits, then grinding is much less costly than lathe turning.

External grinders are divided into three general groups. They are the plain cylindrical, the universal, and the special grinders like the centerless and cam grinders.

The plain cylindrical grinder. This grinder (Fig. 20–17) is used to produce external cylinders, tapers, fillets, undercuts, and shoulders, and may be used for form grinding by dressing the desired contour on the grinding wheel.

In any cylindrical grinder, there are three movements which are very important. They are (1) rotation of the work on its axis, (2) movement of the

Fig. 20–17. Plain hydraulic cylindrical grinder. (Landis Tool Co.)

A. On-and-off control lever
B. Two-speed hand traverse
C. Traverse speed-control valve
D. Traverse reversing lever

E. Traverse tarry control
F. Automatic feed selector
G. Electrical controls
H. Table-swiveling adjustment

J. Amount of slow-grinding feed control
K. Infeed control
L. Footstock spindle lever
M. Coarse and fine-wheel-feed handwheel

work back and forth in front of the wheel, and (3) movement of the wheel into the work. Trouble in cylindrical grinding, with exception of wheel content or make-up, can be attributed to one of the three movements mentioned.

Rotation of the work on its axis is important because, if the centers in the work are bad, or if

Fig. 20–18. Footstock of OD grinder. (Landis Tool Co.)

the machine centers are of poor quality and loose, the work will be irregular in form. The movement of the work back and forth in front of the wheel must be steady and smooth to insure a good finish and accurate sizing of the work. Movement of the wheel spindle in revolving the wheel must be true and smooth, to prevent vibration and to avoid chatter marks on the work. Movement of the wheel into the work must be without play or bind, to ensure accuracy as to depth of cut.

The work in external grinding usually revolves on two dead centers, one in the footstock (Fig. 20–18), and one in the headstock (Fig. 20–19). It is given its rotary motion by means of a drive plate, which revolves about the headstock center, driven by a motor, using pulleys and a belt. The drive plate contains an adjustable arm which can be located at varying distances from the center and into which a drive pin is fitted. This drive pin engages the V slot of the grinder dog (Fig. 20–20) which is attached to the work, and hence the revolving motion of the plate is transmitted to the work.

Besides the rotary motion of the work, it is al-

Fig. 20–19. Headstock or work head of OD grinder. (Brown & Sharpe Mfg. Co.)

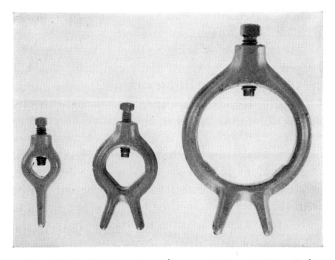

Fig. 20–20. Grinder dogs. (Brown & Sharpe Mfg. Co.)

ways necessary, except in the case of plunge-cut grinding, for the work to be traversed past the grinding wheel. The length of the table traverse should be set so as to permit the wheel to run off the end of the work about one-third of the wheel-face width. If the wheel is not permitted to overrun the end of the work, the job will be oversize at that point because the wheel will not have a chance to finish the cut. If the wheel is permitted to overrun the end of the work completely, the job will be undersize, because the pressure required between the wheel and the work is relaxed.

This permits the work to spring toward the wheel, and so, at the beginning of the traverse, the wheel would cut undersize.

At the end of each traverse, the table stops momentarily to give the wheel a chance to grind the work to size, to permit the wheel to clear itself on the new cut, and to avoid the jarring motion which would be unavoidable with an immediate reversal of the table. If the traversing is not accomplished without jarring, or without a jerking movement, of the table, the work will show high and low spots due to the slight pause, or dwell, of the wheel on the work, which would take place at each jerk or jar of the table. The speed of the traverse depends on the width of the wheel face and the type of finish required on the work. It is generally such that the table will move two-thirds to three-fourths of the wheel face for each revolution of the work.

Steady rest. Long, slender work, besides being supported by the centers at each end, should also be supported with steady rests. Figure 20–21 shows a center steady rest, while Fig. 20–22 shows a back rest.

When using steady rests, as in Figs. 20–23 and 20–24, it is very important to keep the jaws properly adjusted to the work; otherwise the work might get caught between the lower jaw and the

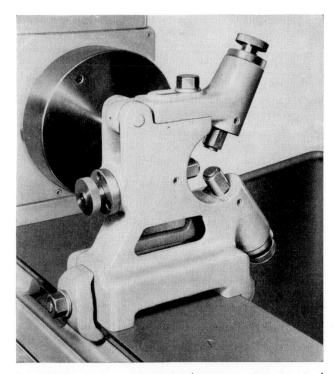

Fig. 20–21. Center steady rest. (Cincinnati Grinders, Inc.)

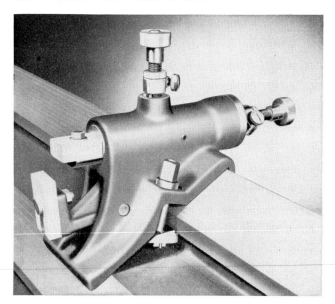

Fig. 20–22. Back rest. (Cincinnati Grinders, Inc.)

grinding wheel and be thrown from the machine, or it might break the grinding wheel.

Feeds. The grinding wheel can be fed to the work either by automatic or hand feed, and feeds as small as 0.00005 in. are obtainable. It is not advisable to use the hand feed except to bring the wheel up to the work, to move it away from the work, or when taking very fine cuts. The automatic feed takes cuts from 0.00025 to 0.004 in. for each traverse of the table. This saves time and wear and tear on the machine, because cuts are more uniform, and gives longer life to the grinding wheel. Generally speaking, roughing cuts may be from 0.001 to 0.004 in. at each reversal, depending on the rigidity of the machine, the work setup, and the amount of stock to be removed. It is common practice when the work is not to be hardened, to leave from 0.006 to 0.010 in. grind stock, but work which is large, long, slender, or easily sprung may have an allowance of from 0.020 to 0.030 in. grind stock; in either case, however, heavy infeeds require good supports for the work. For roughing out the job, use a slow work speed, fast traverse, and heavy feed. For finish-grinding a job, use a high work speed, slow traverse and a light feed.

The more common grades and grain sizes of aluminum oxide wheels used for external grinding are 46-J, 46-K, 60-K, 60-L, 80-O, 120-P.

Work speeds. To the question, How fast should the work speed be? no set answer can be given. Jobs may or may not be of the same metal, same

heat-treatment, or same diameter, any one of which factors affects the speed. Too fast a speed tends to wear away the wheel speedily, while too slow a speed causes the wheel to cut hard and become dull and glazed. If the wheel wears too fast, it requires more frequent dressing and truing, and takes more time to do a given job. Extremely hard steels may have to be ground at 30 sfpm, while very soft steels may require up to 100 sfpm for finishing. Common work speeds are from 30 to 50 sfpm. If the wheel becomes dull or glazed, it will burn the work because of the added friction caused by forcing the wheel to cut. If the work speed is correct and the wheel still has a tendency to become glazed, it is an indication that the bond is too hard and can be corrected by substituting a wheel of the same grain but softer bond.

Operation errors. When cracks, checks, or burns show up on the surface of the work, any one of a combination of the following conditions might be the cause: improper speeds of work, wheel too hard, or the wheel being glazed or loaded. If the wheel is glazed or loaded, it will cause the work to burn and crack even though there is a good supply of lubricant, so that best results can be obtained by keeping the wheel sharp and clean at all times.

Perhaps the greatest obstacle which the operator has to overcome in the grinding of a cylinder is that of taper developing in the work. Conditions which contribute to it are poor machine or work centers, work improperly mounted, worktable out of adjustment, footstock out of line with headstock, or steady rests bearing too heavily or out-of-line with the work.

To correct this tapering, first make sure that the centers of the work are clean and true, and of sufficient depth and clearance to give the machine centers a good bearing. Then, inspect the machine centers for correct taper to fit the machine, see that they are clean and true; mount the work and make sure that the machine centers are engaged properly; and inspect the worktable for side play and have it corrected if necessary. If none of the above factors is causing the taper, then correction can be made by adjusting the knurled screw located at the footstock end of the worktable. The screw should be turned to move the small end of the work away from the wheel. Several adjustments may be necessary to get the work entirely cylindrical and free from taper.

Fig. 20–23. A center steady rest is placed near the grinding wheel while grinding the large diameter of a long shaft. (Brown & Sharpe Mfg. Co.)

Fig. 20–24. Two back rests are used to support a long shaft while traverse grinding. (Landis Tool Co.)

Plunge-cut grinding. Plunge-cut grinding is cylindrical grinding where the length of the work is less than the width of the wheel face, so that the wheel can be fed straight into the work and the cylinder can be completely ground without using the table traverse. When it is necessary to grind a shouldered or stepped cylinder, plunge-cut grinding is used, to maintain a square corner between the cylinder and the shoulder. It should be remembered that a square corner is not necessarily a sharp corner. Figure 20–25 shows an example of plunge-cut grinding.

Fig. 20–25. Plunge-cut grinding a bearing diameter of a short shaft. (Landis Tool Co.)

Important steps in external grinding. The important steps in external-grinding a piece of work are as follows:

1. Check the work for size to make sure grinding stock has been allowed and at the same time note any tapering of the work.
2. Inspect the work centers for being clean and true. Select machine centers of suitable diameters to fill the work centers properly. The footstock center should be cut away enough to permit the grinding wheel to clear the end of the work; a center of this type is known as a one-half-full, or three-quarters-full, center.
3. Attach the grinding dog on the end of the job, making sure that the dog does not damage such parts of the work as threads and keyways, then lubricate the machine centers.
4. Set the table traverse for the length of the work, allowing for overrun of the end and the space that the grinder dog occupies.
5. If necessary, mount the steady rests and adjust the shoes to the work.
6. Dress the grinding wheel, passing the diamond across the face of the wheel quite fast, to make the wheel fast-cutting. Set the work speed at the correct surface speed in feet per minute.
7. Feed the wheel to the work by hand and take a light cut, noting that the wheel starts to cut approximately at the high point of the work, to conform to the check in step 1.
8. Check the work for size and taper and make any table adjustments necessary to ensure that the work will be straight.
9. Rough-grind the job to rough size. If several pieces are to be done, set the stop on the feed ratchet and proceed as before, roughing the balance of the pieces.
10. After the pieces have been roughed out in this manner, place the dog on the rough-ground end of the work and grind the unfinished end. If this end is shorter than the width of the wheel face, it may be plunge-cut-ground. Make sure that the grinding wheel is kept sharp and clean by frequent dressing.
11. To finish-grind, set the machine for fast work speed and slow traverse, and dress the wheel by passing the diamond slowly across the wheel face.
12. Insert the piece to be finish-ground and take a light trial cut. Check it for size and make any corrections necessary for removal of taper. If steady rests are used, keep them adjusted to the work.
13. After the first piece has been ground to finished size re-set the stop on the feed ratchet so that the infeed will produce the required size and then set the shoes on the steady rests for the finished diameter.

The above outline pertains to grinding a plain cylinder. If the work to be ground has shoulders, keyways, or slots, some deviations from the outline must be made. If the work to be ground has a keyway, open at each end, or splines, and steady rests are to be used, it should be filled with key stock or other suitable material to prevent the steady-rest shoes from catching on the work.

Sometimes it is desirable to finish-grind a cylindrical piece of work of one diameter in one operation. To accomplish this, a small angle-iron bracket or other suitable projection may be sweated to the end of the work to act as a driver. Care should be taken to make sure that it is placed so as not to interfere with the overrun of the grinding wheel or the work center. After the grinding is completed, the driver may be removed.

Shoulder work. If the work must be ground to a shoulder, it is advisable to locate the grinding wheel up against the shoulder before starting to grind and then, by plunge-cut grinding, grind the surface to the required diameter. This method will leave the finished diameter with a corner at the shoulder that is fairly sharp and square. After the job has been ground to size at the shoulder, the balance of it may be ground by traversing the table.

JOB ANALYSIS

The following outline is a typical analysis of the procedure in external grinding:

Type of job	Shaft as per sketch in Fig. 20–26
Type of machine	External grinder
Type of steel	SAE 5132
Heat-treatment	Harden to Rockwell 33–35
Kind of grinding wheel	60-L
Operations required	Rough- and finish-grind as per sketch

5. Set footstock to function for correct length of work.
6. Mount the work in the machine and properly adjust the drive pin to the dog.
7. Feed the grinding wheel to diameter A and take a clean-up cut, seeing that the wheel closely follows the work.
8. Check diameter A for straightness, make any necessary table adjustments, take a trial cut, and recheck the work for straightness.
9. With the wheel cutting straight, plunge-cut diameter A at the shoulder and rough-grind, leaving 0.003 to 0.005 in. for finishing. Repeat this operation on A′, B, B′, and C in the order stated, then have the job inspected.
10. Dress the grinding wheel for finishing and, with the machine cutting straight, finish-grind A, A′, B, B′, and C in the order stated.
11. Have job inspected on all dimensions.

Gaging methods. Cylindrical work having dimensions which must be held to close limits requires the use of gages which are calibrated to a finer degree of accuracy than ordinary micrometers. For this purpose a supersensitive comparator is used. There are several makes of comparators, one of which is shown in Fig. 20–27. The indicator is graduated in 0.00005-in. divisions so that very small variations in size may be easily detected. A common method of checking a piece of work is to

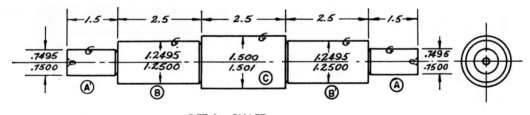

DET 1—SHAFT
1—TYPE SAE 5132 STEEL
STK 1¾ DIA   WT 7½ LB
HARDEN—ROCKWELL 33–35
GRIND

Fig. 20–26. Sketch of a shaft.

PROCEDURE

1. Check all diameters for sufficient grind stock.
2. Check work centers for being free from dirt and nicks.
3. Dress grinding wheel for roughing cut.
4. Mount a grinder dog of correct size on the work.

place a combination of gage blocks equal to the required dimension on the comparator anvil, and to adjust the indicator to read zero. The gage blocks are then removed and the work is placed under the indicator with a sliding or rolling motion, depending on the shape of the work. Any variation between the size of the gage blocks and

Fig. 20–27. Supersensitive comparator. (Federal Products Corp.)

the size of the work is then noted on the indicator dial.

Taper work. Accurate taper work may be produced on the cylindrical grinder by one of two methods, by swiveling either the worktable or the headstock. For slight tapers, the table may be set by means of the swivel adjustments and table graduations, as in Fig. 20–28, but, inasmuch as this can be only approximately accurate, a stand-

Fig. 20–28. Table swiveled 10 deg for grinding taper on wheel spindle. (Landis Tool Co.)

ard taper ring gage, female taper gage, or sine bar is necessary to check the taper. The grinding of tapers is very much the same as grinding a cylinder, the exception being that the swivel table or

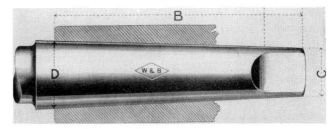

Fig. 20–29. Taper ring gage and tapered shank. (Morse Twist Drill & Machine Co. and Whitman & Barnes)

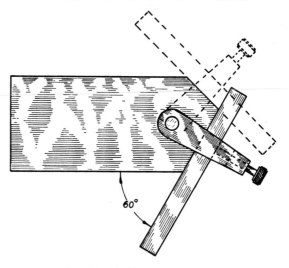

Fig. 20–30. Flat-center gage.

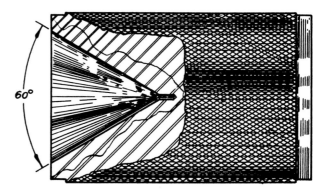

Fig. 20–31. Bell-center gage.

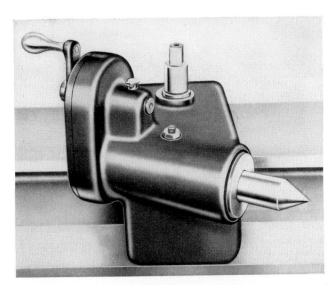

Fig. 20–32. Center grinding fixture. (Cincinnati Grinders, Inc.)

prussian blue about 120 deg apart and then carefully inserted into the ring gage with a slight twisting motion. If the surface being checked does not conform to the surface of the gage, the irregularity

Fig. 20–33. Diamond-holder grinding-wheel dresser. (Brown & Sharpe Mfg. Co.)

wheel-stand slide is set to produce the correct taper angle. Generally, the graduation on the scale marked degrees is one-half of the whole taper angle, while taper per foot or percentage indicates the whole taper angle.

If a taper ring gage (Fig. 20–29) is used for checking the accuracy of the taper, the male section should be given three lengthwise stripes of

rubs the blue off and leaves a bright metallic ring indicating the high spot. If the gage bears only on one or two lines, it indicates that the piece being tested is out of round.

Steep tapers can be produced by swiveling the work head or by dressing the wheel at an angle. If

Fig. 20–34. Radius wheel-truing attachment. (Brown & Sharpe Mfg. Co.)

Fig. 20–35. Universal tool grinder. (Brown & Sharpe Mfg. Co.)

1. Motor-driven headstock has both dead-center and revolving-spindle drive. Swivels on graduated base. Knob at front releases belt tension and frees spindle for truing up work.
2. Swivel table turns on stud to 90 deg either side of zero. Double scale, graduated to degrees, indicates setting from either of two zero marks.
3. Double-ended wheel spindle carried in sturdy slide. Has vertical adjustment of 8⅜ in. Either plain-bearing or antifriction-bearing spindle available.

4. Footstock clamped in position by lever. Spindle operated by spring lever (pressure adjustable). Spindle hand clamp provided.
5. Table reversing dogs quickly positioned along T slot and rack. Have fine thumbscrew adjustment.
6. Spring latch and knob for fine adjustments of swivel table. Latch engages knob.
7. Main start-stop push button conveniently located. Starts and stops wheel spindle and table motors and energizes line to headstock motor switch.
8. Levers provide six changes in rate of power table travel in two series: 7¾, 13 and 24 in. per min and 32, 54 and 100 in. per min.
9. Fine cross-feed operated by small handwheel graduated to read to 0.0001 in. on work diameter; engaged by knob on cross-feed handwheel.
10. Handwheel for hand table travel. Convenient three-position lever (not visible in this view) at side of handwheel permits quick selection of two rates of hand travel or disengagement of handwheel. Knob on front of handwheel can be moved to give play between rim of handwheel and hub; this facilitates "bumping" when it is desired to move table only slightly.
11. Lever may be positioned to start and stop headstock motor or to start and stop headstock motor and power movement of table. Disengages table handwheel when set for power table travel.
12. Table reversing lever; operated manually or by dogs. Has positive stop for grinding to shoulders.

the wheel is to be dressed at an angle, it is absolutely necessary to have the diamond set on the exact center line of the wheel. This is necessary not only to ensure dressing the correct angle on the wheel, but also to obtain a flat face on the wheel rather than one which is concave or convex.

The 60-deg point on a machine center is ground by placing it in the live spindle of the headstock and swiveling it through a 30-deg angle, using the graduations on the base of the headstock. It should be understood that these graduations cannot be relied upon for extreme accuracy of measurement. After a preliminary grinding, the work should be checked with a gage, such as the flat style shown in Fig. 20–30 or the bell-center gage shown in Fig. 20–31. The necessary adjustments can then be made to the machine to ensure accurate results.

Another method for grinding centers is to use a center-grinding fixture (Fig. 20–32) which is designed to hold the center at the proper angle. A handle, attached to a set of gears, is used to revolve the center against the grinding wheel.

The actual operation of grinding-machine centers must be carried out with care, as there is danger of burning the point because of the change in work speed due to the steep taper. This hazard may be overcome by using a slow work speed, a small infeed, a flood of coolant, and starting the cut at the point, moving quickly back towards the shank.

Wheel dressers. On all external grinders, some provision is made for dressing the grinding wheel. The footstock is equipped with a suitable holder so arranged that it is adjustable and can be located on the center line of the wheel spindle. A type of diamond holder or wheel dresser usually furnished with the machine is shown in Fig. 20–33.

Another type of grinding-wheel dresser is the radius wheel-truing attachment shown in Fig. 20–34.

Fig. 20–36. Disk-grinding the face of a casting held on a magnetic chuck. (Brown & Sharpe Mfg. Co.)

The attachment is fastened to the grinder table with a T bolt. A swiveling upright holds a diamond tool which may be adjusted to the size of radius required. The grinding wheel is dressed by swiveling the upright back and forth against the rotating grinding wheel.

Some machines are equipped with a micrometer-adjustment wheel dresser, which consists of a hollow screw body surmounted by a dial graduated to read in thousandths of an inch, which passes through a threaded hole located on the axis of the footstock center. The diamond is inserted in the hollow screw and locked in placed by a setscrew. This dresser proves to be very efficient, especially where the job consists of a number of pieces of the same size. To use it, after the first piece has been reduced to size, the point of the diamond is spotted on the grinding wheel so that the distance from the axis of the footstock center to the tip of the diamond is equal to the radius of the work. The micrometer screw is then locked in place, ensuring the correct sizing ability of the wheel.

Safety items. It is important when operating an external grinder to let the machine run for a few minutes when first starting it, to give it a chance to warm up. During this time, let the coolant run on the wheel to balance it, because, having stood overnight, the coolant has drained to the bottom of the wheel, causing it to be out of balance. Be sure to check the stops, feed trips, and levers to make certain that the wheel does not run into the machine and damage it. See that the driving pin between the drive plate and grinder dog is securely locked in place and properly adjusted. Keep a good stream of coolant running at the point of contact between the wheel and work, as it helps to dissipate the heat, tends to give the work a better finish, and keeps the wheel clean. Keep your hands away from the moving wheel and the work. If something goes wrong, stop the machine by pulling the main switch, and call an instructor or foreman.

Universal grinders

In addition to the external grinder just discussed, another type of grinder which is rapidly growing as a utility machine is the universal tool grinder (Fig. 20–35). This machine is one which can, within its capacity, do the work of many other grinding machines, provided the necessary attachments are available. This machine is truly universal; the wheel-spindle unit is adjustable both horizontally and vertically, and can be swiveled in a horizontal plane 110 deg either side of zero. The headstock has both dead-center and revolving-spindle drive. It is adjustable along the table. It

Fig. 20–37. Grinding the face of a thin disk held on a face chuck. (Brown & Sharpe Mfg. Co.)

Fig. 20–38. Grinding a tapered plug gage. The gage is mounted on dead centers and the swivel table is set to the correct taper. Power table travel is used for traversing the work and fine hand cross-feed is used for feeding the wheel. The length of table movement is governed by means of the dogs, which have both coarse and fine adjustment. (Brown & Sharpe Mfg. Co.)

may be swiveled on its base 100 deg each side of zero. The table may be traversed by hand or by power with adjustable automatic reverse. It may be swiveled 90 deg in either direction. Because of

Fig. 20–39. Grinding a diameter at the end of a long part having no center holes. The work is held in a collet. (Brown & Sharpe Mfg. Co.)

its adaptability, some shops use only universal grinders, while other shops use them for work which might interfere with the continuous operation of specialized machines. Some operations that are performed on a universal tool-grinding machine are shown in Figs. 20–36, 20–37, 20–38, 20–39.

Centerless grinders

The centerless grinder (Fig. 20–40) is a specialized machine which was developed for the rapid production of cylindrical, external-taper, or external-profile work, examples of which are shown in Fig. 20–41.

In centerless grinding, two wheels are employed: one, the cutting or grinding wheel, is used to remove the excess stock; the other, a regulating wheel, is used to control the speed of rotation of the work and rate of feed. The work is supported on a work slide or rest.

This machine has a distinct advantage over other grinders in that the work does not have to be center-drilled, thereby saving the time required for that operation on the lathe. Because the work does not have to be mounted on centers, and since the grinding operation is almost continuous, the time required for loading and unloading is saved. Heavier cuts can be taken with this type of grinder than with ordinary methods, and the amount of material left by the lathe operator to be removed

tains only a few pieces because the machine is simple to set up.

The actual grinding operation depends for the most part on the pressure exerted by the grinding wheel on the work and the operation of the work

Fig. 20–40. Centerless grinder. (Cincinnati Grinders, Inc.)

A. Truing-rate adjustment
B. Micrometer adjustment
C. Grinding-wheel truing device
D. Booster lever
E. Coolant valve
F. Regulating-wheel truing handwheel
G. Regulating-wheel truing device
J. Hand infeed lever
K. Grinding-wheel truing engaging lever

L. Infeed work rest
M. Lower slide clamp
N. Upper slide clamp
P. Master start-stop buttons
Q. Swivel-plate adjusting screw
R. Infeed screw clamp
S. Regulating-wheel speed-change levers
T. Handwheel for adjusting regulating-wheel unit

can be less, therefore saving more time and adding to the life of the grinding wheel. The operation of the machine does not require the services of a skilled mechanic. There are few moving parts in the machine, so upkeep cost is very low, while the output rate is very high.

It is generally thought that, because the external centerless grinder was designed for the grinding of a large number of pieces of the same size, it is not suited for toolroom use, but, actually, much time and money can be saved where the job lot con-

with respect to the wheel centers (Fig. 20–42). In operation, the pressure exerted by the grinding wheel on the work forces the work against the work rest and regulating wheel. The regulating wheel revolves in a direction the same as that of the grinding wheel and has a horizontal movement. It has a speed of 12 to 300 rpm, and at the same time feeds the work through the machine. The rounding of the work depends on how high the work rests are above the center lines of the wheels and the top angle of the work rest.

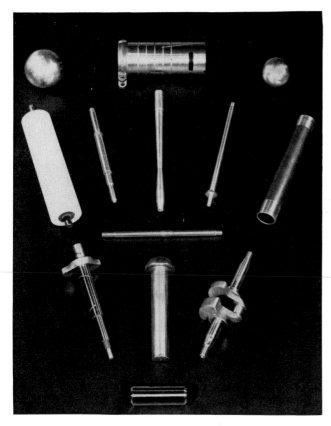

Fig. 20–41. Examples of the kind of jobs that may be ground on the centerless grinder.

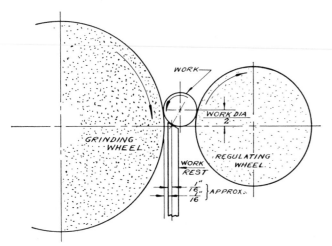

Fig. 20–42. Sketch showing the rotation of the grinding wheel, regulating wheel, and the work.

Methods of feeding. Two common methods used for feeding the work to the machine are the through-feed and infeed. The through-feed method is used for straight cylindrical work. In this case, the work goes in on one side of the machine and comes out on the other side. The work rest for through-feed grinding (Fig. 20–43) has

Fig. 20–43. Through-feed work rest and guide for centerless grinder. (Cincinnati Grinders, Inc.)

adjustable guides on each end to steer the work between the grinding wheels. These guides must be carefully lined up with each other and with the face of the regulating wheel. The height of the rest blade must also be adjusted to fit the diameter of the work.

Infeed grinding is used for jobs that, because of a shoulder or some other obstruction on the part, can only enter the machine so far and then, after the grinding is done, must be withdrawn. The work rest for this operation does not have guides, but does have an adjustable stop on the far end (Fig. 20–44). The lever operates a plunger in the stop to eject the work.

Fig. 20–44. Work rest with ejector for infeed centerless grinding. (Cincinnati Grinders, Inc.)

The amount of material to be ground determines whether the work is passed through the grinding wheels more than once. If an average finish is required, up to 0.008 in. may be ground off during one pass through the machine. If a really fine finish is desired, it is best not to grind off more than 0.003 in. at the final pass.

Safety rules for external grinders

1. Under no circumstances attempt to operate an external grinder unless the wheel is guarded adequately.
2. When it is necessary to replace a large external-grinding wheel, ask the instructor about methods of proper mounting and testing.
3. Before starting the work head, always test the work to see that it is between centers.
4. If the work must be tested for size while it is between centers, be sure to allow ample clearance between your hands and the grinding wheel.
5. Poorly adjusted drivers, loose dogs, defective center holes in the work, and so forth, are a constant danger on the external grinder, causing spinning of the work. Adjust the driver correctly and securely, fasten the drive dog tightly, and inspect the center holes in each piece of work before grinding it.
6. Be extremely careful in removing work from a collet head. Run the table back to a safety stop which will give ample hand clearance between the wheel and work.
7. If the work is heavy, shut the machine down when placing it between centers.
8. Avoid dressing the sides of a large grinding wheel, if possible, but if it is necessary for the job, ask the instructor to help. He will demonstrate the right method of dressing the wheel and how cuts can be taken so as to preserve the corners of the wheel.
9. Do not put your hands on revolving material with any open work in it, such as keyways, slots, and flutes.
10. Be careful in handling sharp tools, such as drills, reamers, and cutters, as severe lacerations may result.

REVIEW QUESTIONS
Cylindrical Grinding

1. What are the common shop terms for cylindrical grinding?
2. What is the purpose of external grinding?
3. What kind of jobs can be produced on the external grinder?
4. How does the work of the external grinder compare with that done on a lathe?
5. Into what three major groups are external grinders divided?
6. What companies manufacture the external grinders used in your shop?
7. Name the important parts of a standard external grinder.
8. What job operations can be done on the plain cylindrical grinder?
9. What movements are important in any cylindrical grinder?
10. Why are each of these movements important?
11. Explain how the job in external grinding is driven when supported between centers.
12. Generally speaking, what should the length of the table traverse be?
13. Why is it important to permit the grinding wheel to overrun the end of the job?
14. What happens to the job if the grinding wheel completely overruns the end of the work?
15. What does the speed of the table traverse depend upon?
16. How fast should the speed of the table traverse be?
17. How is long, slender work supported while being driven between centers?
18. What care should be exercised in the use of steady rests?
19. What provisions are made for feeding the grinding wheel to the work?
20. What depths of cut is it possible to take with the automatic feed?
21. Why is it advisable to use the automatic feed rather than the hand feed?
22. What is the depth of a roughing cut, using the automatic feed?
23. What speed and feed should be used for roughing-out a job? For finish-grinding a job?
24. Give the grades of bond, the size, and the kind of abrasive commonly used for external-grinding wheels?
25. Why is it not possible to have a set rule for the rate of work speed?
26. What work speeds are commonly used?
27. What conditions might cause cracks, checks or burns on the surface of the job?

28. What conditions might cause tapering of the work?
29. How can tapering of the work be overcome?
30. What is meant by plunge-cut grinding?
31. When, in particular, should plunge-cut grinding be used?
32. Why should the job be checked for size before setting the job up?
33. Footstock centers which are cut away are called what kinds of centers?
34. What care must be exercised in attaching the grinder dog to the end of the job?
35. How should the diamond be used to make the wheel fast-cutting?
36. When the wheel is first fed to the work, what notice should be taken of the work contact?
37. Why should the work be checked after the first cut is taken?
38. How should the diamond be used to prepare the wheel for the finishing cut?
39. If the work has keyways or splines, how should it be prepared if steady rests are to be used?
40. How is it possible to grind a cylinder completely at one time without using a grinder dog?
41. If the work has several shoulders, what is the proper way to grind it? Why?
42. Why can micrometers not be used for gaging jobs requiring a high degree of accuracy?
43. What is an amplifying comparator?
44. Explain how to use the amplifier.
45. To what degree of accuracy can the ordinary amplifier be used?
46. How is it possible to produce taper work on the cylindrical grinder?
47. What tools are necessary for producing accurate taper work?
48. How is the taper of the job generally specified?
49. Explain how to use a taper ring gage for producing an accurate taper.
50. In producing steep tapers, what care must be exercised in dressing the wheel?
51. Explain an efficient method of grinding machine centers.
52. How may the accuracy of the 60-deg conical point of the machine center be checked?
53. Name three kinds of diamond holders used on external grinders.
54. What advantage does the micrometer-adjustment diamond holder have over the others?
55. Give six important safety rules for operating external cylindrical grinders.
56. What is meant by a universal tool grinder?
57. What is the advantage of this machine?
58. What are its disadvantages?
59. What kinds of work can be done on the centerless grinder?
60. What is the principle of operation of the centerless external grinder.
61. What advantages does the centerless grinder have over the plain and universal external grinders?
62. Upon what two factors does the actual grinding operation depend in centerless grinding?
63. In what direction does the regulating wheel rotate with respect to the grinding wheel?
64. Upon what two factors does the rapidity of the rounding of the work depend?
65. What is meant by through-feed? Infeed?
66. What is meant by profile work?

SURFACE GRINDERS

Surface grinding is the act of producing and finishing flat surfaces by means of a grinding machine employing a revolving abrasive wheel.

Surface-grinding machines are divided into two major groups according to the shape of the table and how it moves. They are the **planer type**, in which the table is rectangular in shape and traverses under the wheel, and the **rotary type**, in which the table is circular in shape and rotates under the wheel.

Planer types

1. Horizontal spindle using the OD or periphery of the wheel.
2. Horizontal spindle using the rim of a recessed or cupped wheel.
3. Vertical spindle using the rim of a recessed or cupped wheel.

Rotary types

1. Horizontal spindle using the OD or periphery of the wheel.
2. Vertical spindle using the rim of a recessed or cupped wheel.

Fundamentally, any of the above-mentioned machines consists of a spindle with a grinding wheel mounted on it, and a table or magnetic chuck for holding the work, for the purpose of presenting it to the wheel. Each machine has its particular ad-

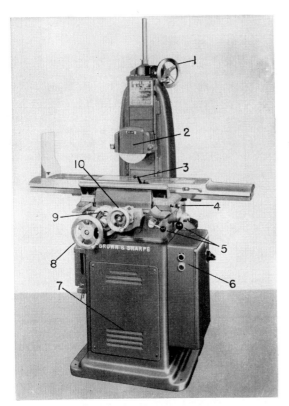

Fig. 20–45. Surface grinder. (Brown & Sharpe Mfg. Co.)

1. Handwheel, graduated to half-thousandths of an inch, provides easy and accurate vertical adjustment of spindle head.
2. Removable-unit-type spindle—plain-bearing or anti-friction-bearing type, readily interchangeable. Heavy wheel guard has removable cover.

3. Table reversing mechanism operated manually through lever shown, or automatically through second lever located on same shaft and tripped by adjustable table dogs.
4. Adjustable dogs permit stopping power movements automatically at any desired point in each direction of cross-feed.
5. Starting lever and trip lever start and stop both longitudinal and transverse power movements. Turning lever at front to right starts power feed; depressing lever at right stops feed instantly.
6. Start-stop push button switch and electrical control compartment conveniently located.
7. Large base compartment has shelf for mounting driving motor for spindle and table. When machine has motorized spindle, provides handy storage space for tools and accessories.
8. Longitudinal table handwheel conveniently located and easily operated. Can be positively disengaged when power travel is used.
9. Adjustable stops provide for any cross-feed from 0.01 to 0.09 in. (or zero feed) at either end of table travel. Knob in center disengages cross-feed mechanism for manual operation.
10. Graduated handwheel permits rapid and accurate transverse adjustment.

vantages, but, for the purpose of general tool-room work this discussion deals principally with the horizontal planer type of surface grinder (Fig. 20–45) which uses the periphery of a disk wheel.

Planer-type surface grinder

Wheels for planer-type surface grinder. Grinding wheels of various shapes are used in the horizontal surface grinder, among the more common being the disk, gage, and thin rubber slotting wheels. The sizes of the wheels may vary from very small wheels of the internal class, which may be used with a high-speed attachment, to wheels 10 in. in diameter having a 1-in. face. The wheels most commonly used on surface grinders are shown in Table 20–1.

Mounting the wheels. The following items are to be considered in mounting a grinding wheel on the horizontal planer type of surface grinder, from the time the wheel is received at the crib until the machine is running:

Table 20–1. COMMONLY USED SURFACE GRINDER WHEELS

Material	Grain	Grade	Abrasive*	Process
Aluminum	30 to 46	H or I	C	Vitrified
Bronze	36 or 46	H	C	Vitrified
Cast iron	30 or 36	I or J	C	Vitrified
Copper	30 or 36	H or I	C	Vitrified
High-speed steel	46	G or H	A	Vitrified
Mild steel (including steel castings)	36 or 46	I, J, or K	A	Vitrified
Monel metal	46	G	A	Vitrified
Nitralloy (before nitriding)	36 or 46	J	A	Vitrified
Nitralloy (after nitriding)	60 to 100	H	A or C	Vitrified
Stainless steel (soft)	36	H	C	Vitrified
Tool steel	36 or 46	H	A	Vitrified
Tungsten carbide (roughing)	60 or 80	G or H	C	Vitrified
Tungsten carbide (finishing)	80 or 100	F or G	C	Vitrified

* C = silicon carbide. A = aluminum oxide.

1. Sound the wheel for cracks. Hold the wheel by the bore and tap it with a nonmetallic object; if the wheel is not cracked, it will give off a dull, ringing sound; if the wheel is cracked, it will give a dull thud.

2. Make sure that the wheel has blotting-paper-type gaskets on both sides around the hole. (Most wheels arrive from the manufacturer with paper washers attached.)

3. Inspect the wheel flanges to make sure they are of the safety type and the proper size.

4. Place the wheel on the spindle. The wheel should slide on the spindle, without bind, or too much play, against the inner safety flange.

5. Put the outer safety flange on.

6. Put the spindle nut on securely.

7. Put the wheel guards in place and tighten them.

8. Make sure that the wheel clears the housing by turning it over by hand.

9. Start the machine and, as the starter button is pressed, step to one side, letting the machine run for at least one full minute before working with it.

10. True the wheel. Don't try to remove all of the runout with one pass of the diamond. Remove it a little at a time.

The wheel speed has been built into the machine by the manufacturer. For safety, don't try to increase it without getting competent advice.

From a safety standpoint, it is very essential to sound the wheel for cracks, because they may not be seen. If the wheel is cracked, and placed on the machine, the centrifugal force when the machine is started up will cause the wheel to burst, thus endangering the operator or nearby fellow workers.

Blotting paper or rubber gaskets should be placed between the safety flanges and the wheel, to distribute evenly the pressures around the wheel when the nut is tightened.

Safety flanges. Safety flanges are wheel flanges which act on the wheel between the spindle and nut. They should be at least one-third the diameter of the wheel and relieved or undercut on the wheel side so that they bear on the wheel only at their outer edges. This bearing surface should be parallel with the opposite side so that when tightened, the nut will bear evenly against the flange, thus as-

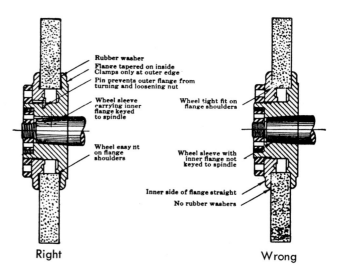

Fig. 20–46. Safety flanges for grinding wheels.

suring equal pressure all around (see Fig. 20–46).

Never force the wheel on the spindle. If it goes on snugly, the lead bushing should be scraped so as to be from 0.003 to 0.005 in. larger than the spindle, which enables the flanges to straighten the wheel without putting an internal strain on it.

The nut threads on to the spindle in a direction opposite to that in which the wheel rotates, so that the resistance offered by the work to the wheel tends to tighten the nut.

When starting the machine, especially after a new wheel has been mounted, or first thing in the morning after the machine has been standing all night, step to one side as the starting button is pressed, and let the machine run for at least one full minute. New wheels are apt to be out of balance due to being moisture-logged on one side, or the wheel spindle may have excessive end play in it, which upon starting would break the wheel. For that reason, be clear of it in case it does break.

Dressing the wheels. In the case of surface grinding where the work is ground dry, it is very necessary to keep the wheel sharp and true if the grinding operation is to be done efficiently. The area of contact between the wheel and work is much greater than it is in cylindrical grinding, which means that a great many more cutting tools (abrasive elements in the wheel) are acting on the work at the same time. The heat generated due to the added cutting tools may be kept at a minimum by keeping the wheel clean and sharp.

A dull or dirty wheel causes the work to burn or have a hard cutting action. Hard cutting action places more strain on the wheel and machine parts, causing them to overheat and operate inefficiently.

To dress a wheel, remove only sufficient material from the face of the wheel to sharpen it. Don't keep feeding the wheel down and hacking away at it with the diamond. Grinding wheels are costly tools and should be shown due consideration. Some grinding-wheel manufacturers claim that about two-thirds of a grinding wheel is wasted due to improper dressing, truing, or handling.

Holding work. Most surface grinders employ a magnetic chuck (Fig. 20–47) for holding the work in place on the machine, but it may be held by clamping it directly to the table or by placing the work in a vise which is fastened to the table. Work may be held on the magnetic chuck in conjunction with a V block, angle plate, sine bar, or special fixtures.

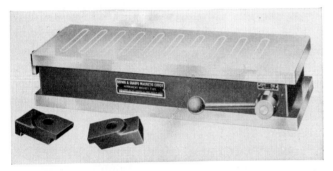

Fig. 20–47. Magnetic chuck. (Brown & Sharpe Mfg. Co.)

The magnetic chuck holds the work in place by exerting a magnetic force on it. The magnetic poles of the chuck are placed close together so that it is possible to hold very small pieces of work. Frequently, however, the work is too small for the chuck to hold it, so that long pieces of iron or steel, having a height less than that of the work, are placed alongside to act as blocks, thus retaining the work on the chuck (see Fig. 20–48). It must be remembered that only magnetic materials such as iron or steel will actually adhere to the chuck. When grinding such materials as bronze, brass, fiber, or certain kinds of stainless steel, the pieces must be held in place on the chuck by bars of iron or steel.

The accuracy of the work, for example, parallelism and squareness, depends on the accuracy of the holding face of the magnetic chuck. For that reason, the holding surface of the chuck must be kept smooth and flat. As soon as the chuck shows

Fig. 20–48. Surface-grinding a number of small pieces held in place on the magnetic chuck by long strips of steel. (Brown & Sharpe Mfg. Co.)

nicks, scratches, or dents, or if the chuck has been removed for any purpose, it should be reground in place on the machine. Do this only on the advice of the instructor or foreman.

Sometimes the chuck is equipped with a back rail, the purpose of which is to support the work parallel to the table travel. This must be removed when the chuck is being reground, so that, when it is replaced, it also must be ground in place to restore its accuracy.

Few jobs are ever done on a surface grinder in the toolroom which do not have to be kept parallel within reasonably close limits. The most frequent causes of difficulty in obtaining parallelism is a dirty or poorly kept work surface on the chuck, or the back rail not being parallel with the table travel. On thick pieces of work, if difficulty is experienced in keeping the opposite faces parallel, it may be overcome by reversing the position of the work on the chuck, putting it in nearly the same location, but without disturbing the wheel setting.

Thin work is especially hard to keep parallel because it warps so easily. The use of a free-cutting wheel and light cuts taken alternately from each side do much to eliminate the warping and hence make it easy to keep the work parallel within reasonable limits. Another method is to place a thin parallel under each end of the work, taking a light cut or series of light cuts alternately from

Fig. 20–49. The use of a coolant does not affect the magnetic chuck and permits heavy grinding cuts with a fine finish. (Brown & Sharpe Mfg. Co.)

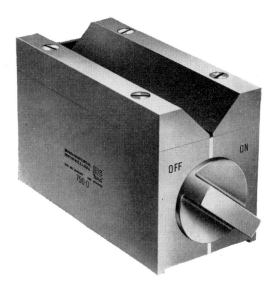

Fig. 20–51. Magnetic V block. (Brown & Sharpe Mfg. Co.)

each side. When using this method, the work should be properly blocked on the table to keep it from sliding. Figures 20–49 and 20–50 illustrate the use of the magnetic chuck.

A magnetic V block (Fig. 20–51) is advantageous for holding iron or steel work of round or rectangular cross section and, also, irregularly shaped pieces which can be placed between, and in con-

tact with, the V faces. It is suited for toolmaking, inspection, and hand operations as well as for light machine work and for wet or dry grinding. When the control is turned on, work is held firmly in the V and, if the V block rests on a magnetically conductive surface, the V block, also, is held firmly to this surface, as in Fig. 20–52. The V block can be used on its sides and end as well as on its base, but it is not held to a magnetically conductive surface when used on its sides. The holding power of the V block can be regulated by giving the control a part turn so that work can be moved or positioned

Fig. 20–50. Large jobs are securely held on the magnetic chuck. (Brown & Sharpe Mfg. Co.)

Fig. 20–52. Magnetic V block is firmly held on the angle plate resting on a magnetic chuck. (Brown & Sharpe Mfg. Co.)

in the V without fully releasing the V block from the conductive surface on which it is placed.

Magnetic-chuck parallels (Fig. 20–53) hold work with projecting surfaces which cannot be held easily on the surface of a magnetic chuck. An example of this nature is shown in Fig. 20–54. The parallels are made of alternating steel and nonmagnetic bronze spacing strips. The magnetic flux passes from the magnetic chuck through the steel strips and the work, holding the work securely to the parallels and the parallels to the working surface of the chuck. Opposite sides are ground parallel

Fig. 20–53. Magnetic chuck parallels. (Brown & Sharpe Mfg. Co.)

Fig. 20–54. Offset parts are held securely for grinding with magnetic chuck parallels. (Brown & Sharpe Mfg. Co.)

and adjacent sides at right angles. Parallels can be used on all four sides, but not on their ends.

Witness marks. Occasionally it is required that the surface of a job be ground **to clean up.** By this is meant that the surface is to be ground so that a very small portion of the original surface can still be seen after the job is done. This is known as leaving *witness marks* on the work. The purpose of leaving these witness marks is to testify that only a small amount of stock was removed from the job. In some jobs, this means that the wheel must be spotted on the work and then traversed over the entire surface to make sure that too much stock is not removed. If the surface is quite regular and has a good finish, it may be given a coat of blue vitriol or copper sulfate before grinding, to show that too much stock was not removed.

Angle-plate work. Ninety-degree angle plates (Fig. 20–55) are used on the surface grinder for supporting the work, while two adjacent faces of the work are ground at 90 deg to each other.

Fig. 20–55. Angle plates. (Taft-Peirce Mfg. Co.)

Obviously the accuracy of the work will depend on the accuracy of the plate. If the two adjacent faces of the plate are ground at exactly 90 deg, and if the edges of the plate are maintained parallel and at 90 deg to the adjacent faces, then it is possible to grind two sides of the work at 90 deg with a third side, thus cutting down on the work setup time.

Adjustable angle plates (Fig. 20–56), which are precision-made, are available. These plates make it possible to grind work that has intricate angles. The end of the block is graduated in degrees. Some of the angle plates of this type, known as *sine angle plates,* which have provisions for setting them with a micrometer or precision gage blocks, are quite suitable for grinding angles which have exacting limits.

Fig. 20–56. Adjustable angle plate. (Taft-Peirce Mfg. Co.)

Grinding work square. To grind a piece of work square after two sides have been ground parallel, place the side to be ground, down on the magnetic chuck. Place a thin parallel or rule alongside of the work, then place the 90-deg angle plate, top

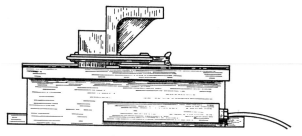

Fig. 20–57. Angle plate resting on a parallel is clamped to the work.

edge down on the rule, bringing the outside face of the plate up against the finished side of the work (Fig. 20–57). Clamp the work and plate together in this position, so that when the angle plate is turned right side up on the magnetic chuck (Fig. 20–58) the work face to be ground will be exposed to the grinding wheel. Make sure that the clamp has been placed far enough below the face to be ground, and that the screw end is located inside the angle plate to reduce the overhang and not interfere with the grinding operation.

Grinding angular surfaces. Angular surfaces can be readily ground on a surface grinder by dressing the wheel to produce the required angle, by using

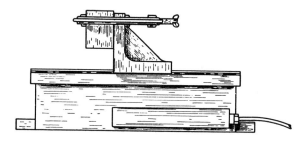

Fig. 20–58. Surface of work to be ground is above the angle plate when inverted.

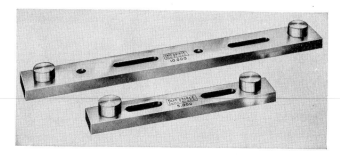

Fig. 20–59. Sine bars. (Taft-Peirce Mfg. Co.)

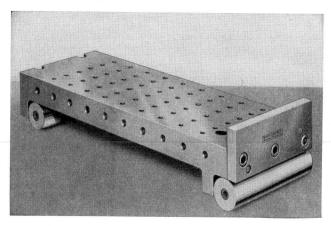

Fig. 20–60. Sine block. (Taft-Peirce Mfg. Co.)

a sine bar (Figs. 20–59 and 20–60) or an adjustable angle plate and setting the work up to the required angle, or by using an adjustable magnetic chuck.

The grinding wheel should not be dressed at an angle except as a last resort, because it decreases the wheel life. If the wheel must be dressed at an angle, make sure it is dressed correctly, that is, dress the wheel so that it will produce the angle required on the work and not the complement of it. For dressing the wheel at an angle, either a standard angle block or sine bar may be used, to guide a sliding flanged block which holds a diamond, as shown in Fig. 20–61. After the angle block or sine bar has been set up, it is located so that the point of the diamond is exactly on the vertical center line of the wheel spindle.

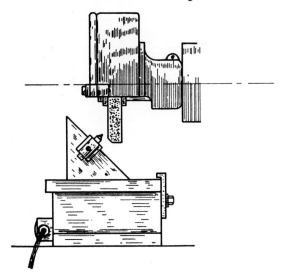

Fig. 20–61. Dressing a grinding wheel to an angle by sliding a diamond tool along the edge of an angle plate.

A grinding wheel may also be dressed with an angle-truing attachment (Fig. 20–62). The upper part is turned and clamped to the required angle using the graduations around the base. The diamond tool is brought close to the grinding wheel

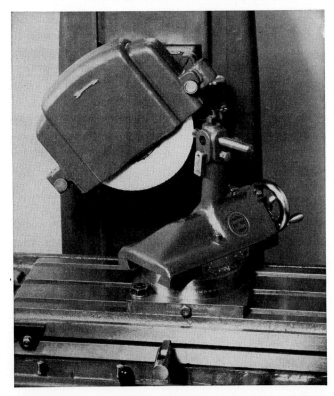

Fig. 20–62. Angle wheel-truing attachment in position to dress wheel to a required angle. (Brown & Sharpe Mfg. Co.)

by the hand feed of the table and the slide of the truing attachment is operated by means of the handwheel to move the diamond tool back and forth across the wheel.

When the work is to be set on an angle, the common practice is to use a standard-angle block or sine bar (Fig. 20–63), in conjunction with a right-angle plate. With some sine bars, all that is necessary is to stack gage blocks or set a planer gage at five or ten times the sine of the angle, depending on the length of the sine bar; then place the work on the sine bar squarely against the 90-deg angle plate and clamp it in place. Other sine bars require the addition of the radius of plugs, or the thickness of the base of the sine bar be added to 5 or 10 times the sine of the angle.

Fig. 20–63. Work is held level on a sine block which is elevated the required distance by a combination of gage blocks.

V blocks are used for holding cylindrical work while grinding flats, slots, radii, and so forth. The blocks used for this purpose are kept square, the sides parallel, the ends parallel, and the V maintained in the exact center of the block.

JOB ANALYSIS

The following outline is a typical analysis of the procedure for grinding two opposite flats central on the outside diameter (OD) of a shaft.

Type of job	Shaft as per sketch (Fig. 20–64)
Type of machine	Horizontal-planer type
Type of steel	SAE 1095
Heat-treatment	Harden to Rockwell 52–64
Kind of grinding wheel	60-K
Operations required	Grind flats to size and central with OD
Tools required	4-in. V block, 10-in. height gage, 1–2 in. micrometers, Ideal indicator

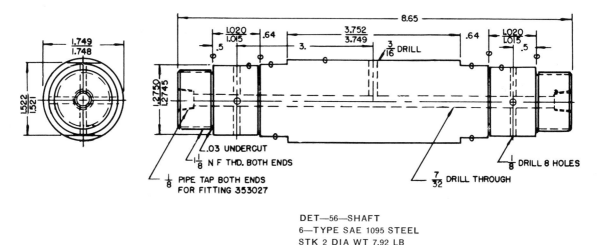

DET—56—SHAFT
6—TYPE SAE 1095 STEEL
STK 2 DIA WT 7.92 LB
HARDEN—ROCKWELL 52–64
GRIND

Fig. 20–64. Sketch of a shaft.

PROCEDURE

1. Check the flats for sufficient grind stock.
2. Place the job in a V block using a 10-in. height gage and Ideal indicator to make sure that the rough flats of the shaft are parallel with the sides of the V block.
3. Using the height gage and indicator, check the cylindrical surface of the shaft that projects from the V block, for being central. This is done by turning the block over on its side, taking a reading with the indicator, then turning the block over to its opposite side and observing if the reading is the same on both sides of the shaft.
4. Check the unground flats for being central, observing which side is high and whether or not it is within the grind stock.
5. Place the job on the chuck with the low side up, and spot the wheel to clean up this side of the flat, leaving witness marks.
6. Reverse the V block to bring the unground side of the shaft up, and take the same cut from this face.
7. Check the job for size, noting by what amount it is oversize.
8. Feed the grinding wheel down an amount equal to one-half the remaining stock and grind both faces, reversing V block as in step 6. This should bring the job to the required size.
9. Check the flats for size and being central; then have it checked by the inspector.

Groove and slot grinding. Certain classes of work on the surface grinder call for considerable skill and patience on the part of the operator. Some of the more common ones are groove or slot grinding, and radius grinding, especially where they have to be maintained within accurate limits relative to another surface.

Probably the most important factor is selection of the proper wheel. Where the groove is wide enough, a gage wheel of medium-hard bond and from 46 to 60 grain size should be used for roughing. If a gage wheel cannot be secured, a disk wheel having the same characteristics can be used, but the sides must be undercut or relieved to avoid tapering on the top of the slot or groove.

Bellmouthing of a slot or groove is a condition where the ends of the slot become gradually wider than the center. On the surface grinder, this condition is generally caused by spindle end play, or pressure on the wheel; the work forces the end play or wheel in one direction, then, as the wheel clears the slot, the work pressure decreases, permitting the spindle to occupy a normal running position. This condition can be overcome by doing most of the grinding in the central section of the groove or slot and only occasionally running the wheel off the ends.

To grind sharp corners on the bottom of the slot, a vitrified wheel of 80-O or 120-P should be used, after the slot has been ground to size.

Form grinding can be done on the surface grinder by dressing the wheel to the desired shape.

In the case of convex or concave radii, a special diamond holder, known as a *radius wheel-truing attachment* provides an efficient, as well as an accurate, method of shaping a grinding wheel to a required radius (see Fig. 20–65). The base of the attachment carries a swivel platen upon which is mounted a slide which can be moved longitudinally by handwheel. An upright, integral with the slide, holds the diamond tool and diamond-tool setting gage; and the diamond may be set parallel to the slide or at right angles and clamped in position by a locking screw.

Fig. 20–65. Radius wheel-truing attachment in position to form radius on edge of wheel. (Brown & Sharpe Mfg. Co.)

For forming concave or convex outlines, the diamond point is located by means of the diamond-tool setting gage (turned upward 180 deg from position shown), and the slide is adjusted longitudinally to the desired radius as indicated by a scale on the slide reading to 1 in. each side of zero by sixty-fourths. The slide is locked in position by a clamping screw, and the diamond is passed across the wheel by swiveling the attachment on its base to produce the desired form. A gib and adjusting screws provide means of compensating for wear in the slide.

CAUTION: The table of the horizontal-planer surface grinder traverses very easily and may be pushed back or forth by leaning accidentally against the end of it. This is a desirable quality of the table in so far as surface finish is concerned but is a dangerous one when removing work from the magnetic chuck. Many an operator has suffered an ugly hand wound on this type of machine because after he moves the table to the right of the wheel, he takes hold of the work and gives it a pull in the direction of the wheel. If the table moves or when the work lets go, the operator's hand or arm is likely to come in contact with the revolving wheel; the result is a nasty burn and cut. To avoid such an accident, move the worktable to the right of the wheel, turn off the magnetic chuck, and then remove the work from the chuck by pulling it in a direction perpendicular to the longitudinal travel of the table.

Horizontal rotary grinder

The horizontal rotary grinder (Fig. 20–66), commonly known as a *ring grinder*, consists of a horizontal wheel spindle having a reciprocating motion similar to that of the shaper ram, and a revolving magnetic-chuck table supported by columns at the front of the machine. The worktable can be raised or lowered and has provisions for tilting the table for concave or convex grinding. The machine is equipped with a coolant supply tank and pump for wet grinding, and, since it uses the periphery of the wheel, it is capable of producing a good finish. This type of machine is used for the production of flat, concave, or convex surfaces which makes it readily adaptable for either toolroom or multiple-production purposes.

Another type of horizontal rotary grinder is shown in Fig. 20–67.

Vertical-spindle rotary grinder

The vertical-spindle rotary grinder (Fig. 20–68) consists of a cylindrical wheel mounted on a vertical spindle and supported on a vertical column. This vertical column provides a means of raising or lowering the wheel. The worktable consists of a revolving magnetic chuck supported on ways or slides, which provide a means of moving the work to and from the wheel. When the work and wheel are engaged, the magnetic chuck rotates in a clockwise direction but the table is locked in place on

Fig. 20–66. Rotary surface grinder with reciprocating head. (Heald Machine Co.)

A. Knob for fine adjustment of work to wheel
B. Handwheel for adjusting chuck to give concave and convex surfaces
C. Handwheel for raising and lowering work chuck
D. Start-and-stop buttons for rotation of magnetic chuck
E. Off-and-on switch for magnetizing chuck
F. Magnetic chuck for holding work

G. Grinding wheel
H. Lever for adjusting speed of wheel slide
J. Dogs for adjusting length of stroke of wheel slide
K. Dog for quick return of wheel slide
L. Wheel-slide reverse lever
M. Lever for adjusting speed of wheel slide and wheel

the ways of the machine. This machine does not give as good a surface finish as the horizontal rotary grinder, but has a use in the toolroom as well as on production.

In using the vertical-spindle rotary grinder, the work is placed on the magnetic chuck in such a manner as to distribute the load equally, as shown in Fig. 20–69. The table is then moved in to bring the center of the chuck under the outer edge of the wheel where it is locked in place. The wheel head is then lowered very gradually until sparks indicate contact between the wheel and work. Then the power feed is thrown in.

If one of the pieces of work has been previously ground to size at one spot and coated with blue vitriol, it may be placed on the chuck and used as a sizing block. The grinding wheel can then be fed into the work until light scratches appear on the vitriolized surface, indicating that the work is

to size. When the correct size is obtained, the downfeed is stopped, the wheel head raised, the worktable moved out, and the job removed.

The more essential points for the efficient operation of a vertical-spindle rotary grinder are given below:

1. The selection of the proper grade and grain of wheel for the job.
2. The selection of the proper wheel feeds and chuck speeds to keep the wheel free-cutting and as nearly self-sharpening as possible.
3. The proper loading and blocking of the work on the chuck.
4. The condition of the working face of the chuck.
5. The condition of the working faces of the work to be ground.
6. The proper and judicious use of the wheel dresser, when required.

Fig. 20–67. Rotary surface grinder. (Heald Machine Co.)

Types of grinding wheels. There are several types of wheels for vertical surface grinding. Those most commonly used are the cylinder, the segment, and the sectored wheels. The advantages and disadvantages of each are detailed below:

The cylinder wheel (Fig. 20–70) is the most popular and generally the most satisfactory-type wheel for Blanchard grinding. The proper cylinder wheel will stay sharp with little or no dressing. Wear will be just sufficient to maintain this sharpness and no more. The grain size will be so selected as to provide clearance for chips, depending upon the nature of the material and the total area of the surface being ground, and as to produce the desired finish. The contact with the work is continuous with the maximum area of abrasive surface in contact. The cylinder wheel should always be selected for fine finishes and where extreme flatness accuracy is required. Because of the broken contact surface, the segment and, to a lesser extent, the sectored wheel, will often cause scratches on a fine finish and a rounding off of the edges of the surfaces being ground. It takes less time for a trained operator to change a cylinder wheel than to install a new set of segments; and, as against setting the segments, there is only a wire band, in

the case of the cylinder wheel, to be cut and removed.

The segment wheel (Fig. 20–71) is popular with many operators. It consists of several abrasive segments securely clamped into a segment chuck. There are several types of these chucks, and, in general, each type requires a special-shape segment. Blanchard manufactures segment chucks for segment wheels of the following diameters: 11, 18, 20, 27, 32, 36, and 42 in. The number of segments per set for each of these chucks, respectively, is 4, 6, 8, 8, 8, 10, 10. Safety, balance, and ease of clamping are necessary requirements for a satisfactory segment wheel. Segments are set out to compensate for wear but should never project more than 2 in. The segments are gripped so securely that only about an inch of the segment in the chuck is required for holding the last 2 in. However, many operators prefer to use backing blocks to prevent any possibility of a segment cocking. The spaces between the segments facilitate the clearance of chips and flow of coolant, which makes the segment wheel particularly suitable for grinding broad surfaces and rough castings. It is not suitable for grinding small pieces or narrow surfaces, especially where a fine finish and flatness accuracy are required. The interrupted grinding surface has a tendency to catch and tip small pieces and throw them from the chuck.

The sectored wheel (Fig. 20–72), is essentially a cylinder wheel of increased rim thickness with V-shaped notches molded into the outer surface. The effect of these V-shaped notches is to give approximately the same number of linear inches of abrasive on any circumference. Thus, each abrasive grain does the same amount of work, and the grains are not overworked on one diameter and wasted on another. The sectored wheel is cool-cutting, free from vibration, and uniform in grade. As in the case of the segment wheel, it is particularly suitable for grinding broad surfaces. This wheel will often give the lowest wheel cost per cubic inch of material removed. It is recommended for all Blanchard grinding except where very fine finishes are required.

Mounting of wheels. Vertical-spindle rotary grinders come equipped with a number of cast iron rings into which cylinder and sectored wheels are mounted for fastening to the faceplate. The wheel is held in the ring with sulfur, which, in its

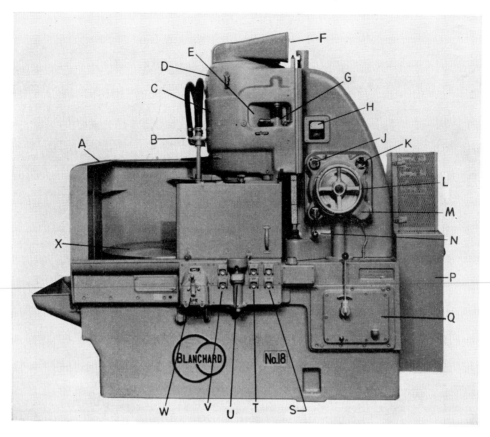

Fig. 20–68. Vertical-spindle rotary grinder. (Blanchard Machine Co.)

A. Steel guards
B. Water cocks
C. 25 hp induction motor
D. Wheel head
E. Air outlet
F. Air inlet
G. Wheel dresser
H. Ammeter

J. Feed variator
K. Oil-flow indicator
L. Feed dial and wheel
M. Oil filter
N. Feed and head-elevating lever
P. Control cabinet
Q. Chuck speed box with oil pump
R. Chuck speed control

S. Pump control
T. Wheel control
U. Table-traverse control
V. Chuck rotation control
W. Chuck switch
X. One-piece steel magnetic chuck

molten state, is poured into the space between the ring and the wheel. The ring and wheel must be clean and the wheel carefully centered in the ring. The outside of the ring may be greased to facilitate removing any sulfur which may be spilled. Care must be taken to avoid getting grease on the inside of the ring. To prevent noxious fumes and the possibility of the sulfur catching fire, it should be heated just above its melting point and no hotter. Sulfur becomes too thick to pour, if overheated.

Wheels may also be mounted on the grinding machine with a solid wheel holder. This solid wheel holder (Fig. 20–73), eliminates the use of wheel rings and sulfur to mount cylinder wheels. The wheel holder provides the advantage of rapid wheel changes and is especially useful when the grinder is on production work, or where a variety of work requires frequent wheel changes.

Handling and storage of wheels. The cylinder wheel, because of its relatively thin section, is more fragile than most other types of grinding wheels. Care must, therefore, be taken in shipping, packing and unpacking, handling, and storage, or breakage may be expected. Wheels should not be dropped or rolled along the floor. Racks should be provided for storage of wheels. It is usually more convenient to rack them vertically, that is, with the axes horizontal. Proper labeling will facilitate finding a desired wheel, if several different grits and grades are carried in stock. Wheels should not

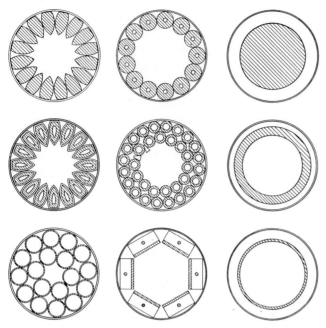

Fig. 20–69. Methods of placing various types of work on the magnetic chuck of a vertical-spindle grinding machine. (Blanchard Machine Co.)

Fig. 20–70. Cylinder grinding wheel and ring adapter. (Blanchard Machine Co.)

Fig. 20–71. Segment grinding wheel. (Blanchard Machine Co.)

be stored in the open or in damp cellars. They must be kept dry and extreme temperature changes avoided.

Finishes. Good finishes can be obtained with medium-grain wheels by the following procedure.

Fig. 20–72. Sectored grinding wheel. (Blanchard Machine Co.)

Fig. 20–73. Solid wheel holder. (Blanchard Machine Co.)

When final size is approached, continue grinding for several turns of the chuck without downfeed of the grinding wheel. This is sometimes referred to as *sparking out*. Raise the wheel by hand from 0.001 to 0.002 in. very slowly. This procedure will give a finish of from 15 to 20 micro-inches on hardened steel when a 24-grit wheel is used or on soft steel when a 46-grit wheel is used.

The same procedure should be followed when using fine-grit wheels for fine finishes. It is absolutely essential to use a free-cutting wheel, since wheels as fine as 220 grit size are quite dense, and a wheel too hard for the job will tend to heat the work and will not produce the accuracy possible with the freer-cutting wheel. In using fine-grit wheels, 100 grit or finer, the regular wheel dresser can be used occasionally if it is necessary, but only light pressure should be used for this operation. To give best results, a silicon carbide dressing stick should be used, holding the stick against the face of the wheel as the wheel idles down to a stop. The inside and outside corners of the wheel should be rounded to about 1/16 in. radius in order to obtain the best finishes possible and eliminate occasional scratches.

Safety rules for surface grinders

1. Test all wheels for cracks or defects before installing them on the spindle.
2. When starting a machine with a new wheel, stand a safe distance to one side until you are sure that the wheel is sound.
3. Whenever there is danger of injury in any way to yourself, in loading, unloading, or checking work on the chuck, **stop** the machine.
4. In removing work from the magnetic chuck, crank the table clear of the grinding wheel and then pull the stock **away** from the wheel.
5. Small, thin pieces of stock, extra-long stock, or stock with small contact surfaces should be thoroughly blocked on the chuck.
6. Do not use an unguarded wheel at any time if it has a diameter greater than 1 1/2 in.
7. Wear goggles when using a rubber wheel on a surface grinder.
8. Do not wipe a chuck with a towel—use an oil brush.
9. Shut off the machine while checking or setting up a job.
10. Use properly undercut safety washers in mounting a wheel.
11. Exhaust hoods are supplied as a safeguard for the health of grinder operators. See that they are properly adjusted at all times and **that** they are not abused.

REVIEW QUESTIONS
Surface Grinding

1. What is meant by surface grinding?
2. What is the difference between the planer and rotary types of surface grinder?
3. Name some of the companies that manufacture surface grinders.
4. Name the principal parts of the surface grinder shown in Fig. 20–45.
5. What wheel shapes are commonly used on the surface grinder?
6. What are the grain and grade sizes of grinding wheels commonly used on surface grinders?
7. How should the wheel be inspected for cracks?
8. What is the purpose of blotting-paper gaskets on the sides of the wheel?
9. What is meant by safety flanges?
10. Why is it necessary to step to one side when starting the machine after it has stood idle all night or after a new wheel has been installed?
11. Why is it necessary to keep surface-grinder wheels sharp and clean?
12. What is the result of continued use of a dull or dirty wheel?
13. Give five common methods of holding work on the surface grinder.
14. Explain the correct method of holding small work on a surface grinder.
15. How are nonmagnetic materials held on the magnetic chuck?
16. What is the purpose of the back rail on the magnetic chuck?
17. What is the purpose of a 90-deg angle plate?
18. In what condition should the angle plate be kept for accurate work?
19. How many faces can be ground square with each other at the same time by use of the 90-deg angle plate?
20. From Figs. 20–57 and 20–58, explain how to set up a job for squaring by use of an angle plate.
21. Give two reasons for work being out of parallel in surface grinding.
22. Give an efficient method for keeping thick work parallel on the surface grinder.
23. How is thin work prevented from warping on the surface grinder?
24. What is meant by grinding the work to clean up?
25. Explain what witness marks are.
26. Briefly explain how to surface-grind a job to leave witness marks on it.
27. When is the V block used for holding work on the surface grinder?
28. Name four factors governing the accuracy of a V block.
29. Briefly explain the procedure in grinding two opposite flats central on a cylindrical shaft.
30. Give two methods for grinding angular work.
31. Why should the grinding wheel **not** be dressed at an angle unless absolutely necessary?

32. When dressing the wheel at an angle, what is an important thing to remember?
33. How is the wheel dressed at the desired angle?
34. What tools are commonly used for setting the work at an angle?
35. What is a sine bar?
36. Explain how the sine bar is used to set the work at an angle.
37. What two surface-grinding operations call for considerable skill and patience on the part of the operator?
38. What shape, grain size, and bond of wheel should be used for slot grinding?
39. How can an ordinary disk wheel be used for grinding?
40. What is meant by bellmouthing of the slot?
41. How can bellmouthing of the slot be prevented?
42. How is it possible to maintain sharp corners in the bottom of a slot?
43. How is it possible to grind radii on the surface grinder?
44. What is the purpose of a radius wheel-truing attachment?
45. Explain briefly how a radius wheel-truing attachment is used?
46. What is the important thing to remember when dressing a radius or angle on a wheel?
47. What is the correct method of removing work from the magnetic chuck of a surface grinder?
48. What machine is frequently referred to as a ring grinder?
49. What is the principle of operation of the ring grinder?
50. What work operations can be performed on the ring grinder?
51. What is the principle of operation of the vertical-spindle rotary surface grinder?
52. Describe the worktable of the vertical-spindle rotary surface grinder and tell how it operates.
53. After the work is loaded on the magnetic chuck, how is it brought into contact with the grinding wheel?
54. How is sizing of the work accomplished on the vertical-spindle rotary surface grinder?
55. Give six important points for the efficient operation of a vertical-spindle rotary surface grinder.
56. What types of wheels are used on the vertical-spindle rotary surface grinder?
57. How may glazing of the wheel be prevented on the vertical-spindle rotary surface grinder?
58. What is safety rule 6 for surface grinders?
59. What is the purpose of exhaust hoods on grinders?
60. What precision tools are commonly used for checking work on the surface grinders?

INTERNAL GRINDERS

Internal grinding is the operation of grinding straight-cylindrical, tapered, or formed holes to accurate size. The work is done on the plain internal grinder (Fig. 20–74) the universal internal grinder, or on other machines especially designed for that purpose.

Internal-grinding machines are divided into three groups, depending on the manner in which the work is held and the technique of operation. The two kinds already mentioned are known as the work-rotating type in which the work is held in place by a chuck, collet, faceplate, or special fixture. Another group of internal grinders is the centerless kind in which a set of rollers hold the work and give it a revolving motion. A third type is the cylinder grinder which holds the work in a fixed, nonrotating position on a reciprocating table and depends on the amount of eccentric wheel-spindle travel to generate the correct size of the hole to be ground.

Work-rotating type

The work-rotating type is the kind of internal grinder commonly used in tool and die rooms. The work head is mounted on the worktable, which in some cases moves back and forth. On most machines, the wheel head moves back and forth, the worktable being in a fixed position. A chuck, faceplate, or drive plate may be attached to the spindle nose of the work head.

Since the work done on internal grinders in toolrooms is generally ground dry, these machines have to be built to much closer specifications than other grinders, because it is harder to protect the vital parts from the ever-present abrasive dust, and because the grinding wheel and work speeds are much faster than on other types of grinders. For the same reasons, internal grinders should be kept well lubricated.

The center line of the grinding wheel and that of the work on internal grinders are in the same

Fig. 20–74. Hydraulic universal internal grinding machine. (Landis Tool Co.)

A. On-and-off control lever
B. Lever to operate collet for holding work
C. Swivel base of work head
D. Hand-traverse wheel
E. Traverse speed-control valve
F. Traverse reversing lever
G. Reversing dogs

H. Traverse-reversal tarry control
J. Automatic feed selector
K. Electrical controls
L. Cross-slide handwheel for feeding grinding wheel into work
M. Grinding-wheel head

horizontal plane, but because the grinding wheel is smaller than the hole to be ground, the two are not in the same vertical plane; for this reason, the grinding wheel must contact the work on the near, or far, side of the hole depending on the construction of the grinding machine. Figure 20–75 shows the relation of the internal-grinding wheel to the work.

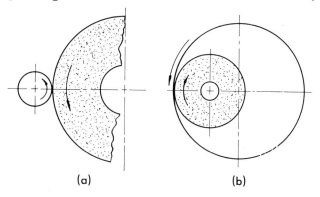

Fig. 20–75. Relation of grinding wheel to work surface. (a) External; (b) internal.

JOB ANALYSIS

The following outline is a typical analysis of the procedure in internal grinding.

Type of job	Bushing as per sketch (see Fig. 20–76)
Type of machine	Internal grinder
Type of steel	SAE 1095
Heat-treatment	Harden to Rockwell 52–64
Kind of grinding wheel	60-K
Operations required	Rough and finish-grind ID as per sketch
Method of holding	Four-jaw chuck

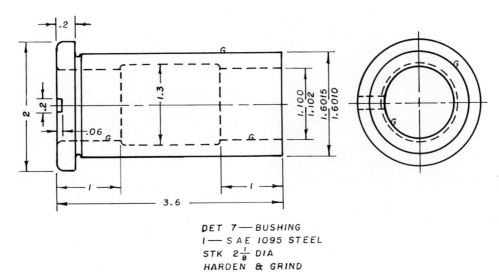

DET 7 — BUSHING
1 — S A E 1095 STEEL
STK 2⅛ DIA
HARDEN & GRIND

Fig. 20–76. Sketch of bushing.

PROCEDURE

1. Check ID for sufficient grind stock.
2. Mount a four-jaw chuck on the headstock and adjust the work in the chuck so that it runs true.
3. Select the proper quill (spindle) and grinding wheel, mount them on the wheel head, and dress the wheel. The proper quill to use is one which is as short and strong as possible, consistent with the length and diameter of the hole to be ground.
4. Adjust the machine for length of stroke, and set the table to grind straight, that is, without taper.
5. Take a trial clean-up cut, removing as little stock as possible.
6. Check the hole for straightness and make any necessary table adjustments.
7. With the wheel cutting straight, rough out the hole to within 0.001 or 0.002 in. of the required size.
8. Dress the grinding wheel for the finishing operation and finish-grind the hole to size.
9. Check the hole with the proper size of gage, noting any bellmouthing or out-of-roundness.
10. Have the first piece of work inspected.

Methods of holding work. A piece of work may be held in a required position on the work head of an internal grinder in many different ways, depending upon the size and shape of the work. The most common method is to hold the work in a four-jaw chuck, as in Fig. 20–77, which shows the

Fig. 20–77. Work held in four-jaw chuck while grinding an internal taper. (Brown & Sharpe Mfg. Co.)

grinding of an internal taper, and Fig. 20–78, which shows the internal grinding of a ring gear.

Another method is to use a magnetic chuck. Fig. 20–79 shows a bushing held in this manner. Work may also be fastened to a faceplate with U clamps and T bolts in the same manner as one would fasten a piece of work to the table of a milling machine or a shaper. It is usually set directly on the faceplate. However, it is sometimes necessary, when grinding work of an uncommon shape, to first attach the job with C clamps to an angle

Fig. 20–78. Grinding the *ID* of a ring gear held in a four-jaw chuck. (Landis Tool Co.)

plate which is then fastened to the faceplate. In like manner, V blocks are sometimes used to hold a job in the required position, the V block being then fastened to the faceplate.

Long pieces of work are held in a chuck at one end and supported near the opposite end by a

Fig. 20–79. Grinding the inside of a bushing held on a magnetic chuck. (Brown & Sharpe Mfg. Co.)

Fig. 20–80. End of a long piece of work is supported by a center rest. (Landis Tool Co.)

steady rest, or, as in Fig. 20–80, with a center rest. A long piece of work that cannot be conveniently placed in a chuck may be held on a center and secured to a drive plate with straps of rawhide at one end, and supported at the other end by a steady or center rest.

When a piece of work is placed in a four-jaw chuck, care must be exercised to get the work running true. Figure 20–81 shows a job in the chuck and the points at which it must be indicated to make sure that it is running true. The dial indicator is placed first at point *A* and the chuck jaws adjusted to give a minimum of runout to the work at that point; then the dial indicator is moved to point *B*. At this point, the work must be forced into

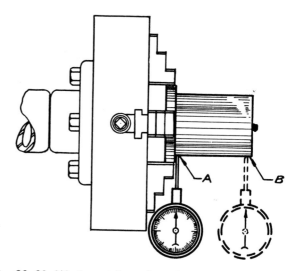

Fig. 20–81. Work must be adjusted in the chuck so that the indicator readings at *A* and *B* are the same.

line by tapping it with a mallet. This procedure should be repeated until the job runs true within the required limits at both ends.

When holding thin-walled bushings in a chuck, the jaws should be tightened only a sufficient amount to hold the work; otherwise, the pressure exerted by the jaws will squeeze the bushing out of shape and so distort the hole. For similar reasons, when clamping work to a faceplate, be sure that the work is firmly seated, and that the pressure is evenly distributed and just sufficient to hold the work firmly.

Figure 20–82 shows a correct and an incorrect method of clamping work to the plate. On the right-hand side, note that the clamp is not parallel with the faceplate because the rest block is too high; that the bolt is too far away from the job; that the parallel, which is placed there to provide end clearance for the grinding wheel, is set too far toward center, and so will interfere with the grinding operation. The bolt, clamp, rest block, and parallel are shown in their correct position on the left-hand side.

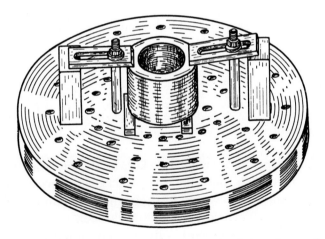

Fig. 20–82. Correct and incorrect methods of clamping work to a faceplate.

Out-of-roundness of the work may be due to the work being improperly supported, overheating of the work, loose work-head spindle, improper clamping, and so forth.

Generally speaking, the operator of an internal grinder is required to do either internal-cylindrical grinding or internal-taper grinding. Internal-cylindrical grinding can be performed only if the wheel and work heads are coordinated so that the axis of rotation of each are moved in parallel

planes. This condition can be brought about by adjusting either the work head on its swiveled base or the worktable, so that the horizontal center line of the work will be parallel to the back and forth movement of the worktable or wheel head.

Internal-taper grinding. Extreme taper is produced in the work by swiveling the work head to one-half the taper angle, according to the graduations on the circular base of the head. Slight tapers may be produced by adjusting the table to the correct taper per foot. These graduations are obviously not accurate enough for precision work, so that a taper plug gage of the correct taper per foot is used for checking the work after a clean-up cut is taken. The plug gage is given a light coat of prussian blue and with a twisting motion is inserted in the hole to be checked. If the two tapers are not identical, a bright metallic line or surface will show on the plug gage, which will indicate whether the taper is too much or not enough. If the head has been swiveled too much, the brightened surface will appear on the small end of the plug gage. If the head has not been swiveled enough, the brightened surface will appear on the large end of the plug gage.

When using plug gages for checking work, be careful that the plug does not freeze in the hole. *Freeze* is the term applied to a condition where the plug is held fast by the work and is brought about by the fact that the heat of grinding causes the work to expand, so that, when a cold plug gage is inserted, the work contracts, thus locking or freezing the plug gage in the work.

When a number of pieces are being ground, this freezing may be prevented by keeping the plug and the work at the same approximate temperature. Leave the plug gage in the hole of the last piece ground until it is necessary to check the hole in the next piece. This keeps the plug gage warm and helps to prevent freezing.

Size of grinding wheel. The diameter of the wheel for internal grinding is based on securing the stoutest-possible quill for maximum support consistent with the size of the hole to be ground. Generally speaking, the diameter of the grinding wheel should not exceed two-thirds of the diameter of the hole. It must be remembered that, as the size of the grinding wheel increases, the diameter of the hole being constant, the greater the area of contact becomes between the grinding wheel and the hole, thus increasing the heating of the work and probable distortion of the hole.

The manufacturers of internal-grinding machines build the limits of the grinding-wheel speed into the machine, and these are such that speeds from 4,000 to 6,500 sfpm can be obtained. These speeds, of course, depend on the size of the grinding wheel.

Various kinds of diamond or tungsten carbide dressers are available for either mechanical or hand dressing of the grinding wheel. Occasionally, grinding wheels are dressed, by the operator's holding a piece of silicon carbide in his hand and passing it along the periphery of the grinding wheel.

The amount of stock left in a hole, to be removed by grinding to bring it up to the required size, depends on the diameter and length of the hole, but is generally from 0.004 to 0.012 in. More grind stock than this means a longer time to complete the grinding job.

Bellmouthing of the work is a condition where the ends of the hole flare out or are increasingly larger than the required diameter. This condition is brought about by permitting the grinding wheel to overrun the ends of the hole, by using a grinding wheel that is too hard, by excessive wheel pressure, or by grinding wheels that are too short. The first condition can be prevented by setting the length of stroke so that, at the extremity of its travel, only one-quarter to one-half of the grinding-wheel face will be uncovered by the work.

The job should be checked for size and straightness after a clean-up cut has been taken, but be sure to move the work and grinding wheel far enough apart to enable the wheel guard (Fig. 20–83) to swing down and cover the wheel. Otherwise serious cuts and burns are apt to be received from the revolving grinding wheel.

Blind holes can be ground on the internal grinder, provided an undercut of sufficient width is made to give the end of the grinding wheel a little overrun of the hole.

Internal centerless grinder

The internal centerless grinder (Fig. 20–84) is especially designed for big runs of work of the same size and kind. It is fully automatic and assures that the hole will be ground concentric with the outside diameter of the work. It is capable of producing straight or taper, blind or through holes, interrupted holes, and holes having a shoulder.

In this type of machine, the work is driven, and its speed controlled, by a regulating roller which causes the work to revolve in the same direction as the grinding wheel. To support the work, a second roller is mounted below the work and may be adjusted for varying distances from the work center. A third roller, known as a pressure roll, is supported on a swing bracket, holds the work in contact with the other two rollers, and moves in and out to allow for loading and unloading the machine. The work head moves back and forth, while the wheel head is fixed longitudinally. This makes for great rigidity of the wheel, which keeps vibration at a minimum.

Cylinder grinder

The cylinder grinder (Fig. 20–85), commonly known as a *planetary grinder,* was designed for the expressed purpose of doing internal grinding on work which was too cumbersome to be revolved on a work head. It is used to good advantage in railroad shops or any shop engaging in heavy-machinery operations.

This machine has a reciprocating table to which

Fig. 20–83. Wheel guard for internal grinding wheel. The wheel guard swings downward to protect operator but does not interfere with fixtures. It can be adjusted for all sizes of wheel heads.

Fig. 20–84. Internal centerless grinder. (Heald Machine Co.)

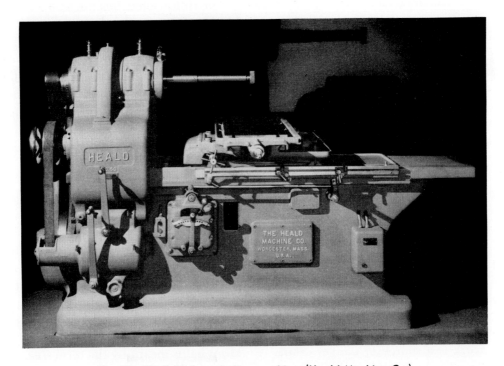

Fig. 20–85. Cylinder grinding machine. (Heald Machine Co.)

the work is clamped in a fixed position. The grinding wheel is mounted on a spindle which, while revolving, travels in an adjustable circular path, the size of the path determining the diameter of the hole.

Grinding wheels for internal grinding

All of the internal-grinding machines discussed here use vitrified wheels of from 1/4 to 2 1/2 in. in diameter and from 3/8 to 2 in. face. The more common grades and grain sizes of aluminum oxide wheels used for internal grinding are: 46-I, 60-I, 46-J, 60-J, 60-L, and 120-P.

Safety rules for internal grinding

1. Internal-grinding wheels are provided with a safety guard that encloses the wheel while the work is being checked. See that this guard is in good operating condition at all times. Do not use the grinder otherwise.
2. Mount all internal-grinding wheels with either paper or brass washers; brass is preferred for small wheels.
3. See that the machine is stopped by pulling the power switch when setting up a job, or while making any necessary changes to guards, stops, or other machine attachments.
4. Wheel breakage happens at times during facing operations. Keep the wheel dressed sharply and use goggles when doing work of this nature.
5. Do not use wheels in excess of 2 1/2 in. diameter on the internal grinder without a special permit from the instructor.
6. Do not try to wipe out the hole that is to be ground, while the work head is in motion. This is a careless practice, resulting in finger and hand injuries.
7. See that all heavy work is properly and securely clamped; use standard planer jacks and grinder clamps. Work that is off center should be counterbalanced.
8. When using thin rubber wheels or extra-hard wheels on the internal grinder, wear goggles as an extra protection from wheel breakage.
9. Any class of work that is too long to allow the proper use of the safety wheel guard while checking the work is a source of danger. Shut the machine down to check work of this nature.

REVIEW QUESTIONS
Internal Grinding

1. What is meant by internal grinding?
2. On what kinds of machines is internal grinding done?
3. Name some companies that make internal-grinding machines.
4. Into what three groups are internal grinders divided?
5. What kinds of internal grinders are commonly used for toolroom work?
6. How is work commonly held in the work-rotating type of internal grinder?
7. Name the parts of the internal grinder which are pertinent to its operation.
8. Why must the internal grinder be built to closer specifications than most other machines?
9. Why must the spindle bearings of the internal grinder be kept especially well lubricated?
10. In the grinding operation, what is the relation of the grinding wheel with respect to the work?
11. Explain, exactly, how to chuck up a job in a four-jaw chuck on the internal grinder.
12. Give six methods for holding work on the internal grinder besides the four-jaw chuck and collets.
13. What care must be exercised in the chucking of thin-walled bushings?
14. Explain, exactly, the correct method of clamping work to a faceplate on the internal grinder.
15. What are the most frequent causes of out-of-roundness of the work in internal grinding?
16. What two work operations is the operator of the internal grinder most frequently called upon to do?
17. What conditions must prevail for the production of internal cylinders on the internal grinder?
18. How can this condition be brought about?
19. How is extreme taper produced on the internal grinder?
20. How are slight tapers produced on the internal grinder?
21. Explain how to produce accurate taper work on the internal grinder.
22. Explain the use of the taper plug gage in producing an accurate taper.
23. What is meant by the term *freeze* when checking a hole with a plug gage?

24. How can freezing be prevented?
25. Upon what two factors does the selection of diameter of the grinding wheel for internal grinding depend?
26. What are the limits of speed in feet per minute for internal-grinding wheels?
27. What is meant by the term *bellmouthing?*
28. What is the most frequent cause of bellmouthing?
29. How can bellmouthing be prevented?
30. When checking work on the internal grinder, how is the operator protected from the rotating grinding wheel?
31. What condition is necessary for the production of blind holes on the internal grinder?

Fig. 20–86. General-purpose bench grinder. (Black & Decker Mfg. Co.)

Fig. 20–87. External-thread grinder. (Ex-Cell-O Corp.)

A. Lead pickup
B. Work drive and lead-screw housing
C. Work head
D. Grinding wheel
E. Coolant valve
F. Tailstock
G. Helix-angle graduation
H. Wheel-spindle motor
J. Signal lights indicating dressing of wheel
K. Machine table slide
L. Electrical compartment
M. Table control dogs
N. Automatic cycle-starting lever
P. Size-setting handwheel
Q. Opening to adjust depth of initial grinding cut
R. Manual-dresser slide adjustment
S. Work-drive motor
T. Control panel

32. What is the purpose of the internal centerless grinder?

33. How is the work held in an internal centerless?

34. For what kinds of work is the internal centerless suited?

35. By what name is the cylinder grinder commonly known?

36. What is the purpose of the cylinder grinder?

37. For what branches of industry is the cylinder grinder especially suited?

38. How is the work held in the cylinder grinder?

39. How is the cylinder grinder adjusted to produce the correct-size hole?

40. Wheels used in internal grinding are made from what kind of bond?

41. What grades of bond and abrasive sizes are commonly used in internal-grinding wheels?

42. How is the operator of a toolroom internal grinder protected from the rotating grinding wheel?

43. What care should be exercised in mounting an internal-grinding wheel?

44. At what two times in particular should the operator of an internal grinder wear goggles?

MISCELLANEOUS GRINDERS FOR TOOL SHARPENING

Floor or bench grinders

A floor or bench grinder (Fig. 20–86) is usually an electric motor mounted on a suitable base and having the rotor shaft extended from each side, with a grinding wheel mounted on each end, for sharpening tool bits, planer tools, boring tools, drills, etc.

Some floor grinders for heavy-duty work have a wheel shaft mounted in heavy bearings which are an integral part of a heavy cast base. The wheel is driven by a belt connecting the wheel-shaft pulley to a motor mounted on the base of the machine.

For grinding cutting tools, these machines should be equipped with fine-grain wheels of a silicate or vitrified bond. For rough grinding, snagging or heavy work, the machine should be equipped with coarse free-cutting wheels.

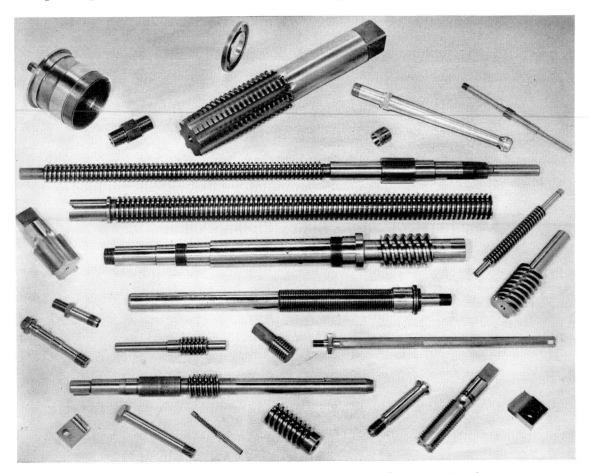

Fig. 20–88. Examples of external-thread grinding. (Ex-Cell-O Corp.)

All floor or bench grinders should be equipped with adjustable eye shields made from fire glass or safety glass and should never be used unless the operator is wearing goggles.

One end of a floor or bench grinder may be equipped with suitable sewed-canvas forms, the periphery of which have been coated with an abrasive to be used as buffers. Buffing wheels are used for the purpose of securing a good finish or polish without respect to surface accuracy. In using a buffer, care must be taken to keep the work from getting caught in the buffing wheel and being pulled into the machine, or serious injury might result.

Thread grinders

Precision thread grinding has an extremely wide application in industry today. Many manufacturers of precision-threaded parts now depend upon thread grinding to obtain the extreme accuracy that the ever-rising standards of modern industry demand. Special machines have been designed for this purpose.

External-thread grinders. An external-thread grinder for general-purpose work is shown in Fig. 20–87. On this type of machine, threads may be ground on work up to 6 in. in diameter and 18 in. long, held between centers. As shown in Fig. 20–88, many different types of threads may be ground, including American National form, 60-deg sharp V, 29-deg Acme, modified buttress, Whitworth, and special thread forms. Threads may be right- or left-handed, straight, tapered, or relieved; also in single and multiple pitches from 1 to 80 threads per inch.

Internal-thread grinders. An internal-thread grinder is shown in Fig. 20–89. This type of machine is designed and built for grinding internally threaded parts on a production basis, with high finish and to close limits. Whether grinding fine threads from the solid, or coarse threads that have previously been roughed and then heat-treated, a tolerance on the pitch diameter of plus or minus 0.0002 in. can be held. Threads ranging from 1 to 9 1/2 in. in diameter and up to 5 in. in length may be ground. Some examples of the type of work usually done on the internal-thread grinder are shown in Fig. 20–90. Some special adapters for the purpose of holding unusual or awkward pieces of work are shown in Figs. 20–91 and 20–92.

Fig. 20–89. Internal-thread grinder. (Ex-Cell-O Corp.)

  A. Work drive and lead-screw housing
  B. Work-head slide
  C. Control for right- or left-hand thread and multiple index
  D. Workpiece
  E. Grinding wheel
  F. Controls and indicating lights
  G. Electrical compartment
  H. Wheel slide
  J. Size-control handwheel assembly
  K. Operator's control panel
  L. Lead pickup and automatic backlash-compensation control

Fig. 20–90. Examples of work done on internal-thread grinder. (Ex-Cell-O Corp.)

Fig. 20–91. A special adapter on the work spindle positions the propeller shaft so that the large, projecting portion can swing without interference while grinding internal threads. (Ex-Cell-O Corp.)

Fig. 20–92. The irregular gun part is held in a special chuck on an internal-thread grinder. (Ex-Cell-O Corp.)

A precision thread grinder for extra-long work is shown in Fig. 20–93. This machine will grind an external thread 50 in. long, on work up to 68 in. in length, held between centers. Longer thread sec-

tions can be ground by turning the work end for end; the lead can be accurately picked up and the threads matched where the sections meet. Using a table extension, work up to 115 in. can be accommodated between centers. Threads up to 8 in. in diameter may be ground when the grinding wheel is a full 18 in. in diameter as in Fig. 20–94. With a grinding wheel 14 in. in diameter, threads up to 12 in. in diameter may be ground.

The thread shown in Fig. 20–94 is being ground with a narrow grinding wheel shaped to the required form of thread. It is known as a single-rib wheel (see Fig. 20–95). An example of an internal thread being ground with a single-rib grinding wheel is shown in Fig. 20–96.

Thread grinding wheels

Thread grinding wheels are also made with multiple ribs. While the truing of single-rib grinding wheels is carried out principally by the use of diamond wheel dressers, the truing of multiple-rib wheels is performed exclusively by rotating crushing rollers (see Fig. 20–97). During the wheel-

Fig. 20–93. An external-thread grinder designed for extra-long work. (Ex-Cell-O Corp.)

Fig. 20–94. Grinding a ball-groove lead screw, 7⅝ in. in diameter and 45 in. long, on an external-thread grinder. (Ex-Cell-O Corp.)

crushing operation, the crushing roller, which is mounted on a slide to permit rotation with axial play, is forced against the wheel by means of a threaded spindle and is driven by the grinding wheel. Figure 20–98 shows the wheel-crushing attachment, which is located behind the grinding wheel. A multiple-rib grinding wheel is shown grinding a tap in Fig. 20–99.

GRINDING SUGGESTIONS

Many grinding-machine and grinding-wheel manufacturers have made some good suggestions relative to safe and economical operation of grinding equipment. It is recommended that apprentices and other users of grinding machines pay close attention to these suggestions. The general adoption of them would go a long way toward the elim-

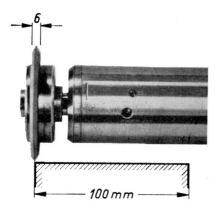

Fig. 20–95. Single-rib thread-grinding wheel. (Kurt Orban Co., Inc.)

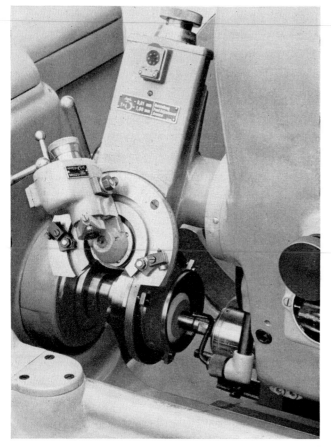

Fig. 20–96. Grinding an internal thread with a single-rib grinding wheel. (Kurt Orban Co., Inc.)

Fig. 20–97. Crushing rollers for dressing multiple-rib grinding wheels. (Kurt Orban Co., Inc.)

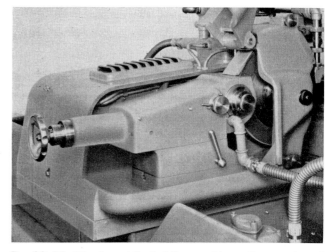

Fig. 20–98. Attachment for holding crushing rollers on thread grinder. (Kurt Orban Co., Inc.)

ination of accidents to the operators and improper use of machines.

1. Handle all grinding wheels carefully.
2. Sound a grinding wheel for cracks before putting it on a machine, especially in the case of cylindrical and surface grinder wheels.
3. Make sure the blotting-paper or rubber gaskets are in place between the wheel and wheel flanges.
4. Where a choice of grinding machines is possible, select the one that is most rigid.

5. The grinding wheel should fit freely on the spindle with about 0.003 to 0.005 in. of play.

6. Use relieved or safety flanges which are at least one-third of the grinding-wheel diameter.

7. The spindle nut should be set up tight enough to hold the wheel securely.

8. Keep all wheel guards tight and in place.

9. After installing a wheel on a surface or cylindrical grinder, turn it over by hand to make sure that it clears the guards and housing.

10. Keep the spindles and bearings well oiled to avoid overheating of the spindle and possible wheel breakage.

11. When starting to work in the morning, press the starter button on the machine and, at the same time, step to one side, letting the machine run for at least 1 min before engaging the wheel with the work.

12. When grinding long, slender work on cylindrical grinders, use steady rests to support the work and keep the shoes properly adjusted to the work. Make sure the driving pin for the grinder dog is firmly located in the arm on the drive plate.

13. When grinding wheels are removed from the machine, handle them carefully and store them in a dry place.

14. When engaging the grinding wheel with the work, avoid excessive pressure; it is ruinous to the wheel, work supports, and spindle bearings.

15. In any grinding machine, it is necessary for the work to be supported properly and for the operator to keep his hands away from the revolving wheel and work.

16. When placing work on the magnetic chuck of surface grinders, the table should be moved far enough away from the grinding wheel so that the operator can locate the work without injury to his hands from contact with the wheel.

Fig. 20–99. Grinding a tap with a multiple-rib wheel. (Ex-Cell-O Corp.)

17. Since the table of a horizontal surface grinder moves along its ways very easily, the work should be removed from the magnetic chuck by sliding it off in a direction perpendicular to the table traverse.

18. Close and easy-fitting goggles should be worn on any dry-grinding operation where there is danger of flying grit getting into the operator's eyes.

19. Exhaust hoods on dry grinders are provided for the benefit of the operator and should be kept in place and free from obstructions.

20. Magnetic chucks are expensive pieces of equipment. Keep them clean. Keep them free from scratches and nicks. Do not leave the machine for any length of time with the switch to the chuck turned on.

Chapter 21 ROUTING OF BENCH TOOL WORK

The term *bench work* is applied to the type of work done at the bench by toolmakers, consisting of planning the work; laying out the work to be done on castings and forgings, the holes to be drilled, tapped, and so forth; and the actual work of chipping, sawing, filing, threading, drilling, reaming, tapping of holes, scraping, and lapping; checking each piece of work after each operation; and the assembling of tools such as drill jigs, dies, gages, and the like.

An order for work to be done in the toolroom is accompanied by a set of blueprints. The order will specify the number of complete units that are re-

quired (see Fig. 21–1). After they have been recorded in the toolroom office, the order and blueprints are delivered to a bench leader who, in turn, assigns the work to a toolmaker who will assume responsibility for the completion of the job. He reads the blueprints to determine what is required and to make sure that the draftsman has given adequate dimensions and specifications for each part of the job. He then plans the job carefully and decides how each detail or piece of work will be made. The sequence of operation and the machines that are to be used must be considered. A mistake in this phase of the work might lead to

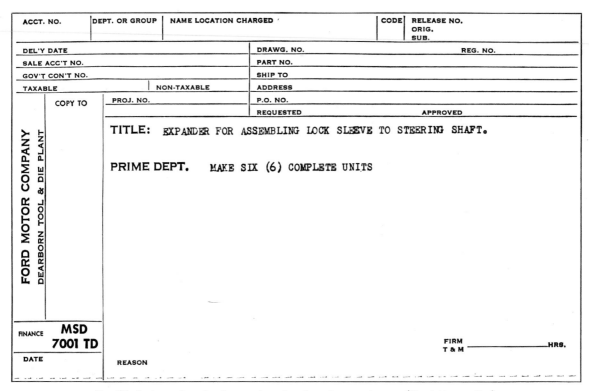

Fig. 21–1. A work order for work to be done in a toolroom. (Ford Motor Co.)

serious results later as the job progresses. If any special tools are necessary for certain operations, such as jigs or fixtures, he must foresee this early enough to have them ready when needed. He must consider the most efficient and economical method that can be used for each part. A toolmaker can save many hours of time and a great deal of expense by analyzing the job, visualizing each operation, and then making a written record of the sequence of operation, thus avoiding mistakes which might otherwise be made.

The first thing to be done is to order the material for making each part, according to the specifications given on the blueprints and in the right quantity for the number of units specified on the order. If the job requires a casting or a forging, these will be ordered first, because it usually takes several days to obtain delivery of them from the foundry or forge shop. In addition to the material for the parts that have to be made in the toolroom, the commercially made parts, such as screws, washers, ball bearings and the like, will be ordered (see Fig. 21–2).

When the stock is received by the toolmaker, it is checked with the blueprint to make certain that the proper material and sizes have been sent. He then writes out a toolroom operation sheet (Fig. 21–3), routing each part of the job in turn to the required departments for machining. The sheet is accompanied by a blueprint or sketch showing the work that is to be done in that department.

Since it is necessary for the toolmaker to be able to locate any part of the job at any time, a complete record of each detail is kept on the tool and die route card (Fig. 21–4). This route card shows where each detail has been sent, the date sent, the date returned, and any remarks pertinent to the job, such as the scrapping of a piece of work.

The toolmaker must follow up his orders to the various departments, making sure that the several details of each job are finished in the proper rotation, and that they are not unnecessarily ignored in favor of other jobs. This must be done daily. Sometimes it is necessary to exercise salesmanship in order to get rush jobs done ahead of less urgent work. As each detail is returned to the bench, it is checked to make sure that it has been machined correctly according to the drawing before sending it to the next department for further machining or heat-treating.

In the case of the bushing shown in Fig. 21–5, it would be planned to send the job (1) to the lathe department for turning, boring, facing, and undercutting; (2) to the mill department to have the slot cut; (3) to the heat-treating department to be hardened; (4) to the grinding department for internal and external grinding.

Figure 21–6 shows an assembly and detail drawing of an expander of which six complete units are required.

1. What size, kind, and quantity of stock should be ordered?

Ans. For detail 1: one piece of SAE 1095—tool steel, 5/8 in. square, 16 in. long. For detail 2: six pieces of SAE 1020—machine steel, 3 1/2 in. in diameter, 1 in. thick. For detail 3: one piece of SAE 1075—drill rod, 7/32 in. in diameter, 22 in.

STOCK LIST

NO. PC.	DET.	DESCRIPTION
1	1	S A E 1095 - Tool Steel, 5/8" sq. x 16"
6	2	S A E 1020 - Machine Steel 3½" dia. x 1"
1	3	S A E 1075 - Drill Rod, 7/32" dia. x 22"
12		½" dia. Steel Balls

SERIAL ___Z___ ACCT. NO. ___ DEPT. CHG. ___ F. W. O. NO. ___ DATE___

DELIVER MATERIAL TO___TOOLROOM___ DIVISION

IMPORTANT—The above material is on order. DO NOT DUPLICATE. All standard details for this order will be held in your TOOL CRIB until released by your Foreman.

ORDERED BY

Fig. 21–2. Stock list; an order for material required for a job. (Ford Motor Co.)

TOOL ROOM OPERATION SHEET — MACH. NO.

SER. NO.	ACCT. NO.	DEPT. CHG.	F. W. O. NO.
DRWG. NO.	PART NO.		DATE
SENT BY BENCH NO.	BAY NO.	OPERATION	LATHE

ESTIMATE TIME	PER PC.		TOTAL HRS.	ACTUAL TIME	PER PC.		TOTAL HRS.
	PER LOT				PER LOT		

NO. PCS.	PATT. DET.	REMARKS	MAKE SKETCH IF NECESSARY
6	1	Machine as per attached blue print.	TYPE OF STEEL BRINELL
6	2		

FOREMAN_____

ORIGINAL—MACHINE FOREMAN'S RECORD

Fig. 21–3. Toolroom operation sheet. (Ford Motor Co.)

TOOL AND DIE ROUTE CARD

AMT.	PATT. DETS.	OUTSIDE DEPT. OUT	IN	LATHE OUT	IN	BULLARD OUT	IN	SCREW MACH. OUT	IN	KELLER OUT	IN	PLANER OUT	IN	SHAPER OUT	IN	MILL OUT	IN	GEAR OUT	IN	HEAT TREAT OUT	IN	GRINDER OUT	IN	BENCH OUT	IN	REMARKS
6	1			7-2	7-5											7-5	7-8			7-9	7-11	7-11	7-12	7-8	7-9	
6	2			7-2	7-5											7-5	7-8			7-9	7-11			7-8	7-9	
6	3																							7-2	7-9	
12	1⅛ BALLS																							7-2	7-3	

Fig. 21–4. Tool and die route card. (Ford Motor Co.)

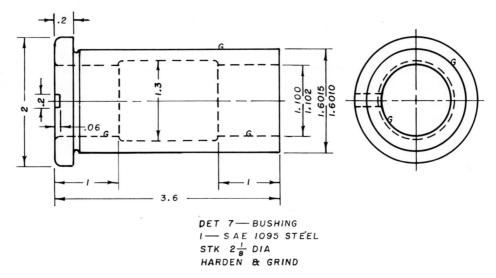

DET 7 — BUSHING
1 — S A E 1095 STEEL
STK 2⅛ DIA
HARDEN & GRIND

Fig. 21–5. Drawing of a bushing.

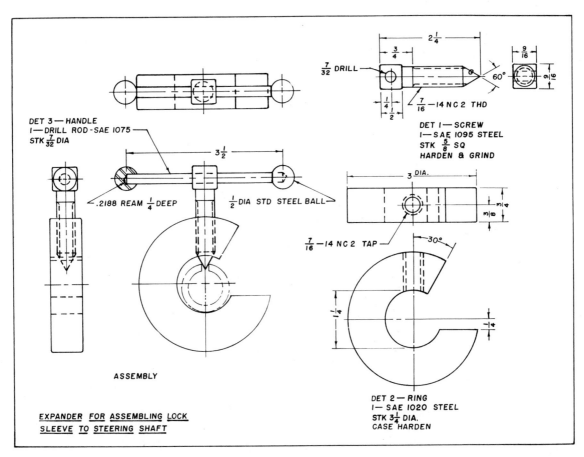

Fig. 21–6. Assembly and detail drawing of an expander.

long; also, twelve 1/2-in.-diameter standard steel balls.

2. List the operations to be performed on detail 1.

Ans. The job would first go to the lathe department to (1) be turned, (2) have the taper cut, (3) have the thread cut, (4) be cut off to length, and (5) have the square end faced. After inspection, the screws would next be sent to the mill department to have the square heads milled to size. The hole would be drilled at the bench. Then the screws would be sent to the heat-treating department to be hardened and tempered. After inspection for the correct degree of hardness, the parts would be sent to the grinding department to have the tapered end ground.

3. List the operations to be performed on detail 2.

Ans. The job would first be sent to the lathe department to be (1) faced on one end, (2) bored, (3) placed on a mandrel, (4) turned, and (5) faced on other end. After inspection the rings would be sent to the mill department to have the opening cut. The hole would be drilled and tapped at the bench. Then the rings would be sent to the heat-treating department for casehardening.

4. List the operations to be performed on detail 3.

Ans. The material would be sawed to length and the ends filed at the bench.

5. List the operations to be performed on the steel balls.

Ans. The balls would be drilled and reamed for a press fit at the bench.

6. After all of the parts have been machined, what does the toolmaker do with them?

Ans. The parts are assembled and sent to the inspection department for final inspection. If the job is approved, the order is marked *closed*, together with the date, and the job is turned over to the bench leader for delivery.

Appendix

ABBREVIATIONS AND SYMBOLS COMMONLY USED IN INDUSTRY

Addendum	ADD.	Gage	GA	Pitch	P or p
Adjust	ADJ	Grind	G or GRD	Pitch diameter	PD
Altitude	alt			Pound	lb
And	&	Hexagon	HEX		
Approximate	approx	Hypotenuse	HYP	Radius	R
		Inch	in. or ''	Right hand	RH
Brown & Sharpe	B&S	Inside diameter	ID	Round head	RD HD
Cast iron	CI	Left hand	LH	Screw	SCR
Center to center	c to c	Linear pitch	LP	Society of Automotive	
Center line	CL or ¢			Engineers	SAE
Centigrade	C	Machine	mach	Socket head	SOC HD
Circular pitch	CP	Machine steel	MS	Spot-faced	SF
Circumference	circum	Maximum	max	Square	sq
Cold-rolled steel	crs	Millimeter	mm	Standard	std
Cotangent	cot	Minimum	min	Stock	STK
Counterbore	CBORE				
Countersink	CSK	National Coarse*	NC	Tangent	tan
Cylinder	cyl	National Fine*	NF	Thread	THD
		National Special*	NS		
Dedendum	DED	Number	No. or #	Unified National Coarse*	UNC
Degree	deg or °			Unified National Fine*	UNF
Detail	DET	Outside diameter	OD	Unified National Special*	UNS
Diameter	dia				
Dimension	DIM.	Pattern	PATT	Weight	wt
Drill rod	DR				
Fahrenheit	F				
Fillister head	FIL HD				
Finish	FIN. or f				
Flat head	FH				
Foot	ft or '				

* On Nov. 18, 1948, the United Kingdom, Canada, and the United States agreed on certain National standards and renamed them Unified National Coarse, Unified National Fine, and Unified National Special accordingly. Those National standards not agreed on are still known as National Coarse, National Fine, and National Special. Sometimes those National standards that were agreed on are still referred to in the trade literature by their old designation of National Coarse, National Fine, or National Special.

Table 1. BASIC SCREW THREAD DIMENSIONS AND TAP DRILL SIZES OF AMERICAN NATIONAL COARSE AND FINE THREAD SERIES

| Screw size | Threads per inch | | Basic dimensions, in. | | | | Commercial tap drill to produce approx 75% full thread | | Body drill | Decimal equiv |
	NC coarse thread series	NF fine thread series	Major diameter	Pitch diameter	Single depth of thread	Minor or root diameter	Tap drill	Decimal equiv		
0	....	80	0.060	0.0519	0.00812	0.0438	$\frac{3}{64}$	0.0469	52	0.0635
1	64	....	0.073	0.0629	0.01015	0.0527	53	0.0595	47	0.0785
1	....	72	0.073	0.0640	0.00902	0.0550	53	0.0595	47	0.0785
2	56	....	0.086	0.0744	0.01160	0.0628	50	0.0700	42	0.0935
2	....	64	0.086	0.0759	0.01015	0.0657	50	0.0700	42	0.0935
3	48	....	0.099	0.0855	0.01353	0.0719	47	0.0785	37	0.1040
3	....	56	0.099	0.0874	0.01160	0.0758	45	0.0820	37	0.1040
4	40	....	0.112	0.0958	0.01624	0.0795	43	0.0890	31	0.1200
4	....	48	0.112	0.0985	0.01353	0.0849	42	0.0935	31	0.1200
5	40	....	0.125	0.1088	0.01624	0.0925	38	0.1015	29	0.1360
5	....	44	0.125	0.1102	0.01476	0.0955	37	0.1040	29	0.1360
6	32	....	0.138	0.1177	0.02030	0.0974	36	0.1065	27	0.1440
6	....	40	0.138	0.1218	0.01624	0.1055	33	0.1130	27	0.1440
8	32	....	0.164	0.1437	0.02030	0.1234	29	0.1360	18	0.1695
8	....	36	0.164	0.1460	0.01804	0.1279	29	0.1360	18	0.1695
10	24	....	0.190	0.1629	0.02706	0.1359	25	0.1495	9	0.1960
10	....	32	0.190	0.1697	0.02030	0.1494	21	0.1590	9	0.1960
12	24	....	0.216	0.1889	0.02706	0.1619	16	0.1770	2	0.2210
12	....	28	0.216	0.1928	0.02320	0.1696	14	0.1820	2	0.2210
$\frac{1}{4}$	20	....	0.2500	0.2175	0.03248	0.1850	7	0.2010		
$\frac{1}{4}$	....	28	0.2500	0.2268	0.02320	0.2036	3	0.2130		
$\frac{5}{16}$	18	....	0.3125	0.2764	0.03608	0.2403	F	0.2570		
$\frac{5}{16}$	....	24	0.3125	0.2854	0.02706	0.2584	I	0.2720		
$\frac{3}{8}$	16	....	0.3750	0.3344	0.04059	0.2938	$\frac{5}{16}$	0.3125		
$\frac{3}{8}$	....	24	0.3750	0.3479	0.02706	0.3209	Q	0.3320		
$\frac{7}{16}$	14	....	0.4375	0.3911	0.04639	0.3447	U	0.3680		
$\frac{7}{16}$	....	20	0.4375	0.4050	0.03248	0.3725	$\frac{25}{64}$	0.3906		
$\frac{1}{2}$	13	....	0.5000	0.4500	0.04996	0.4001	$\frac{27}{64}$	0.4219		
$\frac{1}{2}$	....	20	0.5000	0.4675	0.03248	0.4350	$\frac{29}{64}$	0.4531		
$\frac{9}{16}$	12	....	0.5625	0.5084	0.05413	0.4542	$\frac{31}{64}$	0.4844		
$\frac{9}{16}$	....	18	0.5625	0.5264	0.03608	0.4903	$\frac{33}{64}$	0.5156		
$\frac{5}{8}$	11	....	0.6250	0.5660	0.05905	0.5069	$\frac{17}{32}$	0.5313		
$\frac{5}{8}$	....	18	0.6250	0.5889	0.03608	0.5528	$\frac{37}{64}$	0.5781		
$\frac{3}{4}$	10	....	0.7500	0.6850	0.06495	0.6201	$\frac{21}{32}$	0.6562		
$\frac{3}{4}$	....	16	0.7500	0.7094	0.04059	0.6688	$\frac{11}{16}$	0.6875		
$\frac{7}{8}$	9	....	0.8750	0.8028	0.07217	0.7307	$\frac{49}{64}$	0.7656		
$\frac{7}{8}$	....	14	0.8750	0.8286	0.04639	0.7822	$\frac{13}{16}$	0.8125		
1	8	....	1.0000	0.9188	0.08119	0.8376	$\frac{7}{8}$	0.8750		
1	....	14	1.0000	0.9536	0.04639	0.9072	$\frac{15}{16}$	0.9375		
$1\frac{1}{8}$	7	....	1.1250	1.0322	0.09279	0.9394	$\frac{63}{64}$	0.9844		
$1\frac{1}{8}$	....	12	1.1250	1.0709	0.05413	1.0167	$1\frac{3}{64}$	1.0469		
$1\frac{1}{4}$	7	....	1.2500	1.1572	0.09279	1.0644	$1\frac{7}{64}$	1.1094		
$1\frac{1}{4}$	....	12	1.2500	1.1959	0.05413	1.1417	$1\frac{11}{64}$	1.1719		
$1\frac{3}{8}$	6	....	1.3750	1.2667	0.10825	1.1585	$1\frac{7}{32}$	1.2188		
$1\frac{3}{8}$	....	12	1.3750	1.3209	0.05413	1.2667	$1\frac{19}{64}$	1.2969		
$1\frac{1}{2}$	6	....	1.5000	1.3917	0.10825	1.2835	$1\frac{11}{32}$	1.3438		
$1\frac{1}{2}$	....	12	1.5000	1.4459	0.05413	1.3917	$1\frac{27}{64}$	1.4219		
$1\frac{3}{4}$	5	....	1.7500	1.6201	0.12990	1.4902	$1\frac{9}{16}$	1.5625		
2	$4\frac{1}{2}$	....	2.0000	1.8557	0.14434	1.7113	$1\frac{25}{32}$	1.7813		

Table 2. TAPERS PER FOOT AND CORRESPONDING ANGLES

Taper per foot	Included angle			Angle with center line			Taper per foot	Included angle			Angle with center line		
	Deg	Min	Sec	Deg	Min	Sec		Deg	Min	Sec	Deg	Min	Sec
1/64	0	4	28	0	2	14	1 7/8	8	56	2	4	28	1
1/32	0	8	58	0	4	29	1 15/16	9	13	50	4	36	55
1/16	0	17	54	0	8	57	2	9	31	36	4	45	48
3/32	0	26	52	0	13	26	2 1/8	10	7	10	5	3	35
1/8	0	35	48	0	17	54	2 1/4	10	42	42	5	21	21
5/32	0	44	44	0	22	22	2 3/8	11	18	10	5	39	5
3/16	0	53	44	0	26	52	2 1/2	11	53	36	5	56	48
7/32	1	2	34	0	31	17	2 5/8	12	29	2	6	14	31
1/4	1	11	36	0	35	48	2 3/4	13	4	24	6	32	12
9/32	1	20	30	0	40	15	2 7/8	13	39	42	6	49	51
5/16	1	29	30	0	44	45	3	14	15	0	7	7	30
11/32	1	38	22	0	49	11	3 1/8	14	50	14	7	25	7
3/8	1	47	24	0	53	42	3 1/4	15	25	24	7	42	42
13/32	1	56	24	0	58	12	3 3/8	16	0	34	8	0	17
7/16	2	5	18	1	2	39	3 1/2	16	35	40	8	17	50
15/32	2	14	16	1	7	8	3 5/8	17	10	40	8	35	20
1/2	2	23	10	1	11	35	3 3/4	17	45	40	8	52	50
17/32	2	32	4	1	16	2	3 7/8	18	20	34	9	10	17
9/16	2	41	4	1	20	32	4	18	55	28	9	27	44
19/32	2	50	2	1	25	1	4 1/8	19	30	18	9	45	9
5/8	2	59	2	1	29	31	4 1/4	20	5	2	10	2	31
21/32	3	7	56	1	33	58	4 3/8	20	39	44	10	19	52
11/16	3	16	54	1	38	27	4 1/2	21	14	2	10	37	1
23/32	3	25	50	1	42	55	4 5/8	21	48	54	10	54	27
3/4	3	34	44	1	47	22	4 3/4	22	23	22	11	11	41
25/32	3	43	44	1	51	52	4 7/8	22	57	48	11	28	54
13/16	3	52	38	1	56	19	5	23	32	12	11	46	6
27/32	4	1	36	2	0	48	5 1/8	24	6	28	12	3	14
7/8	4	10	32	2	5	16	5 1/4	24	40	42	12	20	21
29/32	4	19	34	2	9	47	5 3/8	25	14	48	12	37	24
15/16	4	28	24	2	14	12	5 1/2	25	48	48	12	54	24
31/32	4	37	20	2	18	40	5 5/8	26	22	52	13	11	26
1	4	46	18	2	23	9	5 3/4	26	56	46	13	28	23
1 1/16	5	4	12	2	32	6	5 7/8	27	30	34	13	45	17
1 1/8	5	21	44	2	40	52	6	28	4	2	14	2	1
1 3/16	5	39	54	2	49	57	6 1/8	28	37	58	14	18	59
1 1/4	5	57	48	2	58	54	6 1/4	29	11	34	14	35	47
1 5/16	6	15	38	3	7	49	6 3/8	29	45	18	14	52	39
1 3/8	6	33	26	3	16	43	6 1/2	30	18	26	15	9	13
1 7/16	6	51	20	3	25	40	6 5/8	30	51	48	15	25	54
1 1/2	7	9	10	3	34	35	6 3/4	31	25	2	15	42	31
1 9/16	7	26	58	3	43	29	6 7/8	31	58	10	15	59	5
1 5/8	7	44	48	3	52	24	7	32	31	12	16	15	36
1 11/16	8	2	38	4	1	19	7 1/8	33	4	8	16	32	4
1 3/4	8	20	26	4	10	13	7 1/4	33	36	40	16	48	20
1 13/16	8	38	16	4	19	8	7 3/8	34	9	50	17	4	55

Table 3. WIRE GAGE STANDARDS

Wire gage no.	Decimal parts of an inch						
	American or Brown & Sharpe	Birmingham or Stubs wire	Washburn & Moen on steel wire gage	American S. & W. Co.'s music wire	Imperial wire gage	Stubs steel wire	U.S. standard for plate
0000000	0.651354	....	0.4000	....	0.500	....	0.500
000000	0.580049	....	0.4615	0.004	0.464	....	0.46875
00000	0.516549	0.500	0.4305	0.005	0.432	....	0.4375
0000	0.460	0.454	0.3938	0.006	0.400	....	0.40625
000	0.40964	0.425	0.3625	0.007	0.372	....	0.375
00	0.3648	0.380	0.3310	0.008	0.348	....	0.34375
0	0.32486	0.340	0.3065	0.009	0.324	....	0.3125
1	0.2893	0.300	0.2830	0.010	0.300	0.227	0.28125
2	0.25763	0.284	0.2625	0.011	0.276	0.219	0.265625
3	0.22942	0.259	0.2437	0.012	0.252	0.212	0.250
4	0.20431	0.238	0.2253	0.013	0.232	0.207	0.234375
5	0.18194	0.220	0.2070	0.014	0.212	0.204	0.21875
6	0.16202	0.203	0.1920	0.016	0.192	0.201	0.203125
7	0.14428	0.180	0.1770	0.018	0.176	0.199	0.1875
8	0.12849	0.165	0.1620	0.020	0.160	0.197	0.171875
9	0.11443	0.148	0.1483	0.022	0.144	0.194	0.15625
10	0.10189	0.134	0.1350	0.024	0.128	0.191	0.140625
11	0.090742	0.120	0.1205	0.026	0.116	0.188	0.125
12	0.080808	0.109	0.1055	0.029	0.104	0.185	0.109375
13	0.071961	0.095	0.0915	0.031	0.092	0.182	0.09375
14	0.064084	0.083	0.0800	0.033	0.080	0.180	0.078125
15	0.057068	0.072	0.0720	0.035	0.072	0.178	0.0703125
16	0.05082	0.065	0.0625	0.037	0.064	0.175	0.0625
17	0.045257	0.058	0.0540	0.039	0.056	0.172	0.05625
18	0.040303	0.049	0.0475	0.041	0.048	0.168	0.050
19	0.03589	0.042	0.0410	0.043	0.040	0.164	0.04375
20	0.031961	0.035	0.0348	0.045	0.036	0.161	0.0375
21	0.028462	0.032	0.0317	0.047	0.032	0.157	0.034375
22	0.025347	0.028	0.0286	0.049	0.028	0.155	0.03125
23	0.022571	0.025	0.0258	0.051	0.024	0.153	0.028125
24	0.0201	0.022	0.0230	0.055	0.022	0.151	0.025
25	0.0179	0.020	0.0204	0.059	0.020	0.148	0.021875
26	0.01594	0.018	0.0181	0.063	0.018	0.146	0.01875
27	0.014195	0.016	0.0173	0.067	0.0164	0.143	0.0171875
28	0.012641	0.014	0.0162	0.071	0.0149	0.139	0.015625
29	0.011257	0.013	0.0150	0.075	0.0136	0.134	0.0140625
30	0.010025	0.012	0.0140	0.080	0.0124	0.127	0.0125
31	0.008928	0.010	0.0132	0.085	0.0116	0.120	0.0109375
32	0.00795	0.009	0.0128	0.090	0.0108	0.115	0.01015625
33	0.00708	0.008	0.0118	0.095	0.0100	0.112	0.009375
34	0.006304	0.007	0.0104	....	0.0092	0.110	0.00859375
35	0.005614	0.005	0.0095	....	0.0084	0.108	0.0078125
36	0.005	0.004	0.0090	....	0.0076	0.106	0.00703125
37	0.004453	....	0.0085	....	0.0068	0.103	0.006640625
38	0.003965	....	0.0080	....	0.0060	0.101	0.00625
39	0.003531	....	0.0075	....	0.0052	0.099	
40	0.003144	....	0.0070	....	0.0048	0.097	

Table 4. DECIMAL EQUIVALENTS OF PARTS OF AN INCH

Fractions	64ths	32ds	16ths	8ths	4ths	Decimal equivalents	Fractions	64ths	32ds	16ths	8ths	4ths	Decimal equivalents
$\frac{1}{64}$	1	.....	.....	.....	.....	0.015625	$\frac{33}{64}$	33	.....	.....	.....	.....	0.515625
$\frac{1}{32}$	2	1	.....	.....	.....	0.03125	$\frac{17}{32}$	34	17	.....	.....	.....	0.53125
$\frac{3}{64}$	3	.....	.....	.....	.....	0.046875	$\frac{35}{64}$	35	.....	.....	.....	.....	0.546875
$\frac{1}{16}$	4	2	1	.....	.....	0.0625	$\frac{9}{16}$	36	18	9	.....	.....	0.5625
$\frac{5}{64}$	5	.....	.....	.....	.....	0.078125	$\frac{37}{64}$	37	.....	.....	.....	.....	0.578125
$\frac{3}{32}$	6	3	.....	.....	.....	0.09375	$\frac{19}{32}$	38	19	.....	.....	.....	0.59375
$\frac{7}{64}$	7	.....	.....	.....	.....	0.109375	$\frac{39}{64}$	39	.....	.....	.....	.....	0.609375
$\frac{1}{8}$	8	4	2	1	.....	0.125	$\frac{5}{8}$	40	20	10	5	.....	0.625
$\frac{9}{64}$	9	.....	.....	.....	.....	0.140625	$\frac{41}{64}$	41	.....	.....	.....	.....	0.640625
$\frac{5}{32}$	10	5	.....	.....	.....	0.15625	$\frac{21}{32}$	42	21	.....	.....	.....	0.65625
$\frac{11}{64}$	11	.....	.....	.....	.....	0.171875	$\frac{43}{64}$	43	.....	.....	.....	.....	0.671875
$\frac{3}{16}$	12	6	3	.....	.....	0.1875	$\frac{11}{16}$	44	22	11	.....	.....	0.6875
$\frac{13}{64}$	13	.....	.....	.....	.....	0.203125	$\frac{45}{64}$	45	.....	.....	.....	.....	0.703125
$\frac{7}{32}$	14	7	.....	.....	.....	0.21875	$\frac{23}{32}$	46	23	.....	.....	.....	0.71875
$\frac{15}{64}$	15	.....	.....	.....	.....	0.234375	$\frac{47}{64}$	47	.....	.....	.....	.....	0.734375
$\frac{1}{4}$	16	8	4	2	1	0.250	$\frac{3}{4}$	48	24	12	6	3	0.750
$\frac{17}{64}$	17	.....	.....	.....	.....	0.265625	$\frac{49}{64}$	49	.....	.....	.....	.....	0.765625
$\frac{9}{32}$	18	9	.....	.....	.....	0.28125	$\frac{25}{32}$	50	25	.....	.....	.....	0.78125
$\frac{19}{64}$	19	.....	.....	.....	.....	0.296875	$\frac{51}{64}$	51	.....	.....	.....	.....	0.796875
$\frac{5}{16}$	20	10	5	.....	.....	0.3125	$\frac{13}{16}$	52	26	13	.....	.....	0.8125
$\frac{21}{64}$	21	.....	.....	.....	.....	0.328125	$\frac{53}{64}$	53	.....	.....	.....	.....	0.828125
$\frac{11}{32}$	22	11	.....	.....	.....	0.34375	$\frac{27}{32}$	54	27	.....	.....	.....	0.84375
$\frac{23}{64}$	23	.....	.....	.....	.....	0.359375	$\frac{55}{64}$	55	.....	.....	.....	.....	0.859375
$\frac{3}{8}$	24	12	6	3	.....	0.375	$\frac{7}{8}$	56	28	14	7	.....	0.875
$\frac{25}{64}$	25	.....	.....	.....	.....	0.390625	$\frac{57}{64}$	57	.....	.....	.....	.....	0.890625
$\frac{13}{32}$	26	13	.....	.....	.....	0.40625	$\frac{29}{32}$	58	29	.....	.....	.....	0.90625
$\frac{27}{64}$	27	.....	.....	.....	.....	0.421875	$\frac{59}{64}$	59	.....	.....	.....	.....	0.921875
$\frac{7}{16}$	28	14	7	.....	.....	0.4375	$\frac{15}{16}$	60	30	15	.....	.....	0.9375
$\frac{29}{64}$	29	.....	.....	.....	.....	0.453125	$\frac{61}{64}$	61	.....	.....	.....	.....	0.953125
$\frac{15}{32}$	30	15	.....	.....	.....	0.46875	$\frac{31}{32}$	62	31	.....	.....	.....	0.96875
$\frac{31}{64}$	31	.....	.....	.....	.....	0.484375	$\frac{63}{64}$	63	.....	.....	.....	.....	0.984375
$\frac{1}{2}$	32	16	8	4	2	0.500	1 inch	64	32	16	8	4	1.000

Table 5. DECIMAL EQUIVALENTS OF MILLIMETERS

Mm	Inches	Mm	Inches	Mm	Inches	Mm	Inches
0.1	0.00394	4.4	0.17322	8.7	0.34251	13.0	0.51181
0.2	0.00787	4.5	0.17716	8.8	0.34645	13.1	0.51574
0.3	0.01181	4.6	0.18110	8.9	0.35039	13.2	0.51968
0.4	0.01575	4.7	0.18503	9.0	0.35433	13.3	0.52362
0.5	0.01968	4.8	0.18897	9.1	0.35826	13.4	0.52755
0.6	0.02362	4.9	0.19291	9.2	0.36220	13.5	0.53149
0.7	0.02756	5.0	0.19685	9.3	0.36614	13.6	0.53543
0.8	0.03149	5.1	0.20078	9.4	0.37007	13.7	0.53936
0.9	0.03543	5.2	0.20472	9.5	0.37401	13.8	0.54330
1.0	0.03937	5.3	0.20866	9.6	0.37795	13.9	0.54724
1.1	0.04330	5.4	0.21259	9.7	0.38188	14.0	0.55118
1.2	0.04724	5.5	0.21653	9.8	0.38582	14.1	0.55511
1.3	0.05118	5.6	0.22047	9.9	0.38976	14.2	0.55905
1.4	0.05512	5.7	0.22440	10.0	0.39370	14.3	0.56299
1.5	0.05905	5.8	0.22834	10.1	0.39763	14.4	0.56692
1.6	0.06299	5.9	0.23228	10.2	0.40157	14.5	0.57086
1.7	0.06692	6.0	0.23622	10.3	0.40551	14.6	0.57480
1.8	0.07086	6.1	0.24015	10.4	0.40944	14.7	0.57873
1.9	0.07480	6.2	0.24409	10.5	0.41338	14.8	0.58267
2.0	0.07874	6.3	0.24803	10.6	0.41732	14.9	0.58661
2.1	0.08267	6.4	0.25196	10.7	0.42125	15.0	0.59055
2.2	0.08661	6.5	0.25590	10.8	0.42519	15.5	0.61023
2.3	0.09055	6.6	0.25984	10.9	0.42913	16.0	0.62992
2.4	0.09448	6.7	0.26377	11.0	0.43307	16.5	0.64960
2.5	0.09842	6.8	0.26771	11.1	0.43700	17.0	0.66929
2.6	0.10236	6.9	0.27165	11.2	0.44094	17.5	0.68897
2.7	0.10629	7.0	0.27559	11.3	0.44488	18.0	0.70866
2.8	0.11023	7.1	0.27952	11.4	0.44881	18.5	0.72834
2.9	0.11417	7.2	0.28346	11.5	0.45275	19.0	0.74803
3.0	0.11811	7.3	0.28740	11.6	0.45669	19.5	0.76771
3.1	0.12204	7.4	0.29133	11.7	0.46062	20.0	0.78740
3.2	0.12598	7.5	0.29527	11.8	0.46456	20.5	0.80708
3.3	0.12992	7.6	0.29921	11.9	0.46850	21.0	0.82677
3.4	0.13385	7.7	0.30314	12.0	0.47244	21.5	0.84645
3.5	0.13779	7.8	0.30708	12.1	0.47637	22.0	0.86614
3.6	0.14173	7.9	0.31102	12.2	0.48031	22.5	0.88582
3.7	0.14566	8.0	0.31496	12.3	0.48425	23.0	0.90551
3.8	0.14960	8.1	0.31889	12.4	0.48818	23.5	0.92519
3.9	0.15354	8.2	0.32283	12.5	0.49212	24.0	0.94488
4.0	0.15748	8.3	0.32677	12.6	0.49606	24.5	0.96456
4.1	0.16141	8.4	0.33070	12.7	0.49999	25.0	0.98425
4.2	0.16535	8.5	0.33464	12.8	0.50393	25.5	1.00393
4.3	0.16929	8.6	0.33858	12.9	0.50787	26.0	1.02362

FORMULAS

Circumference of a circle	Diameter multiplied by 3.1416
	Diameter divided by 0.3183
Diameter of a circle	Circumference multiplied by 0.3183
	Circumference divided by 3.1416
Side of a square inscribed in a given circle	Diameter multiplied by 0.7071
	Circumference multiplied by 0.2251
	Circumference divided by 4.4428
Side of a square with area of a given circle	Diameter multiplied by 0.8862
	Diameter divided by 1.1284
	Circumference multiplied by 0.2821
	Circumference divided by 3.545
Diameter of a circle with area of a given square	Side multiplied by 1.128
Diameter of a circle circumscribing a given square	Side multiplied by 1.4142
Area of a circle	The square of the diameter multiplied by 0.7854
	The square of the radius multiplied by 3.1416
Area of the surface of a sphere or globe	The square of the diameter multiplied by 3.1416

NUMBERS THAT ARE PERFECT SQUARES AND CUBES—1 to 1728

Square	Cube	Square root	Cube root	Square	Cube	Square root	Cube root
1	1	1	1	441		21	
4		2		484		22	
	8		2		512		8
9		3		529		23	
16		4		576		24	
25		5		625		25	
	27		3	676		26	
36		6			729	27	9
49		7		784		28	
	64	8	4	841		29	
81		9		900		30	
100		10		961		31	
121		11			1000		10
	125		5	1024		32	
144		12		1089		33	
169		13		1156		34	
196		14		1225		35	
	216		6	1296		36	
225		15			1331		11
256		16		1369		37	
289		17		1444		38	
324		18		1521		39	
	343		7	1600		40	
361		19		1681		41	
400		20			1728		12

FORMULAS

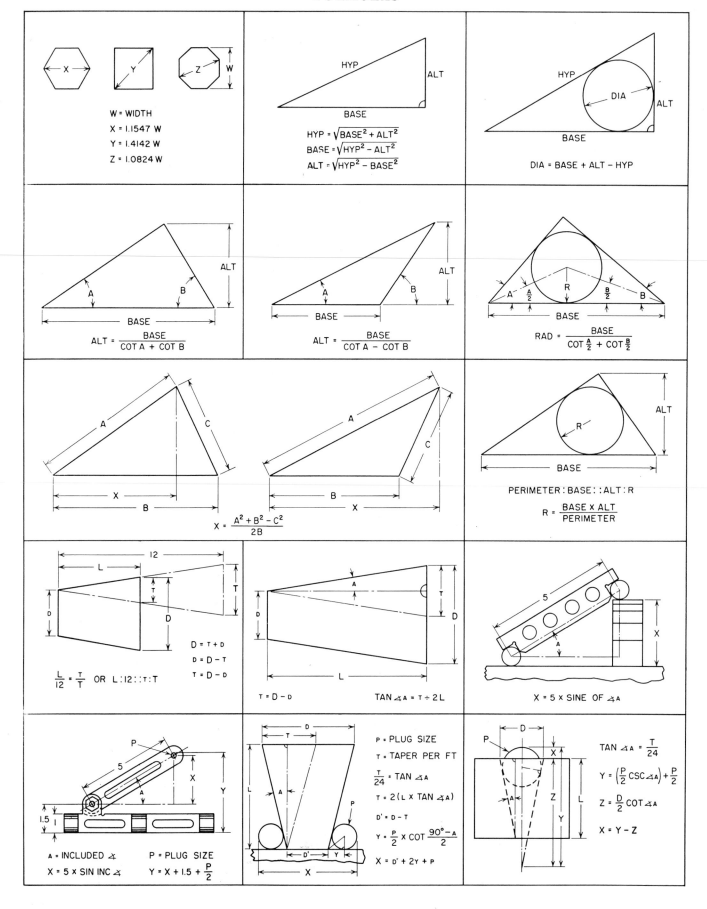

W = WIDTH
X = 1.1547 W
Y = 1.4142 W
Z = 1.0824 W

$$HYP = \sqrt{BASE^2 + ALT^2}$$
$$BASE = \sqrt{HYP^2 - ALT^2}$$
$$ALT = \sqrt{HYP^2 - BASE^2}$$

DIA = BASE + ALT − HYP

$$ALT = \frac{BASE}{COT\ A + COT\ B}$$

$$ALT = \frac{BASE}{COT\ A - COT\ B}$$

$$RAD = \frac{BASE}{COT\frac{A}{2} + COT\frac{B}{2}}$$

$$X = \frac{A^2 + B^2 - C^2}{2B}$$

PERIMETER : BASE : : ALT : R

$$R = \frac{BASE \times ALT}{PERIMETER}$$

$$\frac{L}{12} = \frac{T}{T} \quad OR \quad L:12::T:T$$

D = T + d
d = D − T
T = D − d

T = D − d

TAN ∠A = T ÷ 2L

X = 5 × SINE OF ∠A

A = INCLUDED ∠
X = 5 × SIN INC ∠

P = PLUG SIZE
$$Y = X + 1.5 + \frac{P}{2}$$

P = PLUG SIZE
T = TAPER PER FT
$$\frac{T}{24} = TAN\ ∠A$$
T = 2(L × TAN ∠A)
D' = D − T
$$Y = \frac{P}{2} \times COT\frac{90° - A}{2}$$
X = D' + 2Y + P

$$TAN\ ∠A = \frac{T}{24}$$
$$Y = \left(\frac{P}{2}\ CSC\ ∠A\right) + \frac{P}{2}$$
$$Z = \frac{D}{2}\ COT\ ∠A$$
X = Y − Z

FORMULAS

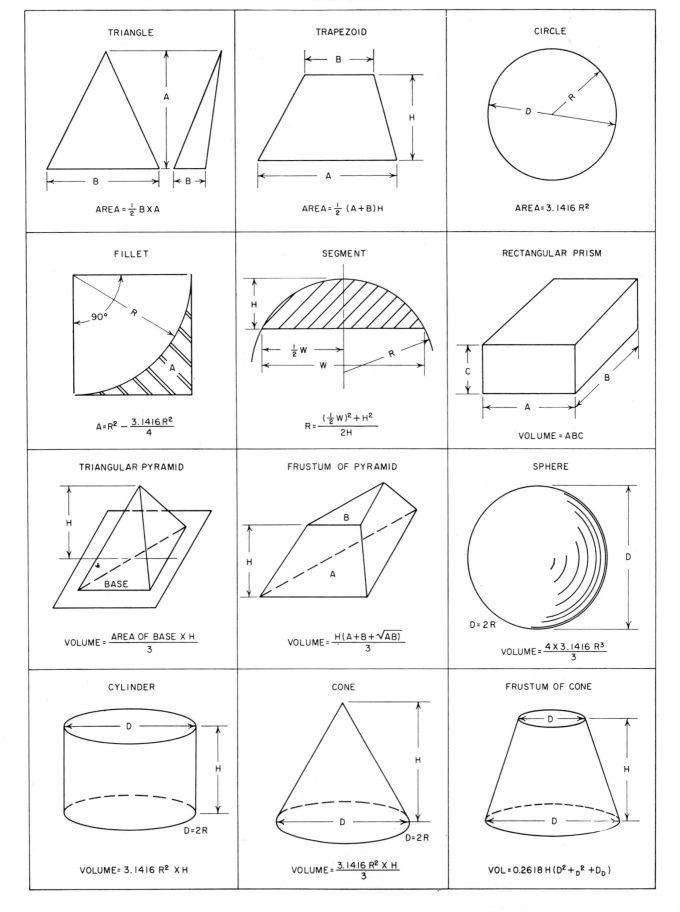

TRIANGLE — AREA $= \frac{1}{2} B \times A$

TRAPEZOID — AREA $= \frac{1}{2}(A+B)H$

CIRCLE — AREA $= 3.1416 R^2$

FILLET — $A = R^2 - \frac{3.1416 R^2}{4}$

SEGMENT — $R = \frac{(\frac{1}{2}W)^2 + H^2}{2H}$

RECTANGULAR PRISM — VOLUME $= ABC$

TRIANGULAR PYRAMID — VOLUME $= \frac{\text{AREA OF BASE} \times H}{3}$

FRUSTUM OF PYRAMID — VOLUME $= \frac{H(A+B+\sqrt{AB})}{3}$

SPHERE — $D = 2R$ — VOLUME $= \frac{4 \times 3.1416 R^3}{3}$

CYLINDER — $D = 2R$ — VOLUME $= 3.1416 R^2 \times H$

CONE — $D = 2R$ — VOLUME $= \frac{3.1416 R^2 \times H}{3}$

FRUSTUM OF CONE — VOL $= 0.2618 H (D^2 + D^2 + D_D)$

Table 6. KEYWAY DATA

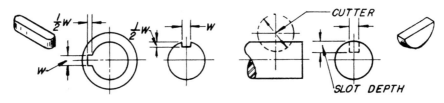

Shaft dia	Square keyways	Woodruff keyways*			
		Key no.	Thickness	Cutter dia	Slot depth
0.500	$\frac{1}{8} \times \frac{1}{16}$	404	0.1250	0.500	0.1405
0.562	$\frac{1}{8} \times \frac{1}{16}$	404	0.1250	0.500	0.1405
0.625	$\frac{5}{32} \times \frac{5}{64}$	505	0.1562	0.625	0.1669
0.688	$\frac{3}{16} \times \frac{3}{32}$	606	0.1875	0.750	0.2193
0.750	$\frac{3}{16} \times \frac{3}{32}$	606	0.1875	0.750	0.2193
0.812	$\frac{3}{16} \times \frac{3}{32}$	606	0.1875	0.750	0.2193
0.875	$\frac{7}{32} \times \frac{7}{64}$	607	0.1875	0.875	0.2763
0.938	$\frac{1}{4} \times \frac{1}{8}$	807	0.2500	0.875	0.2500
1.000	$\frac{1}{4} \times \frac{1}{8}$	808	0.2500	1.000	0.3130
1.125	$\frac{5}{16} \times \frac{5}{32}$	1009	0.3125	1.125	0.3228
1.250	$\frac{5}{16} \times \frac{5}{32}$	1010	0.3125	1.250	0.3858
1.375	$\frac{3}{8} \times \frac{3}{16}$	1210	0.3750	1.250	0.3595
1.500	$\frac{3}{8} \times \frac{3}{16}$	1212	0.3750	1.500	0.4535
1.625	$\frac{3}{8} \times \frac{3}{16}$	1212	0.3750	1.500	0.4535
1.750	$\frac{7}{16} \times \frac{7}{32}$				
1.875	$\frac{1}{2} \times \frac{1}{4}$				
2.000	$\frac{1}{2} \times \frac{1}{4}$				
2.250	$\frac{5}{8} \times \frac{5}{16}$				
2.500	$\frac{5}{8} \times \frac{5}{16}$				
2.750	$\frac{3}{4} \times \frac{3}{8}$				
3.000	$\frac{3}{4} \times \frac{3}{8}$				
3.250	$\frac{3}{4} \times \frac{3}{8}$				
3.500	$\frac{7}{8} \times \frac{7}{16}$				
4.000	$1 \times \frac{1}{2}$				

* The depth of a Woodruff keyway is measured from the edge of the slot.

Table 7. CARBON STEELS*

SAE number	1948 AISI number	Carbon	Manganese	Phosphorus	Sulfur	SAE number	1948 AISI number	Carbon	Manganese	Phosphorus	Sulfur
1008	C 1008	0.10 max	0.25/0.50	0.040	0.050	1041	C 1041	0.36/0.44	1.35/1.65	0.040	0.050
1010	C 1010	0.08/0.13	0.30/0.60	0.040	0.050	1042	C 1042	0.40/0.47	0.60/0.90	0.040	0.050
	C 1012	0.10/0.15	0.30/0.60	0.040	0.050	1043	C 1043	0.40/0.47	0.70/1.00	0.040	0.050
1015	C 1015	0.13/0.18	0.30/0.60	0.040	0.050	1045	C 1045	0.43/0.50	0.60/0.90	0.040	0.050
1016	C 1016	0.13/0.18	0.60/0.90	0.040	0.050	1046	C 1046	0.43/0.50	0.70/1.00	0.040	0.050
1017	C 1017	0.15/0.20	0.30/0.60	0.040	0.050		C 1049	0.46/0.53	0.60/0.90	0.040	0.050
1018	C 1018	0.15/0.20	0.60/0.90	0.040	0.050	1050	C 1050	0.48/0.55	0.60/0.90	0.040	0.050
1019	C 1019	0.15/0.20	0.70/1.00	0.040	0.050	1052	C 1052	0.47/0.55	1.20/1.50	0.040	0.050
1020	C 1020	0.18/0.23	0.30/0.60	0.040	0.050		C 1053	0.48/0.55	0.70/1.00	0.040	0.050
	C 1021	0.18/0.23	0.60/0.90	0.040	0.050	1055	C 1055	0.50/0.60	0.60/0.90	0.040	0.050
1022	C 1022	0.18/0.23	0.70/1.00	0.040	0.050	1060	C 1060	0.55/0.65	0.60/0.90	0.040	0.050
	C 1023	0.20/0.25	0.30/0.60	0.040	0.050	1065	C 1065	0.60/0.70	0.60/0.90	0.040	0.050
1024	C 1024	0.19/0.25	1.35/1.65	0.040	0.050		C 1069	0.65/0.75	0.40/0.70	0.040	0.050
1025	C 1025	0.22/0.28	0.30/0.60	0.040	0.050	1070	C 1070	0.65/0.75	0.60/0.90	0.040	0.050
	C 1026	0.22/0.28	0.60/0.90	0.040	0.050		C 1072	0.65/0.76	1.00/1.30	0.040	0.050
1027	C 1027	0.22/0.29	1.20/1.50	0.040	0.050		C 1075	0.70/0.80	0.40/0.70	0.040	0.050
	C 1029	0.25/0.31	0.60/0.90	0.040	0.050	1078	C 1078	0.72/0.85	0.30/0.60	0.040	0.050
1030	C 1030	0.28/0.34	0.60/0.90	0.040	0.050	1080	C 1080	0.75/0.88	0.60/0.90	0.040	0.050
1033	C 1033	0.30/0.36	0.70/1.00	0.040	0.050		C 1084	0.80/0.93	0.60/0.90	0.040	0.050
1035	C 1035	0.32/0.38	0.60/0.90	0.040	0.050	1085	C 1085	0.80/0.93	0.70/1.00	0.040	0.050
1036	C 1036	0.30/0.37	1.20/1.50	0.040	0.050		C 1086	0.82/0.96	0.30/0.50	0.040	0.050
	C 1037	0.35/0.42	0.40/0.70	0.040	0.050	1090	C 1090	0.85/0.98	0.60/0.90	0.040	0.050
1038	C 1038	0.35/0.42	0.60/0.90	0.040	0.050	1095	C 1095	0.90/1.03	0.30/0.50	0.040	0.050
	C 1039	0.37/0.44	0.70/1.00	0.040	0.050		B 1010	0.13 max	0.30/0.60	0.07/0.12	0.060
1040	C 1040	0.37/0.44	0.60/0.90	0.040	0.050						

Free-cutting steels (open-hearth screw steels)

SAE number	1948 AISI number	Carbon	Manganese	Phosphorus	Sulfur	SAE number	1948 AISI number	Carbon	Manganese	Phosphorus	Sulfur
	C 1108	0.08/0.13	0.50/0.80	0.040	0.07/0.12		C 1132	0.27/0.34	1.35/1.65	0.040	0.08/0.13
1109	C 1109	0.08/0.13	0.60/0.90	0.040	0.08/0.13	1137	C 1137	0.32/0.39	1.35/1.65	0.040	0.08/0.13
	C 1110	0.08/0.13	0.30/0.60	0.040	0.08/0.13	1138	C 1138	0.34/0.40	0.70/1.00	0.040	0.08/0.13
	C 1113	0.10/0.16	1.00/1.30	0.040	0.24/0.33	1140	C 1140	0.37/0.44	0.70/1.00	0.040	0.08/0.13
1115	C 1115	0.13/0.18	0.60/0.90	0.040	0.08/0.13	1141	C 1141	0.37/0.45	1.35/1.65	0.040	0.08/0.13
1116	C 1116	0.14/0.20	1.10/1.40	0.040	0.16/0.23	1144	C 1144	0.40/0.48	1.35/1.65	0.040	0.24/0.33
1117	C 1117	0.14/0.20	1.00/1.30	0.040	0.08/0.13	1145	C 1145	0.42/0.49	0.70/1.00	0.040	0.04/0.07
1118	C 1118	0.14/0.20	1.30/1.60	0.040	0.08/0.13	1146	C 1146	0.42/0.49	0.70/1.00	0.040	0.08/0.13
1119	C 1119	0.14/0.20	1.00/1.30	0.040	0.24/0.33		C 1148	0.45/0.52	0.70/1.00	0.040	0.04/0.07
1120	C 1120	0.18/0.23	0.70/1.00	0.040	0.08/0.13	1151	C 1151	0.48/0.55	0.70/1.00	0.040	0.08/0.13
	C 1125	0.22/0.28	0.60/0.90	0.040	0.08/0.13						

Free-cutting steels (Bessemer screw steels)

SAE number	1948 AISI number	Carbon	Manganese	Phosphorus	Sulfur	SAE number	1948 AISI number	Carbon	Manganese	Phosphorus	Sulfur
1111	B 1111	0.13 max	0.60/0.90	0.07/0.12	0.08/0.15	1113	B 1113	0.13 max	0.70/1.00	0.07/0.12	0.24/0.33
1112	B 1112	0.13 max	0.70/1.00	0.07/0.12	0.16/0.23						

* From combined standard steel lists of American Iron and Steel Institute and Society of Automotive Engineers, Inc.

Table 8. COMBINED STANDARD STEEL TABLE*

SAE number	1948 AISI number	Chemical composition limits, percent								
		Carbon	Manganese	Phosphorus max	Sulfur max	Silicon	Nickel	Chromium	Molybdenum	Vanadium
Manganese Steels (manganese in alloy range)										
1320	1320	0.18/0.23	1.60/1.90	0.040	0.040	0.20/0.35				
	1321	0.17/0.22	1.80/2.10	0.050	0.050	0.20/0.35				
1330	1330	0.28/0.33	1.60/1.90	0.040	0.040	0.20/0.35				
1335	1335	0.33/0.38	1.60/1.90	0.040	0.040	0.20/0.35				
1340	1340	0.38/0.43	1.60/1.90	0.040	0.040	0.20/0.35				
Nickel Steels										
2317	2317	0.15/0.20	0.40/0.60	0.040	0.040	0.20/0.35	3.25/3.75			
2330	2330	0.28/0.33	0.60/0.80	0.040	0.040	0.20/0.35	3.25/3.75			
	2335	0.33/0.38	0.60/0.80	0.040	0.040	0.20/0.35	3.25/3.75			
2340	2340	0.38/0.43	0.70/0.90	0.040	0.040	0.20/0.35	3.25/3.75			
2345	2345	0.43/0.48	0.70/0.90	0.040	0.040	0.20/0.35	3.25/3.75			
2512	E 2512	0.09/0.14	0.45/0.60	0.025	0.025	0.20/0.35	4.75/5.25			
2515	2515	0.12/0.17	0.40/0.60	0.040	0.040	0.20/0.35	4.75/5.25			
2517	E 2517	0.15/0.20	0.45/0.60	0.025	0.025	0.20/0.35	4.75/5.25			
Nickel-chromium Steels										
3115	3115	0.13/0.18	0.40/0.60	0.040	0.040	0.20/0.35	1.10/1.40	0.55/0.75		
3120	3120	0.17/0.22	0.60/0.80	0.040	0.040	0.20/0.35	1.10/1.40	0.55/0.75		
3130	3130	0.28/0.33	0.60/0.80	0.040	0.040	0.20/0.35	1.10/1.40	0.55/0.75		
3135	3135	0.33/0.38	0.60/0.80	0.040	0.040	0.20/0.35	1.10/1.40	0.55/0.75		
3140	3140	0.38/0.43	0.70/0.90	0.040	0.040	0.20/0.35	1.10/1.40	0.55/0.75		
3141	3141	0.38/0.43	0.70/0.90	0.040	0.040	0.20/0.35	1.10/1.40	0.70/0.90		
3145	3145	0.43/0.48	0.70/0.90	0.040	0.040	0.20/0.35	1.10/1.40	0.70/0.90		
3150	3150	0.48/0.53	0.70/0.90	0.040	0.040	0.20/0.35	1.10/1.40	0.70/0.90		
3310	E 3310	0.08/0.13	0.45/0.60	0.025	0.025	0.20/0.35	3.25/3.75	1.40/1.75		
3316	E 3316	0.14/0.19	0.45/0.60	0.025	0.025	0.20/0.35	3.25/3.75	1.40/1.75		
Molybdenum Steels										
4017	4017	0.15/0.20	0.70/0.90	0.040	0.040	0.20/0.35	....	....	0.20/0.30	
4023	4023	0.20/0.25	0.70/0.90	0.040	0.040	0.20/0.35	....	....	0.20/0.30	
4024	4024	0.20/0.25	0.70/0.90	0.040	0.035/0.050	0.20/0.35	....	....	0.20/0.30	
4027	4027	0.25/0.30	0.70/0.90	0.040	0.040	0.20/0.35	....	....	0.20/0.30	
4028	4028	0.25/0.30	0.70/0.90	0.040	0.035/0.050	0.20/0.35	....	....	0.20/0.30	
4032	4032	0.30/0.35	0.70/0.90	0.040	0.040	0.20/0.35	....	....	0.20/0.30	

* From combined standard steel lists of American Iron and Steel Institute and Society of Automotive Engineers, Inc.

Table 8. COMBINED STANDARD STEEL TABLE—Continued

SAE number	1948 AISI number	Chemical composition limits, percent								
		Carbon	Manganese	Phosphorus max	Sulfur max	Silicon	Nickel	Chromium	Molybdenum	Vanadium
Molybdenum Steels—Continued										
4037	4037	0.35/0.40	0.70/0.90	0.040	0.040	0.20/0.35	....	....	0.20/0.30	
4042	4042	0.40/0.45	0.70/0.90	0.040	0.040	0.20/0.35	....	....	0.20/0.30	
4047	4047	0.45/0.50	0.70/0.90	0.040	0.040	0.20/0.35	....	....	0.20/0.30	
4053	4053	0.50/0.56	0.75/1.00	0.040	0.040	0.20/0.35	....	....	0.20/0.30	
4063	4063	0.60/0.67	0.75/1.00	0.040	0.040	0.20/0.35	....	....	0.20/0.30	
4068	4068	0.63/0.70	0.75/1.00	0.040	0.040	0.20/0.35	....	....	0.20/0.30	
4130	4130	0.28/0.33	0.40/0.60	0.040	0.040	0.20/0.35	....	0.80/1.10	0.15/0.25	
	E 4132	0.30/0.35	0.40/0.60	0.025	0.025	0.20/0.35	....	0.80/1.10	0.18/0.25	
	E 4135	0.33/0.38	0.70/0.90	0.025	0.025	0.20/0.35	....	0.80/1.10	0.18/0.25	
4137	4137	0.35/0.40	0.70/0.90	0.040	0.040	0.20/0.35	....	0.80/1.10	0.15/0.25	
	E 4137	0.35/0.40	0.70/0.90	0.025	0.025	0.20/0.35	....	0.80/1.10	0.18/0.25	
4140	4140	0.38/0.43	0.75/1.00	0.040	0.040	0.20/0.35	....	0.80/1.10	0.15/0.25	
	4142	0.40/0.45	0.75/1.00	0.040	0.040	0.20/0.35	....	0.80/1.10	0.15/0.25	
4145	4145	0.43/0.48	0.75/1.00	0.040	0.040	0.20/0.35	....	0.80/1.10	0.15/0.25	
	4147	0.45/0.50	0.75/1.00	0.040	0.040	0.20/0.35	....	0.80/1.10	0.15/0.25	
4150	4150	0.48/0.53	0.75/1.00	0.040	0.040	0.20/0.35	....	0.80/1.10	0.15/0.25	
4317	4317	0.15/0.20	0.45/0.65	0.040	0.040	0.20/0.35	1.65/2.00	0.40/0.60	0.20/0.30	
4320	4320	0.17/0.22	0.45/0.65	0.040	0.040	0.20/0.35	1.65/2.00	0.40/0.60	0.20/0.30	
	4337	0.35/0.40	0.60/0.80	0.040	0.040	0.20/0.35	1.65/2.00	0.70/0.90	0.20/0.30	
4340	4340	0.38/0.43	0.60/0.80	0.040	0.040	0.20/0.35	1.65/2.00	0.70/0.90	0.20/0.30	
4608	4608	0.06/0.11	0.25/0.45	0.040	0.040	0.25 max	1.40/1.75	....	0.15/0.25	
4615	4615	0.13/0.18	0.45/0.65	0.040	0.040	0.20/0.35	1.65/2.00	....	0.20/0.30	
4617	E 4617	0.15/0.20	0.45/0.65	0.025	0.025	0.20/0.35	1.65/2.00	....	0.20/0.27	
4620	4620	0.17/0.22	0.45/0.65	0.040	0.040	0.20/0.35	1.65/2.00	....	0.20/0.30	
X-4620	X 4620	0.18/0.23	0.50/0.70	0.040	0.040	0.20/0.35	1.65/2.00	....	0.20/0.30	
	E 4620	0.17/0.22	0.45/0.65	0.025	0.025	0.20/0.35	1.65/2.00	....	0.20/0.27	
4621	4621	0.18/0.23	0.70/0.90	0.040	0.040	0.20/0.35	1.65/2.00	....	0.20/0.30	
4640	4640	0.38/0.43	0.60/0.80	0.040	0.040	0.20/0.35	1.65/2.00	....	0.20/0.30	
	E 4640	0.38/0.43	0.60/0.80	0.025	0.025	0.20/0.35	1.65/2.00	....	0.20/0.27	
4812	4812	0.10/0.15	0.40/0.60	0.040	0.040	0.20/0.35	3.25/3.75	....	0.20/0.30	
4815	4815	0.13/0.18	0.40/0.60	0.040	0.040	0.20/0.35	3.25/3.75	....	0.20/0.30	
4817	4817	0.15/0.20	0.40/0.60	0.040	0.040	0.20/0.35	3.25/3.75	....	0.20/0.30	
4820	4820	0.18/0.23	0.50/0.70	0.040	0.040	0.20/0.35	3.25/3.75	....	0.20/0.30	

Table 8. COMBINED STANDARD STEEL TABLE—Continued

SAE number	1948 AISI number	Chemical composition limits, percent								
		Carbon	Manganese	Phosphorus max	Sulfur max	Silicon	Nickel	Chromium	Molybdenum	Vanadium
Chromium Steels										
5045	5045	0.43/0.48	0.70/0.90	0.040	0.040	0.20/0.35	....	0.55/0.75		
5046	5046	0.43/0.50	0.75/1.00	0.040	0.040	0.20/0.35	....	0.20/0.35		
5120	5120	0.17/0.22	0.70/0.90	0.040	0.040	0.20/0.35	....	0.70/0.90		
5130	5130	0.28/0.33	0.70/0.90	0.040	0.040	0.20/0.35	....	0.80/1.10		
5132	5132	0.30/0.35	0.60/0.80	0.040	0.040	0.20/0.35	....	0.75/1.00		
5135	5135	0.33/0.38	0.60/0.80	0.040	0.040	0.20/0.35	....	0.80/1.05		
5140	5140	0.38/0.43	0.70/0.90	0.040	0.040	0.20/0.35	....	0.70/0.90		
5145	5145	0.43/0.48	0.70/0.90	0.040	0.040	0.20/0.35	....	0.70/0.90		
5147	5147	0.45/0.52	0.70/0.95	0.040	0.040	0.20/0.35	....	0.85/1.15		
5150	5150	0.48/0.53	0.70/0.90	0.040	0.040	0.20/0.35	....	0.70/0.90		
5152	5152	0.48/0.55	0.70/0.90	0.040	0.040	0.20/0.35	....	0.90/1.20		
	5160	0.55/0.65	0.75/1.00	0.040	0.040	0.20/0.35	....	0.70/0.90		
50100	E 50100	0.95/1.10	0.25/0.45	0.025	0.025	0.20/0.35	....	0.40/0.60		
51100	E 51100	0.95/1.10	0.25/0.45	0.025	0.025	0.20/0.35	....	0.90/1.15		
52100	E 52100	0.95/1.10	0.25/0.45	0.025	0.025	0.20/0.35	....	1.30/1.60		
Chromium-Vanadium Steels										
	6120	0.17/0.22	0.70/0.90	0.040	0.040	0.20/0.35	....	0.70/0.90	....	0.10 min
	6145	0.43/0.48	0.70/0.90	0.040	0.040	0.20/0.35	....	0.80/1.10	....	0.15 min
6150	6150	0.48/0.53	0.70/0.90	0.040	0.040	0.20/0.35	....	0.80/1.10	....	0.15 min
	6152	0.48/0.55	0.70/0.90	0.040	0.040	0.20/0.35	....	0.80/1.10	....	0.10 min
Nickel-Chromium-Molybdenum Steels										
8615	8615	0.13/0.18	0.70/0.90	0.040	0.040	0.20/0.35	0.40/0.70	0.40/0.60	0.15/0.25	
8617	8617	0.15/0.20	0.70/0.90	0.040	0.040	0.20/0.35	0.40/0.70	0.40/0.60	0.15/0.25	
8620	8620	0.18/0.23	0.70/0.90	0.040	0.040	0.20/0.35	0.40/0.70	0.40/0.60	0.15/0.25	
8622	8622	0.20/0.25	0.70/0.90	0.040	0.040	0.20/0.35	0.40/0.70	0.40/0.60	0.15/0.25	
8625	8625	0.23/0.28	0.70/0.90	0.040	0.040	0.20/0.35	0.40/0.70	0.40/0.60	0.15/0.25	
8627	8627	0.25/0.30	0.70/0.90	0.040	0.040	0.20/0.35	0.40/0.70	0.40/0.60	0.15/0.25	
8630	8630	0.28/0.33	0.70/0.90	0.040	0.040	0.20/0.35	0.40/0.70	0.40/0.60	0.15/0.25	
8632	8632	0.30/0.35	0.70/0.90	0.040	0.040	0.20/0.35	0.40/0.70	0.40/0.60	0.15/0.25	
8635	8635	0.33/0.38	0.75/1.00	0.040	0.040	0.20/0.35	0.40/0.70	0.40/0.60	0.15/0.25	
8637	8637	0.35/0.40	0.75/1.00	0.040	0.040	0.20/0.35	0.40/0.70	0.40/0.60	0.15/0.25	
8640	8640	0.38/0.43	0.75/1.00	0.040	0.040	0.20/0.35	0.40/0.70	0.40/0.60	0.15/0.25	
8641	8641	0.38/0.43	0.75/1.00	0.040	0.040/0.060	0.20/0.35	0.40/0.70	0.40/0.60	0.15/0.25	

Table 8. COMBINED STANDARD STEEL TABLE—Continued

SAE number	1948 AISI number	Chemical composition limits, percent								
		Carbon	Manganese	Phosphorus max	Sulfur max	Silicon	Nickel	Chromium	Molybdenum	Vanadium

Nickel-Chromium-Molybdenum Steels—Continued

SAE number	1948 AISI number	Carbon	Manganese	Phosphorus max	Sulfur max	Silicon	Nickel	Chromium	Molybdenum	Vanadium
8642	8642	0.40/0.45	0.75/1.00	0.040	0.040	0.20/0.35	0.40/0.70	0.40/0.60	0.15/0.25	
8645	8645	0.43/0.48	0.75/1.00	0.040	0.040	0.20/0.35	0.40/0.70	0.40/0.60	0.15/0.25	
8647	8647	0.45/0.50	0.75/1.00	0.040	0.040	0.20/0.35	0.40/0.70	0.40/0.60	0.15/0.25	
8650	8650	0.48/0.53	0.75/1.00	0.040	0.040	0.20/0.35	0.40/0.70	0.40/0.70	0.15/0.25	
8653	8653	0.50/0.56	0.75/1.00	0.040	0.040	0.20/0.35	0.40/0.70	0.50/0.80	0.15/0.25	
8655	8655	0.50/0.60	0.75/1.00	0.040	0.040	0.20/0.35	0.40/0.70	0.40/0.60	0.15/0.25	
8660	8660	0.55/0.65	0.75/1.00	0.040	0.040	0.20/0.35	0.40/0.70	0.40/0.60	0.15/0.25	
	8719	0.18/0.23	0.60/0.80	0.040	0.040	0.20/0.35	0.40/0.70	0.40/0.60	0.20/0.30	
8720	8720	0.18/0.23	0.70/0.90	0.040	0.040	0.20/0.35	0.40/0.70	0.40/0.60	0.20/0.30	
8735	8735	0.33/0.38	0.75/1.00	0.040	0.040	0.20/0.35	0.40/0.70	0.40/0.60	0.20/0.30	
8740	8740	0.38/0.43	0.75/1.00	0.040	0.040	0.20/0.35	0.40/0.70	0.40/0.60	0.20/0.30	
	8742	0.40/0.45	0.75/1.00	0.040	0.040	0.20/0.35	0.40/0.70	0.40/0.60	0.20/0.30	
8745	8745	0.43/0.48	0.75/1.00	0.040	0.040	0.20/0.35	0.40/0.70	0.40/0.60	0.20/0.30	
....	8747	0.45/0.50	0.75/1.00	0.040	0.040	0.20/0.35	0.40/0.70	0.40/0.60	0.20/0.30	
8750	8750	0.48/0.53	0.75/1.00	0.040	0.040	0.20/0.35	0.40/0.70	0.40/0.60	0.20/0.30	
9255	9255	0.50/0.60	0.70/0.95	0.040	0.040	1.80/2.20				
9260	9260	0.55/0.65	0.70/1.00	0.040	0.040	1.80/2.20				
9261	9261	0.55/0.65	0.75/1.00	0.040	0.040	1.80/2.20	....	0.10/0.25		
9262	9262	0.55/0.65	0.75/1.00	0.040	0.040	1.80/2.20	....	0.25/0.40		
9310	E 9310	0.08/0.13	0.45/0.65	0.025	0.025	0.20/0.35	3.00/3.50	1.00/1.40	0.08/0.15	
9315	E 9315	0.13/0.18	0.45/0.65	0.025	0.025	0.20/0.35	3.00/3.50	1.00/1.40	0.08/0.15	
9317	E 9317	0.15/0.20	0.45/0.65	0.025	0.025	0.20/0.35	3.00/3.50	1.00/1.40	0.08/0.15	
9437	9437	0.35/0.40	0.90/1.20	0.040	0.040	0.20/0.35	0.30/0.60	0.30/0.50	0.08/0.15	
9440	9440	0.38/0.43	0.90/1.20	0.040	0.040	0.20/0.35	0.30/0.60	0.30/0.50	0.08/0.15	
9442	9442	0.40/0.45	1.00/1.30	0.040	0.040	0.20/0.35	0.30/0.60	0.30/0.50	0.08/0.15	
9445	9445	0.43/0.48	1.00/1.30	0.040	0.040	0.20/0.35	0.30/0.60	0.30/0.50	0.08/0.15	
9747	9747	0.45/0.50	0.50/0.80	0.040	0.040	0.20/0.35	0.40/0.70	0.10/0.25	0.15/0.25	
9763	9763	0.60/0.67	0.50/0.80	0.040	0.040	0.20/0.35	0.40/0.70	0.10/0.25	0.15/0.25	
9840	9840	0.38/0.43	0.70/0.90	0.040	0.040	0.20/0.35	0.85/1.15	0.70/0.90	0.20/0.30	
9845	9845	0.43/0.48	0.70/0.90	0.040	0.040	0.20/0.35	0.85/1.15	0.70/0.90	0.20/0.30	
9850	9850	0.48/0.53	0.70/0.90	0.040	0.040	0.20/0.35	0.85/1.15	0.70/0.90	0.20/0.30	

Table 9. AMERICAN STANDARD TAPERS (MORSE)*

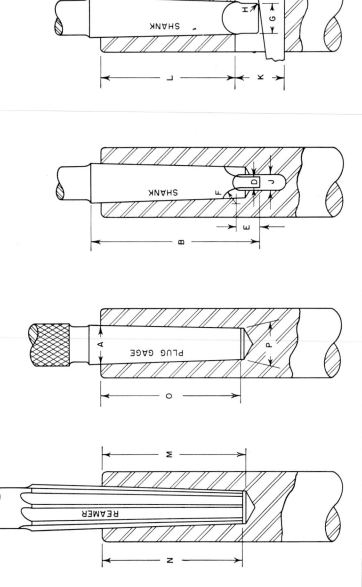

No. of taper	Dia of plug at small end, P	Dia of gage line, A	Shank Whole length, B	Shank Depth, C	Depth of drilled hole, M	Depth of reamed hole, N	Standard plug depth, O	Tang Thickness, D	Tang Length, E	Tang Radius, F	Tang Diameter, G	Tang Radius, H	Tang slot Width, J	Tang slot Length, K	End of socket to tang slot, L	Taper per inch	Taper per foot	No. of drift
0†	0.252	0.356	2 11/32	2 7/32	2 1/16	2 1/32	2	0.156	1/4	5/32	15/64	3/64	0.166	9/16	1 15/16	0.052000	0.62400	0†
1	0.369	0.475	2 9/16	2 7/16	2 3/16	2 5/32	2 1/8	0.203	3/8	3/16	11/32	3/64	0.213	3/4	2 1/16	0.049882	0.59858	1
2	0.572	0.700	3 1/16	2 15/16	2 21/32	2 39/64	2 9/16	0.250	7/16	1/4	17/32	1/16	0.260	7/8	2 1/2	0.049951	0.59941	2
3	0.778	0.938	3 7/8	3 11/16	3 5/16	3 1/4	3 3/16	0.312	9/16	9/32	23/32	5/64	0.322	1 3/16	3 1/16	0.050196	0.60235	3
4	1.020	1.231	4 7/8	4 5/8	4 3/16	4 1/8	4 1/16	0.469	5/8	5/16	31/32	3/32	0.479	1 1/4	3 7/8	0.051938	0.62326	4
5	1.475	1.748	6 1/8	5 7/8	5 5/16	5 1/4	5 3/16	0.625	3/4	3/8	1 13/32	1/8	0.635	1 1/2	4 15/16	0.052626	0.63151	5
6	2.116	2.494	8 9/16	8 1/4	7 13/32	7 21/64	7 1/4	0.750	1 1/8	1/2	2	5/32	0.760	1 3/4	7	0.052137	0.62565	5‡
7	2.750	3.270	11 5/8	11 1/4	10 5/32	10 5/64	10	1.125	1 3/8	3/4	2 5/8	3/16	1.135	2 5/8	9 1/2	0.052000	0.62400	

* The dimensions agree essentially with dimensions of the American Standard on Machine Tapers.
† The size 0 taper is not listed in the American Standard on Machine Tapers.
‡ The No. 5 drift will also eject No. 6 taper shank tools.

Table 10. BROWN AND SHARPE TAPERS*

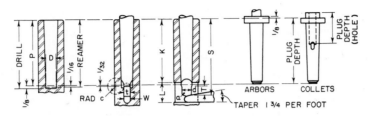

TAPER 1 3/4 PER FOOT

No. of taper	Taper per foot	Dia of plug at small end, D	Plug depth, P B&S standard	Plug depth, P For mill. mach	Plug depth, P misc	Keyway from end of spindle, K	Shank depth, S	Length of keyway, L	Width of keyway, W	Length of arbor tongue, T	Dia of arbor tongue, d	Thickness of arbor tongue, t	Radius of tongue circle, c	Radius of tongue, a	Limit for tongue —to project through test tool
1	0.50200	0.20000	$1\frac{5}{16}$	...	...	$1\frac{5}{16}$	$1\frac{3}{16}$	$\frac{3}{8}$	0.135	$\frac{3}{16}$	0.170	$\frac{1}{8}$	$\frac{3}{16}$	0.030	0.003
2	0.50200	0.25000	$1\frac{3}{16}$	...	...	$1\frac{1}{64}$	$1\frac{1}{2}$	$\frac{1}{2}$	0.166	$\frac{1}{4}$	0.220	$\frac{5}{32}$	$\frac{3}{16}$	0.030	0.003
3	0.50200	0.31250	$1\frac{1}{2}$	...	...	$1\frac{15}{32}$	$1\frac{7}{8}$	$\frac{5}{8}$	0.197	$\frac{5}{16}$	0.282	$\frac{3}{16}$	$\frac{3}{16}$	0.040	0.003
			...	...	$1\frac{3}{4}$	$1\frac{23}{32}$	$2\frac{1}{8}$	$\frac{5}{8}$	0.197	$\frac{5}{16}$	0.282	$\frac{3}{16}$	$\frac{3}{16}$	0.040	0.003
			...	...	2	$1\frac{31}{32}$	$2\frac{3}{8}$	$\frac{5}{8}$	0.197	$\frac{5}{16}$	0.282	$\frac{3}{16}$	$\frac{3}{16}$	0.040	0.003
4	0.50240	0.35000	...	$1\frac{1}{4}$	...	$1\frac{3}{64}$	$1\frac{21}{32}$	$\frac{11}{16}$	0.228	$\frac{11}{32}$	0.320	$\frac{7}{32}$	$\frac{5}{16}$	0.050	0.003
			$1\frac{11}{16}$	...	...	$1\frac{41}{64}$	$2\frac{3}{32}$	$\frac{11}{16}$	0.228	$\frac{11}{32}$	0.320	$\frac{7}{32}$	$\frac{5}{16}$	0.050	0.003
5	0.50160	0.45000	...	$1\frac{3}{4}$	...	$1\frac{11}{16}$	$2\frac{3}{16}$	$\frac{3}{4}$	0.260	$\frac{3}{8}$	0.420	$\frac{1}{4}$	$\frac{5}{16}$	0.060	0.003
			...	...	2	$1\frac{15}{16}$	$2\frac{7}{16}$	$\frac{3}{4}$	0.260	$\frac{3}{8}$	0.420	$\frac{1}{4}$	$\frac{5}{16}$	0.060	0.003
			$2\frac{1}{8}$	...	...	$2\frac{1}{16}$	$2\frac{9}{16}$	$\frac{3}{4}$	0.260	$\frac{3}{8}$	0.420	$\frac{1}{4}$	$\frac{5}{16}$	0.060	0.003
6	0.50329	0.50000	$2\frac{3}{8}$	...	...	$2\frac{19}{64}$	$2\frac{7}{8}$	$\frac{7}{8}$	0.291	$\frac{7}{16}$	0.460	$\frac{9}{32}$	$\frac{5}{16}$	0.060	0.005
7	0.50147	0.60000	...	...	$2\frac{1}{2}$	$2\frac{13}{32}$	$3\frac{1}{32}$	$\frac{15}{16}$	0.322	$\frac{15}{32}$	0.560	$\frac{5}{16}$	$\frac{3}{8}$	0.070	0.005
			$2\frac{7}{8}$	...	...	$2\frac{25}{32}$	$3\frac{13}{32}$	$\frac{15}{16}$	0.322	$\frac{15}{32}$	0.560	$\frac{5}{16}$	$\frac{3}{8}$	0.070	0.005
			...	3	...	$2\frac{29}{32}$	$3\frac{17}{32}$	$\frac{15}{16}$	0.322	$\frac{15}{32}$	0.560	$\frac{5}{16}$	$\frac{3}{8}$	0.070	0.005
8	0.50100	0.75000	$3\frac{9}{16}$	...	...	$3\frac{29}{64}$	$4\frac{1}{8}$	1	0.353	$\frac{1}{2}$	0.710	$\frac{11}{32}$	$\frac{3}{8}$	0.080	0.005
9	0.50085	0.90010	...	4	...	$3\frac{7}{8}$	$4\frac{5}{8}$	$1\frac{1}{8}$	0.385	$\frac{9}{16}$	0.860	$\frac{3}{8}$	$\frac{7}{16}$	0.100	0.005
			$4\frac{1}{4}$	...	...	$4\frac{1}{8}$	$4\frac{7}{8}$	$1\frac{1}{8}$	0.385	$\frac{9}{16}$	0.860	$\frac{3}{8}$	$\frac{7}{16}$	0.100	0.005
10	0.51612	1.04465	5	...	...	$4\frac{27}{32}$	$5\frac{23}{32}$	$1\frac{5}{16}$	0.447	$\frac{21}{32}$	1.010	$\frac{7}{16}$	$\frac{7}{16}$	0.110	0.005
			...	$5\frac{11}{16}$	...	$5\frac{7}{32}$	$6\frac{3}{32}$	$1\frac{5}{16}$	0.447	$\frac{21}{32}$	1.010	$\frac{7}{16}$	$\frac{7}{16}$	0.110	0.005
			...	...	$6\frac{7}{32}$	$6\frac{1}{16}$	$6\frac{15}{16}$	$1\frac{5}{16}$	0.447	$\frac{21}{32}$	1.010	$\frac{7}{16}$	$\frac{7}{16}$	0.110	0.005
11	0.50100	1.24995	$5\frac{15}{16}$	...	...	$5\frac{25}{32}$	$6\frac{21}{32}$	$1\frac{5}{16}$	0.447	$\frac{21}{32}$	1.210	$\frac{7}{16}$	$\frac{1}{2}$	0.130	0.005
			...	$6\frac{3}{4}$	...	$6\frac{19}{32}$	$7\frac{15}{32}$	$1\frac{5}{16}$	0.447	$\frac{21}{32}$	1.210	$\frac{7}{16}$	$\frac{1}{2}$	0.130	0.005
12	0.49973	1.50010	$7\frac{1}{8}$	$7\frac{1}{8}$	...	$6\frac{15}{16}$	$7\frac{15}{16}$	$1\frac{1}{2}$	0.510	$\frac{3}{4}$	1.460	$\frac{1}{2}$	$\frac{1}{2}$	0.150	0.005
			...	...	$6\frac{1}{4}$										
13	0.50020	1.75005	$7\frac{3}{4}$	...	...	$7\frac{9}{16}$	$8\frac{9}{16}$	$1\frac{1}{2}$	0.510	$\frac{3}{4}$	1.710	$\frac{1}{2}$	$\frac{5}{8}$	0.170	0.010
14	0.50000	2.00000	$8\frac{1}{4}$	$8\frac{1}{4}$	...	$8\frac{1}{32}$	$9\frac{5}{32}$	$1\frac{11}{16}$	0.572	$\frac{27}{32}$	1.960	$\frac{9}{16}$	$\frac{3}{4}$	0.190	0.010
15	0.50000	2.25000	$8\frac{3}{4}$	...	...	$8\frac{17}{32}$	$9\frac{21}{32}$	$1\frac{11}{16}$	0.572	$\frac{27}{32}$	2.210	$\frac{9}{16}$	$\frac{7}{8}$	0.210	0.010
16	0.50000	2.50000	$9\frac{1}{4}$	...	...	9	$10\frac{1}{4}$	$1\frac{7}{8}$	0.635	$\frac{15}{16}$	2.450	$\frac{5}{8}$	1	0.230	0.010
17	0.50000	2.75000	$9\frac{3}{4}$												
18	0.50000	3.00000	$10\frac{1}{4}$												

* All dimensions are in inches.

Table 11. JARNO TAPERS

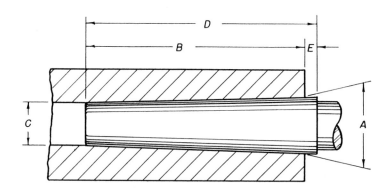

Taper per foot = 0.600

No. of taper	Large end of hole, A	Depth of hole, B	Small end of hole, C	Length of shank, D	Clearance, E
1	0.125	0.5	0.1	$\frac{9}{16}$	$\frac{1}{16}$
2	0.250	1.0	0.2	$1\frac{1}{8}$	$\frac{1}{8}$
3	0.375	1.5	0.3	$1\frac{5}{8}$	$\frac{1}{8}$
4	0.500	2.0	0.4	$2\frac{3}{16}$	$\frac{3}{16}$
5	0.625	2.5	0.5	$2\frac{11}{16}$	$\frac{3}{16}$
6	0.750	3.0	0.6	$3\frac{3}{16}$	$\frac{3}{16}$
7	0.875	3.5	0.7	$3\frac{11}{16}$	$\frac{3}{16}$
8	1.000	4.0	0.8	$4\frac{3}{16}$	$\frac{3}{16}$
9	1.125	4.5	0.9	$4\frac{11}{16}$	$\frac{3}{16}$
10	1.250	5.0	1.0	$5\frac{1}{4}$	$\frac{1}{4}$
11	1.375	5.5	1.1	$5\frac{3}{4}$	$\frac{1}{4}$
12	1.500	6.0	1.2	$6\frac{1}{4}$	$\frac{1}{4}$
13	1.625	6.5	1.3	$6\frac{3}{4}$	$\frac{1}{4}$
14	1.750	7.0	1.4	$7\frac{1}{4}$	$\frac{1}{4}$
15	1.875	7.5	1.5	$7\frac{3}{4}$	$\frac{1}{4}$
16	2.000	8.0	1.6	$8\frac{3}{8}$	$\frac{3}{8}$
17	2.125	8.5	1.7	$8\frac{7}{8}$	$\frac{3}{8}$
18	2.250	9.0	1.8	$9\frac{3}{8}$	$\frac{3}{8}$
19	2.375	9.5	1.9	$9\frac{7}{8}$	$\frac{3}{8}$
20	2.500	10.0	2.0	$10\frac{3}{8}$	$\frac{3}{8}$

Table 12. TAPER PINS

All sizes have a taper of 0.250 per foot

Size no. of pin	Length of pin	Large end of pin	Small end of reamer	Drill size for reamer
0	1	0.156	0.135	28
1	$1\frac{1}{4}$	0.172	0.146	25
2	$1\frac{1}{2}$	0.193	0.162	19
3	$1\frac{3}{4}$	0.219	0.183	12
4	2	0.250	0.208	3
5	$2\frac{1}{4}$	0.289	0.242	$\frac{1}{4}$
6	$3\frac{1}{4}$	0.341	0.279	$\frac{9}{32}$
7	$3\frac{3}{4}$	0.409	0.331	$\frac{11}{32}$
8	$4\frac{1}{2}$	0.492	0.398	$\frac{13}{32}$
9	$5\frac{1}{4}$	0.591	0.482	$\frac{31}{64}$
10	6	0.706	0.581	$\frac{19}{32}$
11	$7\frac{1}{4}$	0.857	0.706	$\frac{23}{32}$
12	$8\frac{3}{4}$	1.013	0.842	$\frac{55}{64}$

AVOIRDUPOIS WEIGHT

16 drams or 437.5 grains = 1 ounce
16 ounces or 7,000 grains = 1 pound
2,000 pounds = 1 net or short ton
2,240 pounds = 1 gross or long ton
2,204.6 pounds = 1 metric ton

BOARD MEASURE

One foot board measure is a piece of wood 12 inches square by 1 inch thick, or 144 cubic inches. A piece of wood 2 by 4, 12 feet long contains 8 feet board measure.

DRY MEASURE

2 pints = 1 quart
8 quarts = 1 peck
4 pecks = 1 bushel
1 standard U.S. bushel = 1.2445 cubic feet
1 British imperial bushel = 1.2837 cubic feet

LIQUID MEASURE

4 gills = 1 pint
2 pints = 1 quart
4 quarts = 1 gallon

1 U.S. gallon = 231 cubic inches
1 British imperial gallon = 1.2 U.S. gallon
7.48 U.S. gallons = 1 cubic foot

LONG MEASURE

12 inches = 1 foot
3 feet = 1 yard
1,760 yards = 1 mile
5,280 feet = 1 mile
16.5 feet = 1 rod

PAPER MEASURE

24 sheets = 1 quire
20 quires = 1 ream
2 reams = 1 bundle
5 bundles = 1 bale

SHIPPING MEASURE

1 U.S. shipping ton = 40 cubic feet
1 U.S. shipping ton = 32.143 U.S. bushels
1 U.S. shipping ton = 31.16 imperial bushels
1 British shipping ton = 42 cubic feet
1 British shipping ton = 33.75 U.S. bushels

1 British shipping ton = 32.718 imperial bushels
1 register ton* = 100 cubic feet

* Register ton is used to measure the internal capacity of a ship.

SQUARE MEASURE

144 square inches = 1 square foot
9 square feet = 1 square yard
30.25 square yards = 1 square rod
160 square rods = 1 acre
640 acres = 1 square mile

TEMPERATURE

Freezing, Fahrenheit scale = 32 degrees
Freezing, centigrade scale = 0 degrees
Boiling, Fahrenheit scale = 212 degrees
Boiling, centigrade scale = 100 degrees

If any degree on the centigrade scale, either above or below zero, be multiplied by 1.8, the result will, in either case, be the number of degrees above or below 32 degrees Fahrenheit.

TROY WEIGHT

24 grains = 1 pennyweight
20 pennyweights = 1 ounce
12 ounces = 1 pound

WEIGHT OF WATER

1 cubic centimeter = 1 gram or 0.035 ounce
1 cubic inch = 0.5787 ounce
1 cubic foot = 62.48 pounds
1 U.S. gallon = 8.355 pounds
1 British imperial gallon = 10 pounds
32 cubic feet = 1 net ton (2,000 pounds)
35.84 cubic feet = 1 long ton (2,240 pounds)
1 net ton = 240 U.S. gallons
1 long ton = 268 U.S. gallons

ENGLISH-METRIC EQUIVALENTS

1 inch = 2.54 centimeters
1 centimeter = 0.3937 inch
1 meter = 39.37 inches
1 kilometer = 0.62 mile
1 quart = 0.946 liter
1 U.S. gallon = 3.785 liters
1 British gallon = 4.543 liters
1 liter = 1.06 quarts
1 pound = 0.454 kilogram
1 kilogram = 2.205 pounds
1 watt = 44.24 foot-pounds per minute
1 horsepower = 33,000 foot-pounds per minute
1 kilowatt = 1.34 horsepower

WEIGHT OF MATERIALS PER CUBIC FOOT

Material	Pounds	Material	Pounds
Aluminum	168	Nickel	555
Brass	525	Oak, white	52
Brick	125	Petroleum	55
Bronze	550	Pine, white	25
Cement	90	Pine, yellow	34
Coal	50	Salt	45
Coke	27	Sand	95
Copper	556	Silver	655
Gold	1,203	Steel	480
Gravel	90	Sulfur	125
Ice	59	Tin	456
Iron	490	Tungsten	1,203
Lead	707	Vanadium	372
Maple	50	Water	62.4
Mercury	850	Zinc	445

Correlated List of Visual Aids

The visual aids listed below and on the following pages can be used to supplement much of the material in this book. For the convenience of users the films have been grouped by chapters, but it is recommended that each film be reviewed before use in order to determine its suitability for a particular group or unit of study.

Motion pictures and filmstrips are included in the following list, the character of each being indicated by the self-explanatory abbreviations "MP" and "FS." Immediately following this identification is the name of the producer; and if the distributor is different from the producer, the name of the distributor follows the name of the producer. Abbreviations are used for these names and are identified in the Sources of Films Listed at the end of the bibliography. Unless otherwise indicated, the motion pictures are 16mm sound black-and-white and the filmstrips are 35mm silent black-and-white. The length of motion pictures is given in minutes (min), of filmstrips in frames (fr). Most of the films can be borrowed or rented from state and local film libraries. A list of these sources is given in *A Directory of 2660 16mm Film Libraries*, available from the Government Printing Office, Washington 25, D.C.

This bibliography is a selective one, and film users should also examine the latest annual editions and supplements of *Educational Film Guide* and *Filmstrip Guide*, published by the H. W. Wilson Company, New York. The guides, standard reference books, are available in most school, college, and public libraries. Readers should also write to various manufacturers of hand and machine tools for copies of charts, posters, diagrams, models, and other visual aids.

GENERAL

Tool and Die Making—Keystone of Mass Production (MP MTP 22min color). Shows how lathes, drilling machines, shapers, and other machine tools are made; their use in industry; and the training of an apprentice in the tool and die making trade. (Sponsored by the National Tool and Die Manufacturers Association.)

CHAPTER 1. Small Tools

A.B.C. of Hand Tools (MP GM). Two animated Disney films, each 18min color. Part 1 covers ham-

mers, screw drivers, pliers, and wrenches. Part 2 covers files, saws, chisels, planes, and punches.

Care and Use of Hand Tools (MP series USA/UWF). Six motion pictures with titles and running times as follows: *Bars, Punches, and Drifts* (15min); *Chisels* (12min); *Hack Saws* (18min); *Hammers* (11 min); *Pliers and Screw Drivers* (15min); *Wrenches* (19min).

Scraping Flat Surfaces (MP USOE/UWF 14min). Explains how surface plates are used to check the flatness of surfaces. Shows different types of scrapers and tells how to remove high spots and to determine when a surface is scraped flat. (Correlated filmstrip, same title, 33 frames.)

CHAPTER 3. Hack Saws and Sawing

Filing and Hacksawing (FS McGraw 41fr). Shows the kinds of files and their uses, the selection of hack-saw blades, and the right and wrong methods of using hack saws.

Sawing an Internal Irregular Shape (MP USOE/UWF 32min). How to drill the saw-starting hole, make the saw selection, set up a band-saw machine, weld saw bands, saw an internal contour shape, and remove and store a band saw. (Correlated filmstrip, same title, 43 frames.)

CHAPTER 4. Files and Filing

Filing (MP USN/UWF 15min). Describes the importance of files and filing in a machinist's work; shows filing techniques and various types of files and file cuts.

Filing an Internal Irregular Shape (MP USOE/UWF 27min). How to make file selection, set up a metal-cutting band-saw machine for filing, file a die, lay out a punch using a die as a template, file a punch, check the filing of a punch with a die, and fine-finish file. (Correlated filmstrip, same title, 31 frames.)

Fundamentals of Filing (MP USOE/UWF 12 min). How to care for, handle, and clean files and how to select different metals. (Correlated filmstrip, same title, 52 frames.)

CHAPTER 5. Soldering

Hand Soldering (MP USOE/UWF 20min). Gives the theory of soldering. Shows how to prepare soldering irons and torches, clean and prepare the work, fasten joints, solder wire and lug joints, and seal seams. (Correlated filmstrip, same title, 54 frames.)

CHAPTER 6. Measuring Tools

The Steel Rule (MP USOE/UWF 14min). How to read steel rules, use flexible hook- and rule-type gages, lay out holes with a combination square and scribe them with a divider, and use inside and outside calipers to transfer dimensions to and from steel rules. (Correlated filmstrip, same title, 52 frames.)

Centering Small Stock (MP USOE/UWF 12min). How to locate the center of round, square, and rectangular pieces of stock, using surface gage, hermaphrodite calipers, center head and steel rule, and combination square. (Correlated filmstrip, same title, 34 frames.)

The Micrometer (MP USOE/UWF 15min). Shows various types of micrometers; tells how to use a micrometer, read the barrel and thimble scales, check the accuracy of readings, and take care of the instrument. (Correlated filmstrip, same title, 38 frames.)

Height Gages and Test Indicators (MP USOE/UWF 12min). Gives the principles and parts of the vernier height gage; tells how to use the gage to lay out holes and to set test indicators and how to use test indicators to check the accuracy of machined surfaces. (Correlated filmstrip, same title, 34 frames.)

Verniers (MP USOE/UWF 19min). Gives the principle of the vernier scale and its application to a micrometer and to inside and outside calipers; tells how to use and read vernier micrometers and vernier calipers. (Correlated filmstrip, same title, 37 frames.)

The Bevel Protractor (MP USOE/UWF 15min). Gives the principles of the vernier bevel protractor; tells how to set and read the bevel protractor and how to use the protractor to lay out angular work and to check angles. (Correlated filmstrip, same title, 34 frames.)

CHAPTER 7. Drills and Drilling Operations

Basic Machines: The Drill Press (MP USOE/UWF 10min). Tells the functions, characteristics, and basic operations of the drill press. (Correlated filmstrip, same title, 32 frames.)

Operations on the Drill Press (MP-FS series USOE/UWF). Five motion pictures and correlated filmstrips with the following titles and running times: *Drilling and Tapping Cast Steel* (19min); *Drilling to a Layout and Spotfacing Cast Iron* (15min); *Drilling a Hole in a Pin* (10min); *Locating Holes, Drilling, and Tapping in Cast Iron* (18min); *Countersinking, Counterboring, and Spotfacing* (20min).

CHAPTER 8. Tapers

Reaming with Taper Hand Reamers (MP USOE/ UWF 15min). How to hand-ream a tapered hole through a shaft and collar, fit a taper pin in the reamed hole, and ream bearing caps for fitting dowel pins. (Correlated filmstrip, same title, 41 frames.)

CHAPTER 9. Threads

Cutting Threads with Taps and Dies (MP USOE/ UWF 19min). Gives the principles of cutting threads with taps and dies; describes tapping full threads in a blind hole, tapping through holes, and cutting threads with an adjustable die. (Correlated filmstrip, same title, 48 frames.)

Inspection of Threads (MP USOE/UWF 22min). How to identify the different parts of an American National standard thread, inspect external threads with a roll snap gage, adjust the roll snap gage, and inspect internal threads with a plug gage. (Correlated filmstrip, same title, 49 frames.)

CHAPTER 10. Gearing

Operations on the Gear Hobbing Machine (MP-FS series USOE/UWF). Five motion pictures and correlated filmstrips with the following titles and running times: *Hobbing a Spur Gear, Part 1: Setting Up the Change Gears* (15min); *Hobbing a Spur Gear, Part 2: Setting Up and Hobbing the Work* (24min); *Hobbing a Square Tooth Spline Shaft* (17min); *Hobbing a Worm Gear: Infeed Method* (18min); *Hobbing a Helical Gear: Two Cuts, Nondifferential Method* (17min).

Principles of Gearing: An Introduction (MP USOE/UWF 18min). Discusses friction gears and toothed gears; explains the law of gearing, positive driving, involute profiles, pressure angles, cycloid profiles, velocity rates, and circular pitch. (Correlated filmstrip, same title, 37 frames.)

CHAPTER 11. Cutting Tools

Carbide Cutting Tools (MP-FS series USOE/ UWF). Five motion pictures and correlated filmstrips with the following titles and running times: *Brazing Carbide Tools* (18min); *Grinding Single-point Carbide Tools* (26min); *Grinding Multiple-point Carbide Tools* (20min); *Cutting with Carbide Tools, Part 1: Single Point* (19min); *Cutting with Carbide Tools, Part 2: Milling Cutters* (15min).

Fundamentals of End Cutting Tools (MP USOE/ UWF 12min). Discusses radius, threading, sheer-cut finishing, roundnose finishing, and side-facing tools; gives the correct setting of the tools and the type of cut each one makes. (Correlated filmstrip, same title, 30 frames.)

Fundamentals of Side Cutting Tools (MP USOE/ UWF 11min). How side cutting tools are shaped and how they cut; how generated heat is dissipated. (Correlated filmstrip, same title, 27 frames.)

CHAPTER 12. Shaper

Basic Machines: The Shaper (MP USOE/UWF 15min). Gives the functions, characteristics, and basic operations of the shaper. (Correlated filmstrip, same title, 40 frames.)

Operations on the Shaper (MP-FS series USOE/ UWF). Three motion pictures and correlated filmstrips with the following titles and running times: *Cutting a Keyway on End of a Finished Shaft* (13min); *Machining a Cast Iron Rectangular Block* (25min); *Machining a Tool Steel V Block* (21min).

Operations on the Spindle Shaper (MP-FS series USOE/UWF). Three motion pictures and correlated filmstrips with the following titles and running times: *Rabbeting and Shaping an Edge on Straight Stock* (18min); *Shaping after Template and Shaping Curved Edges* (17min); *Cutting Grooves with Circular Saw Blades* (22min).

CHAPTER 13. Planer

Planing a Dovetail Slide (MP USOE/UWF 28 min). How to set up the workpiece, cutting tools, and machine; how to make rough and finish cuts in the clearance slot; and how to make angle cuts. (Correlated filmstrip, same title, 38 frames.)

Planing a Flat Surface (MP USOE/UWF 22 min). Discusses the function of a planer; tells how to mount the workpiece, set the tool and table for the cut, and make a first and second roughing cut and a first and second finishing cut. (Correlated filmstrip, same title, 48 frames.)

CHAPTER 14. Lathes

Basic Machines: The Lathe (MP USOE/UWF 15min). Gives the functions, characteristics, and basic operations of the engine lathe. (Correlated filmstrip, same title, 49 frames.)

Operations on the Engine Lathe (MP-FS series USOE/UWF). Seventeen motion pictures and correlated filmstrips with the following titles and running times: *Rough Turning between Centers* (15min); *Turning Work of Two Diameters* (14min); *Cutting a Taper with the Compound Rest and with a Taper Attachment* (11min); *Drilling, Boring, and Reaming Work Held in Chuck* (11min); *Cutting an External National Fine Thread* (12min); *Turning a Taper with the Tailstock Set Over* (17min); *Cutting an External Acme Thread* (16min); *Cutting an Internal Acme Thread* (22min); *Cutting an Internal Taper Pipe Thread* (20min); *Turning Work Held on a Fixture* (21min); *Boring to Close Tolerances* (17min); *Machining Work Held in Chuck: Use of Reference Surfaces* (24min); *Turning Work Held on a Mandrel* (20min); *Using a Steady Rest* (25min); *Using a Follower Rest* (21min); *Using a Boring Bar between Centers: Work Held on Carriage* (22min); *Using a Steady Rest When Boring* (21min).

Operations on the Wood Lathe (MP-FS series USOE/UWF). Five motion pictures and correlated filmstrips with the following titles and running times: *Turning a Cylinder between Centers* (17min); *Turning Taper Work* (12min); *Turning Work on a Face Plate* (15min); *Turning Work in a Chuck* (15min); *Face Turning a Collar* (16min).

CHAPTER 15. Turret Lathes

Operations on the Turret Lathe (MP-FS series USOE/UWF). Seven motion pictures and correlated filmstrips with the following titles and running times: *The Turret Lathe, an Introduction* (17min); *Chuck Work, Part 1: Setting Up Hexagon Turret Tools* (22 min); *Chuck Work, Part 2: Setting Up Tools for Combined Cuts* (16min); *Setting Up and Machining Bar Stock* (34min); *Bar Work: Magnesium, Part 1: Setting Up Bar Mechanism and Roller Turner* (18min); *Bar Work: Magnesium, Part 2: Setting Up Multiple Roller Turner and Turning a Taper* (17min); *Bar Work: Magnesium, Part 3: Necking and Threading by Use of Attachment and by Die Head* (23min).

Operations on the Vertical Boring Mill (MP-FS series USOE/UWF). Three motion pictures and correlated filmstrips with the following titles and running times: *Rough-facing, Turning, and Drilling* (31min); *Rough-facing, Boring, and Turning a Shoulder* (22 min); *Facing, Turning, Boring, Grooving, and Chamfering* (31min).

CHAPTER 16. Milling Machines

Basic Machines: The Milling Machine (MP USOE/UWF 15min). Gives the functions, characteristics, and basic operations of the milling machine. (Correlated filmstrip, same title, 41 frames.)

Operations on the Horizontal Boring Mill (MP-FS series USOE/UWF). Six motion pictures and correlated filmstrips with the following titles and running times: *Setup for Face Milling with a Fixture* (20min); *Face Milling with a Fixture* (16min); *Contour Face Milling* (17min); *Setup for Rough Line-boring* (15 min); *Rough Line-boring* (19min); *Drilling, Tapping, Stub-boring, and Reaming* (22min).

Operations on the Milling Machine (MP-FS series USOE/UWF). Ten motion pictures and correlated filmstrips with the following titles and running times:

The Milling Machine (8min); *Cutting Keyways* (15 min); *Straddle and Surface Milling to Close Tolerances* (27min); *Straddle Milling* (17min); *Plain Indexing and Cutting a Spur Gear* (26min); *Milling a Template* (17min); *Cutting a Short Rack* (18min); *Boring Holes with Offset Boring Head* (28min); *Milling a Helical Cutter* (18min); *Cutting Teeth on a Worm Gear* (17min).

Operations on the Vertical Milling Machine (MP-FS series USOE/UWF). Five motion pictures and correlated filmstrips with the following titles and running times: *Using a Shell End Mill* (21min); *Cutting a Dovetail Taper Slide* (26min); *Cutting a Round End Keyway* (22min); *Milling a Helical Groove* (28min); *Milling a Circular T-slot* (22min).

CHAPTER 17. Gages and Gage Blocks

Fixed Gages (MP USOE/UWF 17min). Discusses types and uses of gages for precision measurement—snap, ring, plug, taper plug, taper ring, flush pin, and screw plug gages. (Correlated filmstrip, same title, 35 frames.)

Gage Blocks and Accessories (MP USOE/UWF 23min). Why accessories are used with gage blocks; how to inspect a plug gage, an adjustable snap gage, a profile gage, a ring gage, and a screw-thread pitch; how to build a height gage and scriber. (Correlated filmstrip, same title, 33 frames.)

Precision Gage Blocks (MP USOE/UWF 18 min). Shows various uses of gage blocks in setting inspection gages; tells how to calculate gage blocks and how to clean and assemble the blocks. (Correlated filmstrip, same title, 28 frames.)

CHAPTER 18. Heat-treatment

Heat Treatment of Steel (MP-FS series USOE/UWF). Three motion pictures and correlated filmstrips with the following titles and running times: *Elements of Hardening* (15min); *Elements of Tempering, Normalizing, and Annealing* (15min); *Elements of Surface Hardening* (14min).

Hardness Testing: Rockwell (MP USOE/UWF 18min). Explains the need for hardness testing; shows how to set up the Rockwell hardness tester, select and seat the penetrator, select and mount the anvil, adjust the timing of the machine, and test flat and curved surfaces. (Correlated filmstrip, same title, 49 frames.)

CHAPTER 19. Abrasives and Grinding Wheels

Lessons in Use and Care of Grinding Wheels (MP series Norton). Three color motion pictures with the following titles and running times: *Grinding Wheel,*

Its Care and Use (17min); *Grinding Wheel Markings* (18min); *Grinding Wheel Safety* (20min).

CHAPTER 20. Grinding Machines

Lessons in Grinding (MP series Norton). Five color motion pictures with the following titles and running times: *Cutter Sharpening* (14min); *Cylindrical Grinder* (20min); *Diamond Wheel, Its Care and Use* (18min); *Grinding Carbide Tools* (26min); *Surface Grinder* (17min).

Norton Abrasives in Tool Grinding (MP Norton 10min color). Illustrates various grinding operations performed in the toolroom and the use of abrasives in these operations.

Offhand Grinding with Norton Abrasive (MP Norton 10min color). Illustrates various operations performed with portable grinders and the use of abrasives in these operations.

Operations of the Center-type Grinder (MP-FS series USOE/UWF). Five motion pictures and correlated filmstrips with the following titles and running times: *Grinding a Plain Pin, Part 1: The Grinding Wheel* (17min); *Grinding a Plain Pin, Part 2: Grinding Operations* (17min); *Grinding a Slender Shaft with Back Rest* (17min); *Plunge Cut Grinding* (15 min); *Grinding a Taper* (19min).

Operations on the Centerless Grinder (MP-FS series USOE/UWF). Five motion pictures and correlated filmstrips with the following titles and running times: *Thrufeed Grinding a Straight Pin, Part 1* (29 min); *Thrufeed Grinding a Straight Pin, Part 2* (28 min); *Infeed Grinding Shouldered Work* (23min); *Infeed Grinding a Shaft of Two Diameters* (31min); *Endfeed Grinding a Tapered Pin* (26min).

Operations on the Cutter Grinder (MP-FS series USOE/UWF). Five motion pictures and correlated filmstrips with the following titles and running times: *Sharpening a Side Milling Cutter* (23min); *Sharpening a Plain Helical Cutter* (16min); *Sharpening a Shell End Mill* (17min); *Sharpening a Form Relieved Cutter* (18min); *Sharpening an Angular Cutter* (15 min).

Operations on the Internal Grinder (MP-FS series USOE/UWF). Three motion pictures and correlated filmstrips with the following titles and running times: *Grinding a Straight Hole* (18min); *Grinding a Deep Hole* (18min); *Grinding and Facing a Blind Hole* (17min).

Operations on the Surface Grinder (MP-FS series USOE/UWF). Five motion pictures and correlated filmstrips with the following titles and running times: *Grinding a Parallel Bar, Part 1: Setting Up the Machine* (14min); *Grinding a Parallel Bar, Part 2: Grind-*

ing Operations (15min); *Grinding a Template* (15 min); *Grinding a V Block* (22min); *Grinding Thin Discs* (15min).

SOURCES OF FILMS LISTED

GM—General Motors Corp., 3044 West Grand Blvd., Detroit 2, Mich., and 405 Montgomery St., San Francisco 4, Calif.

McGraw—McGraw-Hill Book Co., Inc., Text-Film Dept., 330 West 42d St., New York 36, N.Y.

MTP—Modern Talking Picture Service, Inc., 45 Rockefeller Plaza, New York 20, N.Y., and in principal U.S. cities.

Norton—Norton Co., Worcester 6, Mass.

USA—U.S. Army, Washington 25, D.C. (Films distributed by United World Films.)

USN—U.S. Navy, Washington 25, D.C. (Films distributed by United World Films.)

USOE—U.S. Office of Education, Washington 25, D.C. (Films distributed by United World Films.)

UWF—United World Films, Inc., 1445 Park Ave., New York 29, N.Y.

Index